Autism: Sensory-Movement Differences and Diversity
Martha R. Leary and Anne M. Donnellan

Cambridge Book Review Press
310 North Street
Cambridge, Wisconsin 53523
www.cbrpress.com
Editor: Bob Wake

Layout and cover design by Daniel Parent

ISBN-10: 0-9660376-8-5
ISBN-13: 978-0-9660376-8-5
Library of Congress Control Number: 2012939177

Chapter One, "Movement Differences and Diversity in Autism" is a revised and expanded version of *Movement Differences and Diversity in Autism/Mental Retardation*, originally published in 1995 by DRI Press, Madison, Wisconsin.

Chapter Two, "The Evolution of Facilitated Communication," copyright © 2012 by Don Cardinal and Jodi Robledo.

Grateful acknowledgment is made to the following journals and publishers for permission to reprint: *Disability Studies Quarterly:* "Rethinking Autism: Implications of sensory and movement differences"; Oxford University Press: "I Can't Get Started: Stress and the role of movement differences in people with autism" (from *Stress and Coping in Autism*, M. Grace Baron, June Groden, Gerald Groden, and Lewis P. Lipsitt, eds.); *Intellectual and Developmental Disabilities:* "Casting Call for a Supporting Role" and "Moving On: Autism and movement disturbance"; TASH: "Invented Knowledge and Autism: Highlighting our strengths and expanding the conversation."

We dedicate this book to

Arthur L. Schawlow, Sr.
parent, advocate, jazz musician,
Nobel laureate, and friend
1921-1999

and

Pamela Milligan O'Bryan
friend, teacher, parent, and advocate
1918-1999

CONTENTS

7   **Preface**

13   **Chapter 1:**
Movement Differences And Diversity In Autism
         Martha R. Leary and Anne M. Donnellan

135 **Chapter 2:**
The Evolution Of Facilitated Communication
         Don Cardinal and Jodi Robledo

145 **Chapter 3:**
Rethinking Autism: Implications Of Sensory
And Movement Differences For Understanding
And Support
         Anne M. Donnellan, David A. Hill,
         and Martha R. Leary

175 **Chapter 4:**
I Can't Get Started: Stress And The Role Of
Movement Differences In People With Autism
         Anne M. Donnellan, Martha R. Leary,
         and Jodi Patterson Robledo

230 **Chapter 5:**
Casting Call For A Supporting Role
         David A. Hill and Martha R. Leary

237 **Chapter 6:**
Moving On: Autism And Movement Disturbance
         Martha R. Leary and David A. Hill

270 **Chapter 7:**
Invented Knowledge And Autism: Highlighting Our Strengths
And Expanding The Conversation
         Anne M. Donnellan

PREFACE

We shall never cease from exploration
And the end of all our exploring
Will be to arrive where we started
And to know the place for the first time.
—T.S. Eliot, "Little Gidding"

Autism: Sensory-Movement Differences and Diversity is a revised and greatly expanded edition of a book originally published in 1995. Between us we had over 40 years of experience in the field of autism and developmental disabilities when we started this effort in 1991. We spent almost four years studying and talking and learning from others, and slowly we found some of the pieces that had been missing from our perspective of autism, behavior and communication.

For many years we naively believed that we understood the experience of these labeled people. We can be forgiven this assumption, as many learned folks also believed that we understood and praised us for how our insights matched the descriptions found in the professional literature. We believed what we were prepared to believe. People labeled as autistic have added to our understanding, sometimes turning established assumptions into questions. We are learning that many assumptions about autism are based on our own experiences rather than the experiences of the people with that label.

Our book covers some ground on commonly accepted assumptions and takes us on a rocky journey to examine the notion that people might behave in unusual ways because that is the way their bodies are organized. This volume also includes several papers written by Martha, Anne and our colleague David Hill. We have included them here to provide the reader with a compilation of our writings on important topics related to sensory movement differences. For each of us, writing these manuscripts has been a collaborative effort. We often use alphabetical order for listing authorship, or take turns assigning first authorship. In each case where there is more than one author, we consider the authorship to be equal. One of us starts a sentence, the other finishes it. We have essentially agreed on every word and sentence in our manuscripts.

The choice of additional manuscripts to include in this new edition reflects the impact of our emerging perspective on how sensory movement differences have shaped our views on understanding intention, interpreting motivation and assigning meaning to our experience of others. Many autistic people, activist parents, adventuresome professionals and our late, great colleagues Herb Lovett and Ralph Maurer have each influenced our assumptions and values regarding support.

Our journey is a shift in perspective on a very large topic. Each person has a unique developmental trajectory reflected in our wonderful neurological diversity. These differences dynamically affect how one develops, how one views the world and is viewed by others. Whether or not you find yourself agreeing with our premises or conclusions, we trust you will find that these ideas help you in your own efforts to understand and think about these important and complex topics.

As you will see in this book, we are not in favor of labeling. These terms often convey the impression that the people labeled are so alike that they are somehow explained by the categories or the syndromes or labels. We reluctantly use the terms to help people focus on the individuals about whom we are writing. But we want to make clear that what most of them have in common is that they are people faced with challenges in their lives that the labels do little, if anything, to clarify.

We suggest that many of their challenges come from sensory movement differences (not to be confused with weakness or paralysis). These sensory movement differences are what this book is about. In presenting those differences, which at times can be very disturbing, we have no wish to contribute to yet another set of labels (the MD's!). Rather, that as we begin to better understand the role of movement difference in human diversity we will realize that each person truly is unique and must be understood and supported in a very individual and personal way.

Researchers and others describe these differences using a variety of terms such as: motor problems; sensory-integration problems; inertia; sensory overload; apraxia; dyspraxia; echolalia; mutism; behavior disorder; catatonia; or clumsiness. To reflect the range and complexity of sensory perception and movement-related phenomena, we use the term "sensory and movement differences" as it encompasses the dynamic interaction of sensation and movement (Gibson 1979; Thelen and Smith 1995) while acknowledging that many differences are merely part of the richness of human diversity.

We begin by taking issue with some assumptions about autism that most people in the field regard as fundamental. We continue to support the respectful and positive behavioral approaches, teaching techniques, and self-control strategies as well as the communication programs and ecological supports that have helped so many individuals. We have updated this edition with an excellent essay written by Don Cardinal and Jodi Robledo on current thinking and research on supported typing or facilitated communication. Our reading list includes many references and examples that we think are useful. We are, however, no longer accepting without question the assumptions underlying much of the work in our field. We believe that the association between intelligence or mental capacity and the condition recognized as autism is an artifact of a nineteenth-century worldview buttressed by early twentieth-century scientific and cultural bias. We seek to show that the technologies that measure the intelligence of persons with autism—whatever that is—by observing individuals' communication and performance are analogous to assessing the intellect of deaf people by having them analyze musical performances, or people with vision impairments by their ability to read maps. Thus, any approaches, attitudes or programs built on those assumptions ought to be reexamined—not discarded—and gleaned for what is truly useful as we move forward in this new millennium.

Having established our position that the conventional understanding of autism tells us little worth knowing about the people who receive the label, we focus on two, often overlooked, aspects of the disabilities associated with these kinds of diagnoses. The first is the degree to which a variety of symptoms of sensory movement difficulties may inhibit effective action, interaction, and communication, and the second is that constellation of adjustments and adaptations labeled people make to ease the circumstances of their lives. Illuminating the subject from these two perspectives has had a holographic impact on our understanding. What had previously seemed two-dimensional and flat becomes a scintillating new image in multiple dimensions that not only has depth and breadth, but also dynamism and life. Most important, this view of the topic returns the labeled person to a central role as a critical and often remarkable player in his or her own life.

We have written this book for all labeled people, the parents, families, friends and professionals who have always known that they or their children and the people they care about had more to give than we knew how to receive, and who deserve more respect than we typically remember to give. Like them, we have long tried to make the needs, wishes, preferences and opinions of people labeled disabled our priority. This book shows how we are learning to better understand those needs and, at least in part, to address those wishes. In this we join our efforts to those of the many thousands who work to open the doors to full participation for a minority that some of us are born into, and that through accident or illness, many more of us join in the course of our lives.

Martha R. Leary
Anne M. Donnellan
April 2012

EYE IN MOTION? REPOSE?
A WINK? A TIC? A SQUINT? A GRIN?
IN RELATIONSHIP REVEALED
STRANGERS BECOME FRIENDS.

—AMD

CHAPTER ONE

Sensory-Movement Differences and Diversity in Autism

Martha R. Leary

Anne M. Donnellan

I. The Upending Experience

We call people severely or profoundly retarded when our assessment strategies will only allow us to say they are severely or profoundly disabled.
—Gunnar Dybwad (personal communication 1993)

Confronting a paradox

In 1962 Thomas Kuhn published *The Structure of Scientific Revolutions,* one of the most influential books of the twentieth century. In it he described paradigms and how they operate. Paradigms are sets of assumptions and rules that people in a particular scientific culture use to describe their field and which they apply when they do research in that field. For example, the paradigm currently used for understanding the earth's position in the universe has allowed research to proceed differently from the limitations imposed by the paradigm, popular until the Renaissance, which put the earth at the center of the universe.

While operating within a particular paradigm a person seldom thinks of it as a limitation of knowledge. Rather, it is considered *the* way to think and to know and to gain knowledge. Yet, each paradigm represents only one particular way to know. It has a limited set of rules, and a finite way of looking at experience and data. It is only when information comes along which cannot be accounted for or understood within that paradigm that researchers in a field of study begin to rethink the knowledge base and question the value of the paradigm.

Until recently, for example, scientists who study the earth believed that the continents rose out of the ocean close to their present locations. But more and more information accumulated that suggested that the great land masses had once been joined together. For over thirty years this concept was ignored or vilified by very eminent scientists. These men were not malicious. They just could not imagine a way of knowing their field that was so different from their training and experience. But the new information about tectonics and continental drift could not be accommodated until the field was able to see itself as hampered by the old paradigm. Then, like the earth itself, the paradigm cracked and crumbled, and a new one formed.

In the area of study that incorporates developmental disabilities, rehabilitation psychology, special education and speech and language pathology, which we will refer to as "our field," the current paradigm is equally inadequate. It includes the notion that some people are slow or even stopped in their development, which results in an inability to speak, think, or feel like their peers. Many of them have been labeled autistic or retarded, or both.

If these labeled people demonstrate unusual behaviors they are considered the "behavior problems." The language is telling: the people are reduced to the status of their behavior because they are thought to be unaware of their own needs, and unable or unwilling to control their behaviors. Having been shown to benefit from certain specialized teaching techniques and environment, they are thought to learn only through such strategies and placements. Being unable to communicate fluently, they are thought to have little or no opinion about their treatment and circumstances. It is basically a mechanistic model of intelligence and knowledge in which the "teacher" supplies the data and the "learner," like a computer, stores what it can until it is time to retrieve it. This allegedly "hard science" view of humans as objects to be contained or controlled has long been repugnant to us. It fits into the warehouse model of care that characterizes much of the helping profession model that moves "clients" between day centers and congregate residential care.

Thankfully, the introduction and use of sophisticated assistive and augmentative communication technology has challenged prevailing theories and "knowledge" about individuals with impaired communication who have been considered retarded. Assistive and augmentative equipment includes a wide variety of electronic and other options that can be evaluated and programmed to meet individual needs. Thousands of people previously believed to lack the necessary cognitive skills—regarded as too "low functioning" for academic work—are using popular personal technology such as the iPad, iPod Touch, iPhone, Androids and the rest to communicate and order their lives. People are showing that they are capable of entering the social and intellectual mainstream when they are provided with the means. People whose parents had been advised to abandon them in institutions—reassured by the most authoritative professionals that their children would neither know nor care—proved to the world that not only did they know they also cared, a lot!

A prime example of such a person is Bob Williams, who was appointed by President Clinton to the office of Commissioner for the Administration on Developmental Disabilities in 1993. Bob, whose arms flap, whose head rocks, can walk no more than a few steps unaided. Dismissed by some professionals as hopelessly retarded, he never got his hands on a communication system until he was thirteen. Once he had an alphabet he soon showed how very bright he is. Now, with the addition of an electronic voice operated by large buttons he can nudge, Bob gives speeches to audiences rapt with attention, and is an effective spokesperson for all people who need this kind of aid and assistance to lead better and more productive lives.

To talk with Bob Williams and others, as we have done, and to see the changes in the experiences of people previously consigned to lives managed entirely by caregivers is to be confronted with an upending event. Upending, because it turns a belief system, a knowledge base, a set of assumptions underlying one's work, on its ear. Their personal stories do not fit the established paradigm. Given an electronic keyboard, a letterboard, a gestural system, signs, or even a piece of chalk—to use the example of Christy Brown, whose story was told in the movie *My Left Foot*—people who were confidently labeled as noncontributory are being appointed to high office and writing bestsellers. The professionals involved in labeling people were following a paradigm which told them that performance equals intelligence, and that one can estimate capacity by observing behavior; wild movements and no intelligible speech equals absence of intelligence. What else might we have missed in our naïve beliefs about people and disabilities?

Two elements stand out in these stories. First, these people were unable to convey their competence effectively by gesture, expression, or voice. And second, with a greater understanding of who they were and what they needed they acquired and demonstrated a wide range of abilities. These facts lead to many questions. How many more people without speech or effective expression are waiting to be given the tools to communicate and participate? Can we ever again assume that a person's overt behaviors truly reflect his or her inner life?

Let us go back to the paradigm issue for a moment. Paradigms work. That is, they help us understand and study things because they are built upon a set of shared assumptions. These assumptions underlie our knowledge and help us make sense of what we see. In our field, assumptions about labeled people are so deeply rooted that we tend to think they are facts. They are not—they are only shared beliefs. Sometimes, when our observations do not fit our assumptions—as, for example, when we try to fit people like Bob Williams or Christy Brown into the paradigm that says "performance equals intelligence"—we need to remember that the people are real but the paradigm is only an invention.

Some people respond to such a challenge by trying to protect the paradigm and hold on to their assumptions. They would rather see that people like Brown and Williams are "merely" exceptions to the rule rather than question the assumptions that guide their judgments and decisions.

We understand that position. However, we take an alternative view. We believe that exceptions "proof" the rule; that is test the rule. When you have enough exceptions you have to start questioning the legitimacy of the rule, the assumptions, and the paradigm. We believe that the safest course is to think about what Anne has called the "Criterion of the Least Dangerous Assumption." In this field of human endeavor, we can seldom be *sure*. At the same time, we seldom have the option to sit around and wait for information that might be a long time in coming. Life compels us to act, to provide, to support, even to decide what is the *best* course. When we cannot be sure, because we have too little information, we should base our efforts on assumptions that, if ultimately found to be wrong, will have the least dangerous effect on outcomes. Choosing to believe that people are incompetent assumes that we can know who they are by what they do not know and/or cannot do as we do. Assuming that the story is not simple, that having a complex human brain suggests the possibility of competence means that we will look for competence and not merely continue to document deficits.

We believe that our field has been too narrow in its approach to understanding people who have unusual support needs and who communicate differently, often with difficulty. It is not that the information we have about people is *all* wrong; or that we should discard the knowledge of the present paradigm. Rather we believe that there is much to gain in rethinking what we think we *know*. As the great Russian psychologist and physician A. R. Luria emphasized, we need to look at an event from as many perspectives or points of view as possible. We hope that our experience and the knowledge we have gained will help us all look, and see, people labeled developmentally different or autistic in new and helpful ways. On the assumption that the acquisition of knowledge, like all the important tasks in life, is a journey rather than a destination, we invite you to take a journey with us from where we were until 1990 to where we are today.

The good old days—that haven't left us yet!

This is our journey, of course, but it happens to coincide with the beginning of applied work in the field of autism. Up until the late 1960s and early 70s, most children labeled autistic/developmentally different were excluded from community education and programming efforts because of their behavior and/or were being given therapies to deal with their withdrawal from social interaction. The orthodox view that was the professional paradigm included the notion that cold "refrigerator" mothers and weak absent fathers had caused their children's autism. Traditional therapies for children and their parents had little positive effect and many of the children were facing or already living in institutions and other segregated environments. The programs that would and could work effectively were extremely rare. Slowly, through the advocacy work of parents and professionals, there was a growing interest in developing programming options outside of the traditional therapeutic models. Both of us entered the field at that time.

Martha started her career working as a Speech and Language Pathologist in Ontario, Canada, in a pilot, community-based, program for autistic children six to twelve years old. She brought her skills in understanding communication to a program model that was based on supporting parents and teachers as therapists, using behavioral technology in natural environments that was the new, emerging data-based model for autism programs at the time. Anne's background in autism is much like Martha's. Trained in psychology and education, Anne began a school for young children on the autism spectrum in 1970 using an operant conditioning approach. As Martha's behaviorism was tempered by her communication background, Anne's was modified by her early work with Beverly Kilman, a more broadly trained psychologist, and with occupational therapists and speech therapists who brought their perspectives on learning to the school. Operant conditioning as a treatment model assumes behavior is shaped by its consequences. At its best it has helped people observe and analyze and measure some critical components of behavior and through that analysis teach many useful skills. At its worst this model assumes that the only thing worth our attention is observable, measurable behavior viewed through the lens of behaviorism (ABA). While we worked within the model it can be fairly said we never fully accepted many of its assumptions.

Most educators and practitioners in those "modern" programs thought of autism as problems of excess behaviors and missing behaviors. People believed (some still do) that the key to success is to arrange events so that children diagnosed with autism/intellectual disabilities learn the consequences of their behavior and, thereby, change and develop more appropriate behaviors. This model of treatment has undoubtedly helped thousands of supported people and their families cope with unusual and often dangerous behavioral challenges and spawned a number of teaching strategies that are extremely valuable. We will discuss some of these very useful teaching techniques later.

This early model of behaviorism also fostered a notion that "the subject," that is a person on the autism spectrum or a person with similar differences, is not usually an active or critical player in the learning process. The emphasis in the published research was often on the details of the behavioral technology. The success of a teaching effort was determined by whether or not the behavior came under the control of the reinforcement or punishment. The response of the subject was either correct or incorrect as defined by the researchers. Behavior that was observable was the only thing worth considering. The researchers determined which behaviors were worth noting. If the individual was unable to use conventional means to tell us what might be happening from his or her perspective, that perspective could be dismissed as unknowable, irrelevant, and ultimately as non-existent. Unfortunately, some professionals have applied these rules for judging behavior and learning too literally.

In some cases, the behavioral control model became highly negative—what is called "aversive" control. An aversive stimulus or event is one that a person would ordinarily work to avoid. Shock, pain, isolation and the like were used not only to control difficult behavior, but to teach signing, color matching, head lifting and other actions. The use of aversives, which courts prohibited for psychiatric patients, criminals and animals, continues to be advocated for some people who are described as "needing" them—that is, those labeled autistic/developmentally different—by those who are apparently unaware of how to use available alternatives effectively. Perhaps most important is that this emphasis on control contributed to the further dehumanization of people on whom the control strategies were used. One sadly revealing quote captures the attitude—a well known behavioral psychologist hearing a talk on "normalizing" the supports we give people with behavioral challenges said: "We have to humanize them before we can normalize them."

As Anne began to train others to work with autistic children, she realized that the emphasis on control was a dangerous misapplication of behavioral principles. Through her work with Gary LaVigna, a behavioral psychologist, Anne helped develop training programs to guide people into positive approaches to teaching; that is, positive practices to support behavior change. This approach particularly stresses the need to alter the situation that might be causing the problem behaviors. This is how Martha and Anne met. Influenced by the study of ethology and pragmatic communication through practitioners such as Richard Frankel and Martha, Anne's interest in the communication value of some of the problem behaviors grew.

Gradually some behaviorally oriented practitioners, ourselves included, began to put the person back into the equation. Designing comprehensive programs that support people to change their behaviors without aversive control often required that we put ourselves in the learners' shoes. We quickly saw what ought to have been self-evident all along: that from the perspective of people with unusual support needs much of what they are being asked to put up with is unreasonable, often illogical, and usually dull. Programs that teach things that no one needs to learn were and still are commonplace. Even today many people are asked to spend their lives in what psychologist Herb Lovett called "day wasting" centers putting together nuts and bolts and then taking them apart. In the name of community training so many students spend school time walking through shopping malls without real purpose that half-jokingly we call it "mall therapy."

Making all this worse are educational and social service systems that have imported the old hospital model into the community. Labeled people are often educated in isolated classrooms and housed in group homes—surrounded by others who also cannot talk and whose behaviors are equally difficult to predict. Labeled people seldom have an opportunity to spend time with people who are not paid to be with them. In the absence of ordinary or alternative means to communicate about their frustration or confusion, or emotions, people employ the means available to them. These are often unusual behaviors, ranging from relatively harmless repetitive movements to dangerous and violent outbursts directed at themselves or others.

As others and we adopted approaches that include assessing the communicative functions of behaviors, and exclude all aversive control procedures such as time out boxes or the use of pain or humiliation, we could see changes in supported people, as well as in the people who supported them. Treating people in a respectful manner often enabled them to respond and behave in ways more appropriate to their age and circumstances. We hoped that incremental changes in knowledge about positive approaches to challenging behavior, coupled with changing societal attitudes of people's rights to be included, would gradually improve the life options for individuals labeled autistic/retarded. We looked forward to participating in this slow but positive social revolution.

Then the ground began to shift, slowly at first but in time the landscape was entirely changed.

The paradigm cracks ...

First came the revolution in communication options, strategies and equipment. It began slowly, a breakthrough here, another there, typically with people who had the label of cerebral palsy and were considered to have significant intellectual disabilities. As a field we had long recognized that some disabled people were bright but physically limited, but as we noted earlier, we had assumed those people were rare exceptions. We had also assumed that their unusual competence would always be apparent if one did a careful assessment using available technologies.

Writer William Horwood provides a fictional example in his 1987 novel, *Skallagrigg*, about a girl with the cerebral palsy label. It became a bestseller in Great Britain and was quickly reissued in paperback. The novel's heroine, Esther, makes progress toward acceptance that parallels the real-life story of American Bob Williams. *Skallagrigg* is a gripping account without a trace of false sentiment. At one point when Esther is humiliated by children her own age her father reflects:

> He knew it was not that people were cruel or malevolent, it was simply that they could not cope with the affront Esther made to normality. ... To believe that such a being could *think* was barely thinkable. For to do so was to imagine what it must be like to be her ...

And yet this affront to normality was happening everywhere. The rules were changing, and the writing so to speak was on the wall for all to see. We were well on the way toward meaningful change. As Anne's colleague Michael Apple says, "To gain insight, to understand the activity of men and women of a specific historical period, one must start out by questioning what to them is unquestionable." So we began to question: If people like Esther were competent was it not more appropriate, that is, less dangerous, to assume *all* people possessed some competence, since there was no known way to guarantee they did not? We were learning to think the unthinkable, and then, inevitably, to question the unquestionable.

In 1990 our theoretical underpinnings were shaken again, and then shattered. Two award-winning movies about subjects with which we were somewhat familiar, and a mathematician of astronomical talents combined to severely challenge some unquestioned assumptions about our field. The movies, *Awakenings* and *My Left Foot*, were brilliant reminders that appearances can be deceptive. People assumed to be unreachable and unteachable retain within themselves the ability to grow and to know. And in case that message was not being received, there was ample media coverage of Stephen Hawking. He is the professor of astronomy and mathematics, who holds the Isaac Newton Chair in physics at Cambridge University and is author of the bestseller, *A Brief History of Time*. His disabilities, which began in young adulthood, rival Bob Williams'. His impact on twentieth-century science is matchless.

... and crumbles

Then Professor Douglas Biklen of Syracuse University delivered a shattering blow to the old paradigm's assumptions about developmental differences when he published a paper in the *Harvard Educational Review*. He described a communication strategy that he had observed in Australia called facilitated communication or FC. This "method" seemed to allow people who are nonverbal and believed to be severely intellectually impaired to demonstrate previously unexpected literacy, knowledge and awareness. When their hands or arms were supported above a keyboard or alphabet, they typed answers to questions, and sometimes conveyed messages with considerable intellectual and social content.

As any thinking people, we were very skeptical. The phenomenon seemed so entirely out of keeping with the scientific knowledge base about autism/retardation. We went to see for ourselves, and having seen it we each individually (and then jointly, once we were able to meet on the topic) knew that nothing would ever be the same in our field. Individuals we knew so well, about whom we had developed considerable "expertise," were doing something totally unexpected and we had no way to explain it to ourselves or others.

Several aspects of what we were observing astonished us. About the first there was no question. People who had never in their lives remained focused on a single interactional activity for more than a few minutes were willingly and attentively doing something intensely social for long stretches of time. Generally, they did not seem to need external rewards or behavioral contingencies or even much coaching to stay with the activity. They often showed a remarkable decrease in challenging behaviors; moreover, many of them were becoming independent communicators. The experience of FC was changing their lives.

Young adults who we had known for up to twenty years as nonverbal, severely retarded and extremely challenged and challenging, were sitting at a conference for three hours, were attending regular classes and were asking peers out on dates! They were not "cured," certainly, but neither were they the people we thought we knew so well.

If FC experiences were no more than random typing of nonsense syllables or other people's words the changes in people's lives still would be of revolutionary importance. *Real People, Regular Lives: Autism, communication, and quality of life* (2011) by Sally R. Young, Ph.D., introduces readers to ten adults who use facilitated communication as an accommodation for the movement differences that prevent them from speaking or typing independently. The book presents individual case histories as well as discussion of ten prominent themes that surround the use of FC. The case histories highlight the ways in which quality of life changed for these individuals after they gained access to expressive communication. The themes that are discussed arose from the writings of the autistic individuals themselves as well as from interviews with their parents and care providers. The book documents the ways in which FC has given nonverbal people a vital tool that allows them to reveal their awareness, competence, intelligence, and deep humanity.

We had many doubts about another aspect of facilitated communication, that is, the communications that were being generated. On the one hand the topics FC users raised were clearly relevant to their lives, and often referred to information about which the facilitators could have no knowledge. On the other hand, often FC users had little educational background in reading or writing, and sometimes used vocabulary that was clearly associated with their facilitators. The "scientific" attempts to study the phenomenon had such a mixed bag of results that people were leaping to confusions rather than conclusions. We were mystified, and to some extent remain so today.

Facilitated communicating is not the topic of the current text. However, some aspects of that controversial topic are relevant to this discussion of professional attitudes and assumptions. Rather than digress to those points here, we have included a new article ("The Evolution of Facilitated Communication") written especially for this book by our colleagues Jodi Robledo and Don Cardinal. We hope you will read the material because we believe that what the FC controversy tells us about our field today mirrors major errors from the past that haunt us still.

It should not come as a surprise that our field is constrained by mistaken notions about the people it was formed to serve. While interest in human behavior is as old as Adam and Eve, it is only in the last century or so that the scientific method has been brought to bear on the topic. Until about the nineteenth century there was little notion of human characteristics as objects of methodical study—as separate from the disciplines of philosophy and theology. Along with the tremendous burgeoning of interest in the physical sciences came an interest in studying ourselves more objectively as a way of understanding the human condition. There was an effort to study topics such as creativity, intelligence, and pathology as natural phenomenon rather than as functions of the soul as they had been viewed for thousands of years.

Modern psychology is still an immature science, and it strives to make sense of a subject far more baffling than physics, chemistry, or geology. And like these others, it has its history of false starts and dead ends. It also labored under a further handicap. And as our friend Vladimir Sloutsky at Ohio State University points out, the last 150 years were times of great political upheaval and conflict. Scientific communities were cut off from each other for long periods of time. Thus psychology as we know it is not a science well informed by other cultures, other ways of knowing, as are some older disciplines like math and astronomy or philosophy. For much of this century knowledge gained in his Russian homeland was unknown or ignored in the west. Our western psychology has a bias that narrows its vision and gives it an ethnocentricity that has yet to be overcome. Let us take a look at an ethnocentric error that we believe still cripples our field.

The myth of mental capacity

Nineteenth-century scientists wished to apply the objective strategies of the natural sciences to the study of human characteristics. They did not question their own objectivity, but in fact it is impossible to be completely objective about any topic. Although many researchers dismiss this notion, the reality is that we all bring our training, experience and perception of the world to our efforts. In their very readable books, *The Mismeasure of Man* by Stephen Jay Gould, and *Minds Made Feeble* by J. David Smith, the authors describe how those early researchers who were interested in intelligence, who wanted to study and understand what made some people smarter than others, came to the task with the biases of their time. They were overwhelmingly white, upper class, educated men of property who, by and large, believed that they occupied their privileged position by virtue of their innate superiority. They knew without even giving it much thought that white males such as themselves were superior to all females and to all males of the "lesser" races. They saw this as self-evident, and so their attempts to study the nature of intelligence assumed this obvious and natural "fact."

They also assumed that intelligence was not just an idea but a thing, and that as a thing it needed a location. That location, they decided, was most likely to be in the brain. Therefore, they supposed that intelligence could be measured by measuring the brain. As few brains were available they studied the next best thing. They measured heads. They also studied skull sizes by filling them with marbles or sand to determine the volume of the brain case.

For some thirty years eminent scientists attempted to rank living and dead people's intelligence by ranking them according to head size. The field was called craniometry and sometimes phrenology. The rationale behind the science went something like this: We know that all women and all non-whites are inferior to us but how much and to what extent they differ we do not know. So we will measure the brains of brilliant men, educated women, prostitutes, criminals, servants, and so forth. When we have enough samples we will understand the details of difference and get a clearer notion of how to rank them. Ranking was very important to this inherently racist and sexist endeavor—the higher the ranking the better the person or the ethnic group.

Unfortunately, the data did not support the underlying assumption that intelligence can be measured by head size. Too many women, criminals, and other "lower types" had large heads. This fact complicated the results and by the end of the century craniometry and phrenology went out of fashion. However, these scientists were not put off from their underlying assumption that intelligence could be assigned a number that would correspond to the natural ranking of human beings. They thought that all that was missing was the proper way to measure it.

The IQ test filled in the space left vacant by the failed attempt to measure intelligence through head size. Now we used tests and statistical analyses, but the vocabulary of head size lingered on. We still think, talk and write about intelligence as a quantity, a matter of capacity—mental capacity—from the Latin word *cappa* meaning head, cover or cap. By capacity we usually mean the ability to receive, absorb or hold, with the implication that there is a limit to this—a maximum capacity, like a quart jug or a twenty-gallon gas tank. "Capacity" is also related to "capability" meaning "power to accomplish," which means that there is a way to measure capacity separate from ability to perform. It is ironic that a scientific and professional community has spent over a century developing and employing a vocabulary that equates a major aspect of human functioning with a milk jug; but all too often that is exactly how intelligence tests are interpreted.

The IQ test was first introduced to North America from Europe about the turn of the century. In France, according to Stephen Jay Gould, Alfred Binet had developed the tests to study whether children might need additional assistance to succeed in school—not as a general measure of intelligence or human worth. In the United States, however, there was a tremendous social and political push at the time to slow the tide of immigration, and to allow in only the most worthy of people. The IQ test seemed perfect for the task of sorting the worthy from the worthless.

In succeeding decades many variations of the Binet tests were developed to do this sorting. Some of the results would have been laughable but for the fact that they had such damaging effects on the people who failed to measure up. Failure was seen as innate to the person being measured, rather than a failure of the measuring stick or of the very logic that human intelligence could be reduced to a few numbers. People were tested under very stressful conditions—after long and dangerous sea voyages, for example—and with little or no concern for their experience, education, culture or sometimes even their native language.

At one stage scientific journals were claiming that the majority of Italians, Greeks, Slavs, and Jews—southern and eastern European immigrants—plus Negroes and Asians were "morons." There was so much racism in the measurement model that few gave any thought to how implausible was the notion that average persons of many nations should rank below average! In a summation of these egregious errors Gould called them "scientific dogma masquerading as objective fact."

The results of such testing were often devastating to immigrant families when some members were admitted and others deported. But that did not dampen the enthusiasm for the tests and testing. The "data" of the testers and their testimony on their scientific "facts" were used to support the Immigrant Restriction Act of 1924 that established quotas severely limiting immigration from areas other than northwestern Europe.

Then came the economic hardships of the 1930s. Many previously successful people, including professionals of all kinds, found themselves in diminished circumstances. The idea that privilege was a function of innate worth began to be less popular. Gradually, but all too slowly, psychologists and other measurement specialists began to address the biases of the tests and to look for fairer tests. It is sad but interesting to note that until the 1970s there often was no requirement that school children be tested in their native language. The search for fairness in testing continues today, but the professional literature is virtually silent on the validity of the measures that are used to label people as mentally retarded. In our "able-ism" we ignore the fact that such measures can have an impact on disabled people fully equivalent to the immigration quotas and other racial biases of an earlier day.

In the second half of the twentieth century the children of the supposedly inferior races used their education and rising political power to challenge the notion that their race, their ethnicity, their native language or their country of origin should condemn them to second-class status. Through lawsuits and anti-discrimination legislation they have been able to change the way they and their children are viewed. Unfortunately, what has still never been adequately challenged are the notions underlying the IQ test—the assumptions of the basic paradigm that are so dangerous. Here, over a hundred years after they were introduced, many still believe that some of those assumptions and biases are facts. Moreover, within and without the professions there is a belief that they are scientifically proven, true, obvious and legitimate, though perhaps still in the process of being better understood through scientific study. Bias continues to masquerade as scientific fact, but today's victims are people who cannot speak for themselves. Some of the dogma assumes that:

1. Intelligence is a thing (or small set of things) that can be defined, measured and given a number.

2. Human beings can be ranked according to these numbers.

3. These numbers correspond to a "capacity" for acquiring knowledge. This capacity is fixed at birth but can be changed (lowered) through brain trauma, accident, or illness—particularly in childhood.

4. Intelligence, as a matter of quantity, capacity or limit, can be understood in terms of "more or less." Thus an IQ score of 60 means that a person has more intelligence or capacity to learn than someone with an IQ score of 35 and less intelligence or capacity to learn than someone with an IQ score of 80.

5. That such tests can demonstrate that some people stop developing. They can have a "mind of a one-year-old" and be 47 years old. That "mental age" is a reasonable reflection of reality even when we have no assurance that we can actually measure the knowledge of the eight-month-old baby or the nonverbal man of 47 years.

Over the past thirty years many people have begun to question the value of the tests and the whole idea of intelligence as a quantity. What has never been properly taken into account, however, are the communication, voluntary movement and performance requirements needed to demonstrate competence on these tests. A non-speaking person cannot show knowledge on an oral test. A person with delayed response cannot show actual ability on a timed test. And a person with a certain movement difficulty cannot perform adequately on a test requiring dexterity. A person with any or all of these characteristics cannot be tested using conventional instruments. Today, psychometricians try to adapt their tests for obvious disabilities. However, some aspects of disability, particularly those involving symptoms of sensory and movement disturbance, are not always obvious.

So the "facts" listed above are not facts at all. They are assumptions which color the way people study human intelligence, particularly in the field of developmental disabilities, intellectual disability, autism spectrum disorder or other disabilities presumed to affect intelligence. That these assumptions have done great harm to people goes without saying. Our reference list includes several books and articles about that history of harm. Here we are interested in stressing the harm these notions have done to our acquisition of knowledge about the phenomena of differences in intelligence and, therefore, to our field.

Because our scientific culture has assumed that there is such a thing as "mental capacity" and that we can reduce all of human diversity and achievement to a number or series of numbers, we failed to study what people, particularly labeled people, were actually doing. We saw some people as deficient rather than different; stopping in their development; or being slow in approaching normal (or even personhood). Much of our science was about studying how different they were from normal. Our educational efforts were geared toward making them normal. In effect, our enterprise of understanding and supporting people who are different is based on putting everyone and everything into mutually exclusive categories: normal versus abnormal; retarded versus non-retarded; etc. Assignment to a category is based on a score that is related to capacity—intellectual capacity.

In such a model if a person is a fine artist but scores low on an IQ test we say she is a retarded person with savant or splinter skills. We present her art as "very special"—worthy of admiration because the person is retarded rather than because her work is art. We do this even though the person's abilities far exceed the ability of us "normals." But those of us in the non-retarded category of human being who cannot draw or are tone deaf do not get labeled "artistically retarded." Nor are our academic specialties like mathematics or linguistics referred to as splinter skills!

Stephen Wiltshire, a famous young artist, is a clear case in point. He has the label of autism. Yet, according to an episode of the British documentary series *Q.E.D.*, at age sixteen his drawings sold for more than £1,000 apiece. On the show a famous psychologist gives him an "intelligence" test with a heavy emphasis on verbal skills. Stephen does poorly. Instead of explaining how this shows the diversity of human development, the psychologist makes a major error. He says that Stephen has half the intelligence of a normal person and goes on to predict how this "fact" will effect his adult career. The psychologist is justly famous for his work in our field. He is also wrong in his comment. If someone were to ask him what "half the intelligence" actually means he would agree that it is a meaningless statement. Fifty is half of one hundred, but an IQ test score of 50 does not mean the person has half the intelligence of people who score 100.

We are emphasizing his comment here only to show that for most of us the ideas and assumptions we hold about intelligence are so deep rooted that we make these kinds of public pronouncements even when we clearly know better. As a field we have the idea of capacity as part of our language and our thinking so that it has become automatic to think this way. We say "lower functioning," "mental level," "lesser intelligence" as if intelligence and retardation were real, quantifiable entities. Intelligence is thought of like the contents of the crockery in Figure 1.1, and people have more or less of it. And the word "retardation" always means less, and always means permanent.

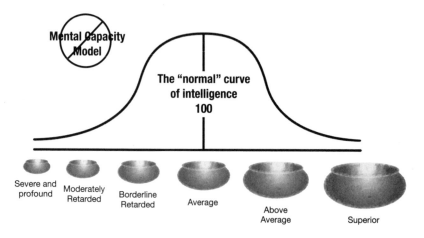

Fig. 1.1. The mind is not a vessel to be filled but a fire to be ignited

As we have mentioned, for some thirty years a few clear-sighted advocates and professionals have been telling us that normal and abnormal, retarded, autistic, etc. are political, social, cultural notions rather than reflections of some objective, clearly discernible reality. They have been saying that like intelligence, autism is not a "thing" at all. We are lending our voices here to the voices of Doug Biklen, Burt Blatt, Bob Bogdan, Judy Duchan, Gunnar Dybwad, Robert Edgerton, Seymour Sarason, and Steve Taylor, to name a few who have been teaching us that "normal" is a fluid term which changes its meaning from context to context. Their writings are referenced in our reading list.

Until now, too few people have listened. We suspect that the reason these voices have not been heard in the past, and the implications of their message acted upon, is that we did not have the information necessary to develop alternative explanations for what we experienced. That is, we did not have a paradigm, a notion of development which could account for the fact that some people who seem slow or infantile or uncomprehending to us—who seem to fit so well the social category we have called retardation—might be "different" without being inherently inferior of deficient.

We are saying what Blatt and others are saying: Autism is not a THING. Just as intelligence is not a thing. These are merely concepts used to describe phenomena we have barely begun to understand, just as we barely understand "normal" learning. We can observe and experience and study the phenomena, but not as a thing (so big, so wide, so tall, occupying so much space). We must study as we experience them—as expressions of individuals' ability to interact with people, ideas, materials and environments. If a person is unable to act in a standardized manner we have essentially no information, yet, about what that means. But we know for sure that it does not help to say he has a "thing" or "condition" called retardation, because that term labels but does not inform.

What we are NOT saying

Before going on it is important here to emphasize what we are not saying. In dismissing the notion of mental capacity and stressing the potential impact of symptoms of sensory and movement differences we are NOT saying any of the following:

We are not saying: Everyone is the same. There is no variation among people in their ability, knowledge or talent.

We are not saying: All of the difficulties experienced by people on the autism spectrum are related to sensory and movement differences.

We are not saying: Everyone on the autism spectrum/developmentally different is OK, even a genius "underneath"—just limited in the ability to let us know what they know.

We are not saying: Having identified the problem of sensory and movement disturbance we can, should and will be able to "fix" it.

We are not saying: Because a difficulty is related to a neurological problem such as symptoms of sensory and movement disturbance we cannot use positive behavioral technology to assist the person to deal with it.

We are not saying: The presence of symptoms of sensory and movement disturbance means that all language, perceptual, cognitive, and emotional functions are operating effectively.

What we ARE saying

Obviously there are differences between and among people and many of those differences will have a significant impact on a person's life. The impact of symptoms of sensory and movement disturbance on a person's ability to think and feel is not well understood. But these differences are *not* a function of capacity as we have historically defined capacity. Capacity, as we have said, is thought of in terms of an ability to "contain"—a measure of volume: *A mind is not a vessel to be filled but a fire to be ignited.*

We think that researchers such as Esther Thelen and Gerald Edelman from recent history and Lev Vygotsky and A. R. Luria from nearly a century ago, provide us with incentives for alternative explanations that lead to new ways of thinking. With the late great Esther Thelen, we are saying that intelligence and ability are functions, at least, of genetics, development, interaction and context that dynamically self-organize. That differences among people are enormous but, to date, very poorly understood. Why is one member of a musical family a prodigy, another tone deaf, and a third an avid painter? Why can one child play soccer brilliantly and her brother trip over his feet despite the best attempts to teach him?

Particularly difficult to understand are the differences that result from unusual genetics or exceptional development experiences. Neuroscientists like Gerald Edelman are helping us to understand that development is entirely *individual*; even identical twins have developed different brains by the time they are born. Much of this development depends on movement, Edelman says. Registering changing experience, responding to emotion, calling up memory—the cornerstone of what we think of as mind—is all movement. We are adding to Edelman's notion of idiosyncratic, individualized development the idea of significant difference. That is, to the extent that people have problems with movement of actions, thoughts, emotions, speech, and memories, they may have had a very different course of development from their earliest days and these differences can continue to affect them and change their experience. They are, likewise, going to be viewed very differently than youngsters with more typical developmental experiences. Therefore, their interactions with the world will be altered as well as the contexts in which they learn.

Perhaps an example will help. An infant son born to deaf parents will likely be given hearing tests and, if found to be deaf or hearing impaired, offered a wide variety of accommodations and communication options. He will almost certainly learn sign language from his parents and their community. According to Oliver Sacks's book, *Seeing Voices*, in learning sign in infancy he will develop brain patterns remarkably different from his "normal" peers. And he will continue to develop in different ways, but we can in no way call those differences "deficiencies." He will develop different social and cultural skills. If given most standardized IQ tests, even with a signing interpreter, he will perform differently, and possibly less well, than his speaking/hearing peers. On tests that tap the developmental experiences of deaf people he would probably score far higher than his hearing friends. Yet it is no surprise but nonetheless sad to learn that for decades deaf children were routinely diagnosed as mentally retarded. Still today, they are often considered to have diminished capacity relative to their hearing peers, even when we clearly know that they can flourish if given the appropriate education and experiences.

So, even where there is a clear impediment (an inability to hear) we learn and understand more by seeing the child as different, *not* as defective. To think of a deaf child as retarded on the basis of a low test score would be dangerous to the child and useless to the teacher.

The term retardation, the idea of retardation, is equally dangerous and worse than useless. It includes the notion that someone can stop developing, has a limited capacity to develop, or is developing on a "regular path," but so *very* slowly that he will never catch up. The idea of retardation keeps us from understanding that he or she may be developing very differently, but developing nonetheless. These differences may be very real and very debilitating but they are not going to be understood if we limit ourselves to old and dangerous assumptions about mental capacity.

An alternative model

> A child whose development is impeded by a defect is not
> merely a child less developed than his peers. Rather he
> has developed differently.—Lev S. Vygotsky

To begin to account for significant differences without including the notion of lack of capacity we found it useful to learn from a school of "Exceptionality" which evolved from a different tradition, the Russian school of "defectology." In English the term has a very negative connotation. It helps to think of the study of constraints or impediments rather than defects.

In the former Soviet Union, where for much of the twentieth century IQ tests were illegal, scientists and practitioners often approached defect or abnormality as a manifestation of human diversity. Their great psychologist Lev Vygotsky suggested that we must study development which includes those who are developmentally different in order to understand all human development. He based his approach on an idea of child development very different from our western idea that some children stop developing normally. Instead, he saw that a constraint or impediment would cause a child to develop differently much as any growing, living organic matter, a tree or a plant for example, which could not grow in one direction would grow around the impediment.

Vygotsky's work, published in Russia 75 years ago, is having a major impact on education and psychology in the west. His writings on diversity and disability have only relatively recently been published in English.

In this short text we cannot begin to present his very complicated and advanced ideas. Taking the idea, however, that development does not stop while an organism lives, but instead takes different paths, can help us begin to view developmental differences and autism from a perspective of ability rather than deficit and damage. Within this perspective we can begin to understand the accommodations that can be made to include people with such differences in the mainstreams of our society. In this Vygotskian view we will never understand human development unless we include the patterns of diversity. "Disability" and difference are part of that diversity and essential to understanding it. Likewise, if we are to have a human community we must have full inclusion because difference and accommodation are essential to building community. In making our case for full inclusion we are not asking that people assume persons with autism or developmental difference have genius, or even competence in all the same areas as each other or their peers. We are merely asking that we *not* assume incompetence or accept exclusion because someone cannot respond in the ways we expect her peers to respond.

In the next section we will explore symptoms of movement differences and the effect that they may have on people labeled autistic and retarded.

II. Sensory and movement disturbance and difference

In section I we introduced the topic of sensory and movement differences, the term given to difficulties some people have in starting, stopping, combining, executing, continuing and switching movements. The movements that we refer to are not just actions and postures. The experience of many people and the clinical observations made by physicians and others have indicated that symptoms of movement disturbance may also affect persons' sensory perceptions, speech, images, thoughts, memories and emotions. We begin our discussion here with a summary description of the issues around sensory and movement differences for people on the autism spectrum or other developmental differences.

The diagnosis of autism is not prescriptive of the type of supports needed for assisting the person to participate, relate and communicate. Relationship is the basis for participation and communication, for all people. People with autism often communicate, behave and participate in unique, very personal ways that may be difficult to relate to and understand. Differences in the way people are able to use their bodies and focus their attention leads many people to assume that a person does not care to participate or communicate and does not desire relationship. These assumptions affect our expectations for people, the way we speak with them and the educational and social opportunities we offer to them. Our assumptions color the support we give to people.

People on the autism spectrum move their bodies in ways that are unfamiliar to most of us. Some people rock, repeatedly touch an object, jump and finger posture while other people come to a standstill in a doorway, sit until cued to move and turn away when someone beckons. As professionals trained to believe what we see, most of us have interpreted these movements as volitional behaviors, communicative acts signaling avoidance of interaction and evidence of diminished cognitive ability. We have taken a "literal" interpretation of what we see and extended it into a notion of what constitutes autism.

Some behaviors may not be intentional, but an artifact of the difficulties a person may have in organizing and regulating sensation and movement. Other behaviors may be subtle signs of the desire for relationship or expressions of meaning. When we focus on our standard expectations for behavior and communication in our fast-paced, super-technological world, we may miss opportunities to know and understand people who are likely among the most patient and best listeners on the planet.

Detailed personal descriptions of sensory and movement differences found in other disabilities have given us some clues as to what it may be like to deal with symptoms such as being overwhelmed by sensory input, having compelling impulses, a loss of conscious control, lack of initiation, akinetic moments and unusual ways of being in the world. Leary and Hill (1996) analyzed the literature on symptoms associated with established movement disorders and those associated with autism. The greatest difference among these disabilities was the interpretation of the symptoms. In Tourette syndrome, Parkinsonism and Catatonia, there was a neurological interpretation of symptoms. There was a social interpretation of the same symptoms if the person had a label of autism. That which is called a "tic" in a person with Tourette syndrome is most often considered a "behavior" (and often a conscious choice) in a person with autism. A "bark" by a person with Tourette or another movement disorder may be viewed as neurological, in autism it is a behavior to be reduced often with a negative intervention.

Humans carry inside, an image of themselves that includes reasons for and the possibility of change. We need to know that we are OK just as we are, even though there are things we may want to learn or to do better. In our journey of change, we need allies who will collaborate with us to find the most comfortable and effective ways for us to learn new ways to participate in our families, with our friends and as contributing members of our communities. Supports for people on the autism spectrum should reflect the respect and dignity due to all people and address the challenges with which people struggle in organizing and regulating themselves in response to the sensory environment and their movement differences.

How we came to understand aspects of sensory and movement difference

Symptoms of movement disturbances may be more easily understood by discussing the history of some of the syndromes that are defined primarily by the presence of movement disturbance, for example, Parkinson's disorder or Tourette syndrome. Research on symptoms of movement disorders goes back to the nineteenth century. The possible connection between symptoms of movement disturbance and "mental" disorders was first discussed in 1874 by Ludwig Kahlbaum, a German physician. A summary of Kahlbaum and others' descriptions of patients can be seen in the list below. In the nineteenth century the term catatonia was used. Later, catatonia came to be defined more narrowly as a kind of schizophrenia characterized by absence of movement. Regardless of the terms used, there has been a continuing awareness of these behaviors in persons diagnosed with a variety of psychiatric and neurological disorders, including autism.

Characteristics of catatonia

Simple disorders of movement:

- Repetitive movements—self-stimulation, repeated actions.
- Abnormal facial movement—expressionless, flaccid or fixed expression, abnormal eye movements, grimaces, teeth-grinding, facial tics, lip movements.
- Abnormal gait—too fast, slow, halting, peculiar, stiff walking.
- Mannerisms—posing, unusual manner of eating, tic-like movements.
- Blocking and freezing—lack of movement, difficulty starting movement, stopping during on-going movement, difficulty completing actions.
- Unusual postures—odd hand and body postures, flexion of neck, trunk or limbs.
- Abnormalities in muscle tone—too little or too much muscle tone, rigid, floppy.

More complex disorders of volition:

- Automatic obedience—excessive compliance, follows commands instantly.
- Echopraxia—forced imitation of another person.
- Lack of imitation—unable to imitate others.
- Negativism—does the opposite of what is expected or routine.
- Stripping.
- Extreme suggestibility.
- Difficulty initiating actions, postures, thoughts.
- Difficulty stopping or switching actions, postures, thoughts.

Very complex disorders of overall behavior:

- General overactivity—continuous movement, difficulty stopping.
- Impulsiveness—action without consciousness of motives, easily aroused without inhibiting components.
- Frenzy—explosive or violent movement episodes.

- Destructiveness, aggression.
- Self-mutilation.
- Extreme response to minor changes.
- Decreased activity—motionless, stays in one place for long periods, difficulty initiating.
- Decreased responsiveness—little or no response to others, aversion to contact with others, stupor or arrest, deepening and intensification of attention.
- Maintenance of postures—including thought and perceptual postures.

Disorders of speech:

- Vocal and verbal tics.
- Stereotyped verbalizations.
- Mutism—lack of speech or decreased use of speech.
- Slowness or delay in answering.
- Labored speech.
- Unusual vocal melody—lack of intonation, sterotyped intonation, monotone voice.
- Unusual loudness of volume—shouting, screaming, whispering.
- Disturbance of rhythm of speech—talks too fact, too slowly, with unusual stress patterns.
- Outbursts of speech.
- Swearing.
- Falsetto voice.
- Repeats names of places, cities, towns.
- Unmotivated laughter.
- Echolalia.
- Repetition of words, phrases, topics.
- Unintelligible speech.

(Sources include: Kahlbaum 1874/1973; Bleuler 1911/1950; Abrams and Taylor 1976; Wing and Attwood 1987; Sacks 1990; Realmuto and August 1991; Lund, Mortimer, Rogers, and McKenna 1991; Johnson 1993.)

Interest in symptoms of movement disturbance was rekindled during the great encephalitis epidemic in the early part of the twentieth century. For ten years people around the world developed a range of unusual symptoms after having *encephalitis lethargica* or "sleepy sickness." The details of this epidemic and its aftermath are described in Oliver Sacks's book *Awakenings*. At the time there was much interest in symptoms of movement disturbance because so many people had been affected by sleepy sickness. However, as time passed and many people with the devastating symptoms were confined to institutions, the interest waned. At the same time internal squabbling and politics among the fields of neurology, psychology and psychiatry resulted in each continuing along their separate ways.

By the end of the epidemic very few paid attention to these movement disturbances in individuals with "mental" problems. In the field of psychiatry for most of the twentieth century, these strange movements were generally thought to be secondary aspects of psychological illness or weakness. They were seen as manifestations of emotional distress rather than intrinsic differences in the way people function. Thus people who were immobile were thought to have withdrawn from the world because of severe trauma. People who wriggled their fingers in front of their eyes were blocking out reality or, later, "merely" engaging in self-stimulation. This particular view of such behavior provided little or no useful insight into the nature of these persons' experience nor how they might be helped.

Twentieth-century psychiatrists have used the term catatonia as a movement disorder specific to schizophrenia. This has led to confusion about the nature of catatonia and has undervalued the neurological basis of movement disorders. In contrast to the view that catatonia is a type of schizophrenia, the literature contains documentation of a wide range of causes of catatonia including: infections (e.g., encephalitis lethargica, herpes simplex); vascular events; brain lesions; metabolic differences (e.g., porphyria, carbon monoxide poisoning); drugs (e.g., alcohol, neuroleptics, lithium); and epilepsy (i.e., non-convulsive epileptic status). It has been refreshing to see the return to the use of the term catatonia to describe movement disturbances regardless of the diagnosis or label given to a person.

More recently, several British neuropsychiatrists led by Daniel Rogers have gone back to the old descriptions (that is, from the nineteenth century) and used them in order to explore symptoms of movement disturbance. In the early years of the twentieth-first century Dr. Lorna Wing, a British physician, autism researcher, parent and lifelong advocate has revived interest in catatonia related to autism. Her publications have summarized data on autistic people who were hospitalized or came to the autism clinic and met criteria for a diagnosis of catatonia as a movement disorder. The term catatonia is applied to the various disturbances in movement, including unusual postures, tics, dystonia, volition or the "will" to move and disturbances of overall behavior and speech.

In *Characteristics of catatonia*, above, we list some of the symptoms that have been associated with catatonia. Our interest is in understanding the symptoms, rather than the label, syndrome or diagnostic category. Many of these symptoms have also been identified as problematic for people with labels of autism, Down syndrome or developmental disability. A review of the literature documenting this association is contained in the journal article, *Moving On: Autism and movement disturbance*, written by Martha and her colleague, David Hill, and referenced in our Reading List. (The complete article is included as Chapter Six of this book.)

Daniel Rogers and his colleagues have established in their work that, although these symptoms of movement disturbance may be present in people with developmental disabilities, the symptoms are often dismissed as bizarre behavior or self-stimulation. For those individuals who have been prescribed anti-psychotic or neuroleptic drugs the strange movements have been attributed to medication side effects. Rogers and his colleagues conducted a series of research projects that took a different look at the relationship of these disturbances to the cluster of symptoms called tardive dyskinesia. This name is given to a variety of physical symptoms (e.g., abnormal, uncontrolled movements, tics and tremors) which occur in individuals who are given certain anti-psychotic drugs. Following the introduction of these drugs in the 1950s, the interest in movement disturbance was again rekindled among physicians.

Possibly because the symptoms came to the attention of physicians who prescribed the anti-psychotic medications, the drugs alone were thought to be responsible for the presence of movement disturbance symptoms. In the tradition of neurology, Rogers and his colleagues began to study the symptoms that were affecting people, rather than the syndrome called tardive dyskinesia. Rogers's studies showed that many patients in chronic care hospitals who had diagnoses of psychosis or mental handicap (a British term for cognitive impairment) showed symptoms of catatonia whether or not they were currently taking drugs, had ever taken them, or had never been on such medications. Analysis of the data showed that the presence of symptoms of movement disturbance cannot be explained solely by the use of anti-psychotic medications.

This is an important point because it forces us to review and revise the relationship between movement problems and the labels of autism, developmental disability, intellectual and cognitive disability, Down syndrome and the like. We can no longer assume that unusual or strange movements are solely side effects of the drugs. Psychiatrists and neurologists also will likely be looking ever more carefully at the effects of drugs on the development of symptoms of movement disturbance. Rogers suggests, for example, that in some conditions the drugs may hasten the progress of the disorder. (Progress, in this context, usually means deterioration of the patient.) In this book we have followed the model of Rogers. We are interested in understanding the role of symptoms of sensory and movement disturbance in the conditions that our society calls autism/intellectual disability.

We will now consider a few of the ways that symptoms of sensory and movement disturbances may contribute to what people may think of as the labels of autism, developmental disability, intellectual and cognitive disability, Down syndrome and "retardation." These include: impressions of retardation; developmental differences; masking of competence; impressions of intentionally bizarre or disturbing behavior; and differences in internal mental processes.

Impressions of retardation

Symptoms of movement differences and disturbances can create an impression of intellectual handicap that is of limited capacity. We human beings judge and evaluate people based on what we see and how we experience them in relation to our expectations. Consider a person who has difficulty initiating an action or saying a word and who spends long periods of time standing in the same posture. It has become natural in our culture to assume that these symptoms mean that the person has limited capacity for understanding and lacks interest in events around him. Our natural assumptions are strongly reinforced when we learn that these symptoms are part of the syndrome of autism/developmental disability. For some other individuals who have *acquired* these differences, the same behaviors may be considered to be symptoms of neurological differences. The presence of these symptoms may or may not indicate limited understanding or lack of interest. It is not possible to know the inner workings of the mind or the capacity for thought based on the presence of these symptoms. We have no standardized tests or medical technology that can give us this insight.

The fact that these symptoms have been either ignored or misunderstood for more than a hundred years has created the impression that they are part of the package of certain syndromes. Our professional field has used the term of retardation, intellectual or cognitive disability to explain people who did not talk and had unpredictable behaviors. Strange movements, stereotypies or "self-stimulation" were somehow a part of the "package" we have called intellectual disability. We seldom looked carefully at the symptoms to try to understand how a person's challenges in organizing and regulating their bodies might affect their ability to communicate, relate and participate in a typical way.

Developmental differences

When a person has *acquired* a disability from an accident, stroke or other trauma, the nature of her disability is different from a disability with the same symptoms that were present from birth. She has had typical developmental experiences and developed skills and social competencies. Consider, however, a child who has had difficulties from infancy, and has no real history of typical interaction. Such a child will have a very different course of development. The presence of symptoms that disrupt the initiation, rhythm and completion of actions and interactions may shape her relationships and create for her strong assumptions about her own ability to participate. As well, when she does not perform as expected we use the label retardation, with all the assumptions and associations it carries to explain her. Those assumptions and her unusual behaviors affect our further expectations and limit our interactions with her. The term "retardation" has included with it the notion of lack of capacity and absence of knowledge, rather than lack of ability to perform on cue. Because we have not understood the possible contributions of neurological differences to what we call retardation, we have treated such children as having diminished capacity.

A child with sensory and movement differences has a developmental experience colored by these factors. Imagine, for a moment, being an infant who cannot calm down or relax his body when Mom picks him up. It is likely that over time mother will pick up that baby far less often than one who seems to enjoy and be comforted by being in her arms. She cannot be faulted for picking up the child less often. Remember we just finished saying that we all—certainly moms included—tend to respond and to judge what is happening in terms of our social expectations. If no one knows to tell her that her baby's body is betraying him, that is sending a message that he is not comforted by her, she is unlikely to guess from her own life experience. Instead, she may think that this is a baby who does not want to interact. The child may continue to develop experiencing fewer interactions than his siblings.

In this regard, some years ago Karel Bobath wrote of how movement difficulties change a child's experience. His ideas certainly apply to the discussion. He described how these disturbances may affect a child's:

- Ability to learn about themselves; for example, very young children put their hands into their mouths.
- Ability to learn about textures, tastes, temperatures of objects.
- Ability to learn about size, for example, their own sizes in relation to objects through reaching.
- Ability to learn about the environment by moving around; about space and spatial development.
- Ability to develop perceptual and motor skills.
- Ability to learn about the power of communication from an early age.
- Ability to develop independence of others.

Masking of competence

Symptoms of movement disturbance may contribute to what we think of as autism by making it impossible for an individual to demonstrate competence. Symptoms affecting movement may have an impact on a person's ability to communicate and relate to others. For example, delay in responding or inability to regulate movements may affect the ability to turn attention from one event to another in a timely fashion, or use conventional signals of communication. When greeted by another child, the child with symptoms of movement disturbance may respond by screaming (too much force in vocalizing), and failing to turn her head or gesture in response (delay in organizing head and arm movements). It is natural to take these behaviors at face value and to feel that the child does not care to interact. The child may not be able to send her partner the conventional signals that communicate, and be unable to inhibit certain signals that carry meaning that was not intended. All communication requires movement.

As we discussed earlier, assessments of intelligence require the subject to perform a particular action or say a particular word within a certain amount of time and under specific and standardized conditions. Therefore, if the person is living with the symptoms associated with a movement disturbance, we have no formal way to assess the person's knowledge or ability. All too often we have forgotten to ask the fundamental question: Can she do what we ask her to do in the time and manner expected? Instead, typically we have assumed that a lack of performance equals a lack of knowledge.

Impressions of intentionally bizarre or disturbing behavior

People may express symptoms of movement disturbance in ways that appear to be intentional behavior. Often support staff, teachers and family members want to know, "Was that a behavior or was it a movement difficulty?" It is not uncommon for people to be asked if they have intentionally done something. In fact, it may not be possible to determine whether the behavior has been "planned" or intended by a person, or whether the behavior has been acted out without intention. The individuality of how symptoms are expressed indicates that each person's behavior is a reflection of both symptoms and personality.

Kate McGinnity and Nan Negri have written *Walk Awhile in My Autism* (CBR Press 2005), which is helpful to students, teachers and others in beginning to understand symptoms associated with sensory and movement differences. Kate and Nan describe their book:

> *Walk Awhile in My Autism* is a book of sensitivity presentations that can be used to promote acceptance and compassion in classrooms and greater communities. Our book is organized as a manual that sets up each activity with what the goal is, what materials will be needed, how to adapt it for younger/older learners and points that can be made. Often, when we want a group of individuals to understand what it is like to have autism, we tell them about it. *Walk Awhile in My Autism*, by contrast, allows the leader of an activity to actually create an aspect of the experience of autism for others. Through this method, classmates (and others) can better identify with and accept their peers with autism as well as become problem solvers and collaborators with their classmates. These activities are useful when doing training for staff, parents, peers and community members.

The belief that problem behaviors are intentional is often the first consideration when there has been an abrupt change in a person's behavior. This is understandable when the behaviors are cause for great concern. However, this conviction may not be the most helpful. This first line of investigation should always include a consult with the family physician to determine whether the person has symptoms of illness. If illness is ruled out, recent changes in the person's life should be considered as possible reasons for abrupt behavior change. When neither of these investigations yields a satisfactory explanation, it may be helpful to do an analysis of the possible role that symptoms of sensory and movement disturbance may play in the behavior change.

Bob is a young man with many interests and capabilities. He loves music and spends a great deal of time each day playing the piano or his electronic keyboard. He also has a label of autism. The people who provide support to Bob have recognized that he has movement differences and have assisted him to accommodate those differences that are problematic for him. Despite this awareness, they were convinced that abrupt changes in Bob's behavior were intentional. The behaviors were described as: not responding even when people spoke loudly to him; swearing at people; saying challenging things to people; belching loudly in public; loud and inappropriate vocalizations and verbalizations; increased self-stimulatory behaviors such as waving his arms wildly in the air; and self-injurious behavior when instructed to stop those behaviors. After engaging in these behaviors, Bob often laughed uncontrollably, indicating to support staff that his behaviors were intentional. People were frustrated and angry with him for his lack of regard for others and his lack of self-control.

With a quick look at the list of symptoms of movement disturbance contained in this section we find that many or all of Bob's recent behaviors are possible symptoms. It may be that Bob is experiencing a particularly difficult time in accommodating symptoms of movement disturbance. When Bob's behaviors are viewed from a movement perspective, it becomes possible to remove the element of blame and to begin discussions with him about the need to find ways to accommodate some of the symptoms that are causing him problems. Some of the strategies may be similar to those listed in the section on accommodations in this chapter. Some of the strategies chosen to assist him may not differ in content from those chosen in the belief that his behaviors are intentional. However, the spirit of intervention and the faith that he will be able to regain self-control are in contrast to a more traditional view that the program changed his behaviors, or that he found out he could not "get away with that" anymore.

Differences in internal mental processes

In the late twentieth century, Margaret Bauman's autopsy studies and Eric Courschesne's Magnetic Resonance Imaging (MRI) studies supported the notion that people diagnosed with autism have differences in the parts of the brain that are associated with sensory integration, movement, the regulation and planning of movement, generation of rhythms, and attention. Most of our knowledge about movement disturbances comes from the literature on individuals who have *acquired* differences. These people develop problems after they have passed through their developmental years. The anatomical evidence suggests that in autism the differences likely occurred in the prenatal or early developmental period. To date, there is still too little information available about people who are experiencing such differences from their earliest years.

Given the state of knowledge about sensory and movement differences in the developmental years, we can only make some tentative statements. In exploring the issue we bear in mind the criterion of the least dangerous assumption. First and foremost, the symptoms of sensory and movement difference are likely to affect more than motor planning, motor control or motor performance differences. Difficulties associated with sensation, memory, perception, emotion and thought have been well documented as accompanying symptoms of movement disturbance in conditions such as Parkinsonism, catatonia and Tourette syndrome. It seems safest for the moment to assume that for some people labeled as autistic/developmentally disabled symptoms of movement disturbances may also affect internal as well as external ability. If, for example, as Gerald Edelman says, memory itself is an internal movement, a disturbance in memory processing or access might result in substantial differences in the person's way of knowing and being in the world. Barbara Moran, a woman with autism who has considerable artistic talent says that when it comes to thinking and using language, "My mind gets there in the end, but it takes the scenic route!"

Symptoms versus syndromes

As long as we toss all differences into one of a few categorical syndromes with labels such as autism, developmental disability and retardation, we will continue to neglect to ask essential questions about how these symptoms affect a person's experience. We have not asked these essential questions because we thought in labeling a symptom or a disorder we had already answered them. We have been caught up in a movement disturbance of our own as depicted in Figure 1.2.

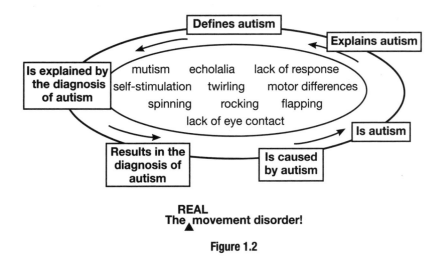

Figure 1.2

Look at the figure and think about what we do when, for example, we diagnose a child as autistic. First we base the diagnosis on certain behavioral characteristics. We then explain those characteristics by the diagnosis. If a child is flapping, has poor eye contact, and has only minimal speech—mostly echolalic—these characteristics help define the child as autistic. Then, if we are asked by his parent, "Why doesn't my son talk?" or "Why does he not look at me? Why is he flapping?" we say it is because he is autistic.

The British neurologist Ian McKinlay has written: "... [A]utism is the 'way people are' rather than a 'thing people have.' It is a reason for investigation, not an explanation in itself." As a neurologist such as McKinlay uses the term, autism is no more explanatory than "anxious." It should cause us to look further at the experience of the persons with the label. In that spirit let us take a closer look.

If we understand that the label neither explains nor even necessarily describes any individual with autism we can begin to ask much more elemental questions: Why is this child not talking? Is it possible that he has some language and understanding but lacks the means to express himself? And what of the child who repeats what other people say, or the girl who can talk only when she is in a panic or very angry? We should be asking: If she can talk some of the time, why is she not talking all of the time? The ability to perform under some circumstances and not under others has also been reported for people with acquired symptoms of movement disturbance. It is time to look in that direction and examine an individual's symptoms in detail. We will likely produce better answers than "... because she is autistic," or "... because he is retarded."

As we learn to ask better questions, to watch with broadened perspective, particularly to take the individual's perspective whenever and however possible, we may really begin to understand these differences. We can at least start to communicate with and about people more effectively; to know what is real and what is created by our attitudes.

Motor disorder, movement disturbance, and sensory and movement difference

Recognition of a symptom of sensory and movement disturbance will not automatically suggest ways to accommodate it. That is not to say we would not try. Trying is the point of this book. Changing the context, the presentation, the rules, the material, the equipment, the teaching strategies and—most importantly—adjusting aspects of our interaction style and relationship may assist the person in ways we have only begun to imagine. We will discuss these kinds of accommodations and others more fully in the following section.

For now we want to stress that accommodations are not attempts to "fix" or eliminate a difference. They are ways that people have devised for themselves or ways to support a person to do what he or she wants to do by finding ways around a difficulty. Identifying the difference does not ensure that we will find a way to accommodate that difference, but it is a step toward finding a balance.

In the model we have presented for understanding the symptoms of sensory and movement difference "movement" refers to more than actions and postures. These symptoms may also affect speech, images, thoughts, perceptions (sensations), memories and emotions. Only the first two are obviously physical, yet at a neurological level all are forms of movement. The English language betrays an implicit understanding of this when we use terms like "shifting opinions," "bringing up memories," and "being emotionally moved." In fact, the Latin root of the word "emotion" is *movere*, meaning "to move."

There are three related terms used in this text—motor disorder, movement disturbance, and movement difference—and we need to distinguish among them. Outside the medical profession "motor" refers almost exclusively to muscular activity, especially that involving the limbs, hands and feet. Neurologists are apt to use motor for a far wider range of movement. This is particularly true of British writers. Daniel Rogers's important book, *Motor Disorders in Psychiatry*, deals with the whole range of behaviors that we prefer to use the term "movement" to describe for a North American audience.

Disorder, disturbance and difference are value-laden terms. The first two, especially "disorder," imply deficiency. The third, "difference"—the term we prefer—does not. We do not dispute that movement differences may create enormous hardship for many; nor are we unaware that movement differences are often the consequence of identifiable trauma, accident, or illness. But whether a difference *disturbs* depends on a number of factors including the context or environment of the person.

For example, rhythmical, repetitive movements of the body are often referred to as self-stimulation or even "self-stims." These are routinely regarded as both undesirable, meaningless behaviors that are indulged in by individuals for pleasure and, in behavioral terms, are self-reinforcing. Treatment programs are sometimes designed and implemented in order to reduce the frequency of self-stimulatory behavior. The goals are usually related to improving a person's attention to task, timely completion of tasks or improving participation in interactions. However, often the goals may be related to making the individual appear more normal. Thus the object of treatment for the man who spins around before sitting down may be to eliminate bizarre or unusual behavior.

In using the term sensory and movement differences, we recognize that the repetitive movements that some call self-stimulation may serve a purpose for a person in accommodating or adjusting his movements to meet the physical, perceptual or emotional demands of the situation. Alternatively, the repetitive movements may not be performed for a reason, may be involuntary or automatic movements and/or the individual may not be conscious or aware of them. The presence of these movement differences makes it necessary for many of us to re-socialize ourselves to accept that some people move very differently. Just as we accept and tolerate other differences among people, a decision to set treatment goals for the elimination of unusual or repetitive behaviors should be based on issues such as personal choice or safety.

Unfortunately, many people assume that all such behavior is a disorder or a disturbance to be controlled by external force if necessary. In our work we try to stress that a behavior does not automatically need to be changed just because it is different. As well, in our interactions with family members, classmates or people in the community who may be unsettled by unusual behaviors, we have found it important to explain briefly that the person who rocks his body and flaps his hands while standing in line at the bank is doing just fine. He just moves differently. In our own experience the more we learn about people with movement differences the less likely we have been to label a behavior as a disturbance. Figure 1.3, which David Hill and Martha developed for explanatory purposes, outlines the concepts. Here are some examples from our own lives:

> **Starting**: Sometimes I cannot start a song until someone gives me the first couple of words. When addressing a group, I may "clear my throat" before starting to speak.

> **Stopping**: I get a thought or tune in my mind that will not go away even when I wish it would (Oliver Sacks writes of these as "ear worms" in his book, *Musicophilia*). Humming tunelessly even after someone has politely asked me to be quiet.

> **Executing**: Realizing that I have stepped on my dance partner's foot and then not being able to dance well from that point on. Sometimes I get nervous and talk faster and louder than I need to.

> **Switching**: I become absorbed in a funny movie or book and then have a hard time joining a serious conversation.

> **Combining**: When I am driving in a wicked storm, I need to turn off the car radio. I find it difficult to have a pleasant conversation while shivering in a cold room. At that point, I usually can only focus on how miserable I am!

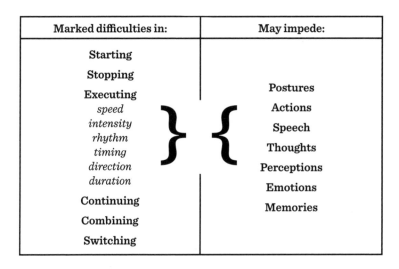

Marked difficulties in:	May impede:
Starting Stopping Executing *speed* *intensity* *rhythm* *timing* *direction* *duration* Continuing Combining Switching	Postures Actions Speech Thoughts Perceptions Emotions Memories

Figure 1.3
Clinical considerations of movement difficulty.
Adapted from Hill and Leary 1993.

While things like this happen to all of us, they may not be obvious to an observer unless we talk about them. For example, if we cannot or do not say that a book or memory has made us sad, a friend may misinterpret our gloomy expression or demeanor as a personal rejection. On the other hand, if it is known that we are overcome with grief because of a recent tragedy, such a response is understood and accepted.

Persons without speech are at a disadvantage in telling us about these difficulties. When they do they are apt to describe them as vastly more inhibiting than the everyday ones we listed above.

The following list of quotes and comments (some prepared by our colleagues Jodi Robledo and Karen Strandt-Conroy) illustrates symptoms of sensory and movement difference described by persons diagnosed with Parkinson's, Tourette syndrome and autism, identified by the initials **P**, **T** and **A** respectively. The sources are cited in parentheses and can be located in the reading list.

> **P**: Rachel would become intensely excited. At these times she would be uncontrollably echolalic, repeating anything one said to her in a shrill screaming voice hundreds or thousands of times in succession (Sacks 1990).

A: Temple Grandin recalled feelings of stress when being asked to perform two motor tasks at the same time: "Getting all the parts to work together is a monumental task" (Grandin and Scariano 1986).

T: Dana states, "When I started to get stuck on words I felt like a record repeating itself" (Tourette Syndrome Foundation).

A: "Speaking for me is still often difficult and occasionally impossible, although this has become easier over the years. I sometimes know in my head what the words are but they do not always come out. Sometimes when they do come out they are incorrect, a fact that I am only sometimes aware of and often pointed out by other people" (Jolliffe, Lansdown, and Robinson 1992).

A: "At worst, the stress of direct, emotionally loaded communication either blocks the brain's ability to retrieve any or all of the words needed to speak a fluent sentence or won't allow the process of articulation to begin, leaving the words echoing within the speaker's head. The frustration of this can lead, as I described, to the deafening scream of frustration that may or may not get out of the speaker's mouth" (Williams 1992).

A: "The more I wanted to say or show something, the more my own Exposure Anxiety was tuned in, hanging on my every expression. My body, my facial expression, my voice and my words were pulled about by some wild horse inside of me. I'd want to say I was sad, my face would be beaming. I'd want to sit calm and still and enjoy a sense of company, my body would be propelled into wild diversion responses demonstrating discomfort and hyperactivity. I'd try to tell someone I liked them and swear at them, try to show caring and be compelled to do something to repel them" (Williams 2003).

P: Gertie C. said she had lived in "a state of 'great inner stillness' and of 'acquiescence': her attention would dwell for hours on whatever object or thought entered its field.

... She would spend hours and days and even weeks reliving peaceful scenes from her own childhood ..." (Sacks 1990).

P: Sudden traumas such as deaths or loss of job were noted to "cause" the onset of the Parkinson condition or the stress would increase the Parkinson's characteristics (Sacks 1990).

A: "Sometimes only one thing can go in at one time. So the sight could go in first, then fade out because the sound is coming in. When the sigh fades only the sound is left, it is the only information the person is getting, which makes it sound louder because it is all he can focus on" (Rand 1999).

P: "The irony is that nothing is wrong with the [Parkinsonian] person's motor system per se. The tendons, the nerves, and the muscles are intact. The problem stems from the communication between the brain's commands for the actions and the body's response time in obeying them" (Carroll).

A: Jim, one of the individuals with autism interviewed, offered insights into his stereotypical movements. Jim stated that "Stereotypical movements aren't things I decide to do for a reason; they're things that happen by themselves when I'm not paying attention to my body" (Cesaroni and Garber 1991).

A: Jim also reported that combining and synchronizing movements was as difficult as trying to make your eyes blink at opposing times (Cesaroni and Garber 1991).

P: Movements are no longer the routine. As one patient put it, "My body doesn't always do what I want it to anymore, so I have to keep telling it who's the boss; where once my body did it all now my head has taken over" (Carroll).

P: "Parkinson's is always with you ... unpredictable, persistent. The only pattern you can be sure of is its consistency. You know each morning when you wake up that the shaking and stiffness will be there bringing new trouble of some kind" (Carroll).

T: "Tourette's syndrome involves every aspect of the affective, the instinctual and the imaginative life" (Sacks 1985).

A: "Autism affects everything all the time" (Jolliffe, Lansdown, and Robinson 1992).

A: "Once I was in mother and baby club, I didn't like it because of all the people talking and it sounded like thunder. That's the same reason why I didn't like going to town in the early days. All the noise was terrible. I did not get on very well at nursery school. On bright days me sight blurred. Sometimes when other kids spoke to me I could scarcely hear them and sometimes they sounded like bullets. I thought I was going to go deaf" (*A is for Autism*).

A: "I was often lazy in school because sometimes me ears distorted the teacher's instructions or me eyes blurred to stop me seeing the blackboard properly. Or sometimes I would hear a word or two at the start and understand it and the next lot of words sort of merged into one another. And I could not make head or tail of it. I can now recall that one could sometimes refer to my vision and hearing as being like an untuned television" (*A is for Autism*).

A: "As a child I wanted to feel the comfort of being held; I craved tender touching. At the same time I withdrew from touch. Being hugged was like being swallowed by a tidal wave" (Temple Grandin, *A is for Autism*).

A: "I still become visually overloaded. It's because my brain can process only a tiny amount of sensory information at a time—the exact opposite of having a multi-track mind, more like having only a fraction of a track. Tinted lenses help some but could never reduce the extra input to nothing unless they were painted solid black. Which sometimes I wish they were. If I could get away with going around blindfolded there are times when that would be easier than being distracted by a bunch of visual clutter that I can't process anyway. Vision has always been my flakiest sense so I'm well adapted to only using it as a backup sense when the others don't work. Unfortunately tinted glasses only go so far to fixing it, just like I have astigmatism and near-sightedness they can't totally fix with regular glasses" (Amanda Baggs, personal communication, April 7, 2012).

A: "A wish I have is that I can be myself, not a fake normal. When I try to play your part by acting normal I am in pain. Weird actions I do, like touching items and spacing out, protect me from sounds and sights that are painful to me. We people with autism experience the world differently, and therefore, we need to react to it in a different manner" (Stup 2011).

An emerging understanding of the symptoms of sensory and movement difference and the resulting difference has made us reexamine work that we did several years ago. In Anne's earlier research with Pat Mirenda a delayed response in conversation was identified for several students. Although it was not the focus of our research at the time, interviewers who were in conversation with twelve young adolescents with minimal verbal skills, all labeled developmentally disabled or autistic, were asked to wait expectantly for as long as it took them to respond. We were surprised to discover that everyone in the study was capable of offering unexpectedly good conversational responses if people were patient enough to wait for them to reply. On average they took fourteen seconds to begin!

Fourteen seconds is a very long time. The normal wait in a conversation in our culture is less than two seconds; after that we typically repeat a question, change the subject, or abandon the conversation. Most likely we would see such a long delay as a failure to respond and make a firm and probably negative judgment about the person we addressed. Now take a minute, if you will, to imagine how different your life might be if it took you fourteen seconds to begin a response and that you had no way of indicating this delay to people who addressed you. How long would it be before you either let yourself be passively managed or blew up in anger to gain some control of your circumstances?

Suppose you also had a difficulty with stopping? Suppose some of your most difficult behavior was automatic, so you were simultaneously blamed for behaviors you could not stop? We are suggesting that many people labeled autistic may have difficulty with both voluntary and automatic behavior, terms that we will discuss in the next section.

Voluntary and automatic movements

An important aspect of understanding movement is the difference between voluntary movement (intentional movement) and automatic behavior (perceptual motor habits). Voluntary or purposeful movements are those we need consciously to think about (however slightly) in order to perform them. Automatic movements are those that, once learned, we perform without much conscious thought. Many of our daily routines, such as driving a car, are performed with sequences of automatic movements that were originally voluntary. It may take a great deal of practice to learn some new skills. Once learned, these automatic movement sequences form the core of our skill base. Many people can ride a bike, walk on a sidewalk or shave in a mirror without giving it much thought.

The classification of movements into automatic and voluntary is not as clear cut as we have described. Although it is sometimes helpful to think of these two categories, almost everything we do is a mix of the two, there being automatic components buried in actions we might consider almost totally voluntary. It is the automatic actions that generally lend smoothness to our behaviors. We gave an example above of how our dance fluency may be lost after we accidentally step on a partner. Our language fluency may also be affected if we are in a situation where we have to think before we speak. In general, the more relaxed, familiar and routine the situation the easier it is to rely on established skills.

A familiar example may help describe the difference as well as the interactions of the automatic and voluntary systems. Think about making a call on the keypad of a telephone. We punch in those numbers with fair ease, even new or less familiar numbers. We may not have deliberately memorized the keypad but the buttons are so much a part of our experience that we can be both smooth and rapid. Something about the act of pushing the buttons in a familiar pattern helps us remember them. A person may have a repertoire of automatic behaviors that include delicate and intricate movements that become totally inhibited when the situation changes and there becomes the need to perform them voluntarily. It is a characteristic of automatic movement sequences, that smooth performance is very context-dependent. When an aspect of the context changes, we may lose our ability to perform automatic sequences with ease. For example, when you use a different phone, it is likely that your fluent ease with the keypad is stymied. Now think about calling a number that has been given in some word code: say, 1-800-HOLIDAY (1-800-465-4328). The word helps us remember the number, but makes pushing the buttons clumsy and slow because our movements have to be so much more deliberate—that is, voluntary.

Here is an illustration of the differences between starting or initiating voluntary and automatic movements for a person with a movement difference such as oral apraxia: a person cannot put his tongue out on request (voluntary movement) but is able to automatically lick ice cream cones or clear peanut butter off his lips. So long as the behavior is central to one's focus and has to be thought about it may be either impossible to do or performed with difficulty. When it becomes peripheral—and calls primarily on automatic rather than volitional movement—it may sometimes be achieved with ease. Sometimes, the more you think about it, the less likely you are to be able to do it.

Colleague Alan Kurtz gives an example of a common difficulty some of his friends with autism have stopping or inhibiting an automatic response:

> Almost inevitably, when I ask a person with autism to smile for the camera s/he offers me what Judy and Sean Barron call the "Fake Smile." It is unnatural, contorted, and overdone. If I wait `for the person to relax or tell him or her that I am done s/he usually beams a naturally beautiful smile. Obviously, the person has the motor skills for the task but it becomes difficult when s/he is put in a demand situation.

Some sensory and movement differences cause more problems than others

All people become accustomed to making the constant adjustments that make participation easier. After sitting in a chair for a few minutes, we make small adjustments to provide our bodies with inner comfort, that is, we move our legs, cross them or shift our weight in order to remain seated. For some people on the autism spectrum the constant adjustments to facilitate participation are often unique and not easily understood by others. The neurological basis for these adjustments is just not something most of us have experienced. The behaviors associated with a neurological symptom are not "learned" or performed as a matter of choice. The often unsympathetic judgments of others may lead people with these neurological differences to believe that their differences are a kind of character flaw, rather than a difference in their ability to organize and regulate sensation and movement.

Differences in the ability to tolerate and the need for touch are common among people on the autism spectrum. This can be seen in simple differences such as not being able to tolerate tags or scratchy textures for clothing. People on the autism spectrum often report that light touch, unexpected touch or touch from a stranger can be disconcerting. Children with touch sensitivities may become overwhelmed by constant touch (even if it is meant to be a pleasant event), especially if the impressions of touch do not quickly fade away as typically happens in most people.

However, differences in this sensory system can lead to larger difficulties. Some people may not adequately experience the kinesthetic feedback from their body that lets them know their position in space. People may seek deep pressure in order to regain a sense of their body image. People seeking deep pressure or joint compression may position themselves under a mattress, under the cushions of the sofa, jump on the floor or bed, wear ten snug-fitting tee shirts or bang their fists on hard surfaces. They may go to the bottom of the swimming pool to feel the increased pressure or simply thrive with the "touch all over" sensation of being in a bathtub or the swimming pool. Temple Grandin explored this aspect of her sensory system long ago when she invented the "Squeeze Machine." Temple reported that when she controlled and felt the deep pressure from her squeeze machine, she felt calm comfort and a lifting away of anxiety. Her insights have been very helpful to others on the autism spectrum in finding appropriate ways to accommodate to sensory and movement differences.

Sensory differences are often very specific and the ways in which they are manifest are extremely personal. Some people cannot tolerate bright lights, loud sounds, certain scents or foods of certain textures. These preferences and sensitivities can change over the years, so that a young boy, who shows great fear of the sound of a lawnmower, may be drawn to that sound as a young adult. Some people seek motion to stimulate the vestibular system such as in car rides, swings and rides at amusement parks. Climbing and seeking heights are also common ways for people to experience their sensory systems more adequately or acutely. Two of the books in our reading list that are terrific resources for understanding sensory and movement needs are *Building Bridges through Sensory Integration* and *Walk Awhile in My Autism*. Consult the upcoming section IV, "Accommodations," for further discussion on supporting people to find good sensory and movement balance in their daily lives.

A neurologically-based movement symptom that can cause particular difficulty is akathisia, causing unpleasant sensations of inner restlessness. People with this symptom may have a periodic inability to sit still or remain motionless. As an outside observer, one might say, "Why can't he just sit still?" Participation in school, social gatherings, meetings, religious ceremonies and most relationships demand that a person be able to stay put—at least long enough to listen to a conversation, eat a meal or say a prayer. But what if you could not stay still? You might find that you need to adjust all of your activities to accommodate to this restlessness. We have held planning meetings with a number of people where we have set up the environment to allow the focus person to pace around the room, even to leave the room to be in a vestibule area in order to keep listening and continue moving. One young man we have met has learned to make tea for his guests by drawing hot water from an urn and remaining in one spot while doing so. But in order to accomplish this he must bend and straighten his legs repeatedly while drawing water into the teacup. One observer dismissively judged that the young man was doing this for attention. We have found that people who do not have personal experiences of sensory and movement differences, may judge behaviors such as this harshly.

Some people are troubled by vocal, verbal or physical tics. Loud vocal tics have especially been a challenge for students in inclusive classrooms and people in gatherings where quiet concentration is required, such as a concert, a theatrical performance, a synagogue or the library. The nature of tics is usually misunderstood by most of us. Tics can be suppressed for a time, but ultimately must be released. The more attention that is paid to the tic, the more difficult it becomes for a person to suppress the tic. A history of having an episode of tics in a particular place will make it more likely to happen upon returning to that place. Things that are forbidden often become tics by the very nature of having been forbidden—making the tic more likely when it is a taboo.

Festination is a neurological symptom that is little understood and is frequently experienced by people with developmental differences and/or autism. Festination is defined as "unnecessary hurry." This symptom seems related to a perception or sensation of rhythm and speed and subsequent regulation of movement. We often hear of people who: always walk very fast and ahead of their partner; eat so fast that they choke on their food and overstuff their mouths; and cannot hold a steady clapping beat, instead racing to an out of control series of progressively smaller and faster claps. Observers usually assume that this speed is a choice and often judge the behavior as indicative of an inattention or a negative personality trait. Oliver Sacks wrote of festination in his post-encephalitic patients as something of which they were unaware, something that happened as a result of their neurological differences. Some of his patients who either moved excessively fast or laboriously slow spoke of having "lost their rhythm."

Akinesia or blocking, stopping or freezing is another neurological symptom found to be common for people with autism spectrum or other developmental disorders. To an outside observer, akinetic episodes can look like a complete lack of movement or response; small movements like repeated touching; moving feet sideways or backward; or reaching toward a particular direction. Akinesia is particularly evident at transition points, such as when attempting to get started or to initiate movement. Akinesia can affect whole body movements, but is also evident for some people in an inability to initiate speech, to move an arm or look in a particular direction. Freezing can also be problematic when a change in perception or adjustments in movement are necessary, such as when passing through doorways or crossing from one ground cover or floor pattern to another.

Some sensory events can cause enormous emotional and physical reactions. One young boy with autism responded consistently to the fire alarm at school by spinning wildly until he fell to the ground. When viewed as a "behavior," we heard unknowing observers claim that he just needed to "learn" to behave properly during fires drills. Truth was this boy was not in control of his body during this spinning. The intense sensory event caused the action in his body.

Bradykinesia, or excessively slow movement, is a neurological symptom often seen in people with sensory and movement differences. People may keep moving, but make little progress in relation to those of us who move at an increasingly faster pace. Dressing, bathing and eating can take hours for a person who moves this slowly. Observers may use the words "unmotivated" or "lazy" in describing people with bradykinesia, without recognizing the amount of effort required for a person to keep up.

Other puzzling symptoms of sensory and movement disturbance are the involuntary performance of unwanted or feared actions, or the intrusion of unwelcome thoughts, memories or emotions. Of course, everyone experiences these in life; however, for most of us intrusive thoughts are usually brief and can be put aside. People with Tourette syndrome, obsessive-compulsive disorder (OCD), autism spectrum disorder or Parkinsonism report having concerns with intrusive thoughts. Involuntary behaviors or thoughts of feared actions may be brief and tic-like, or complex rituals that take minutes to complete; and may, as Gertie C. told Oliver Sacks, last for days extending into months.

Perhaps this is a good point to return to Kahlbaum's table of symptoms of movement disturbance on pages 38 and 39 and review the list in the light of what we have written about difficulties in starting, stopping or inhibiting voluntary and automatic movements. Many of these symptoms are commonly found in people labeled autistic or mentally retarded. How differently would you begin to judge that person if you were to see the strange behaviors and silences in the context of sensory and movement differences?

What happens if you put yourself in the person's place? For us, we begin to see some "behaviors" quite differently than we had in the past. A person may be struggling to stay in an interaction, to contain a behavior, or to keep from disturbing a situation with involuntary movements, noises or rituals. Our attention is drawn to the person when they fail to inhibit a behavior, but we fail to see the incredible number of times he was able to inhibit behaviors successfully. With such a perception we begin to see our relationship to that person very differently. This is a person to learn from as well as to teach. This is a person to work with, not to work on. This is a person who has likely found strategies to accommodate for his or her differences, and to keep *disturbance* to a minimum. Our job is to support, help expand and extend those strategies, not *for* the person, but *with* the person.

III. Sensory and movement differences and effective teaching strategies

One way we have been able to accommodate people with sensory and movement differences in the past has been through the use of good, clear teaching strategies often based on the principles of behavioral psychology. The reading list will help you identify several good books on this topic. We particularly recommend Anne and her colleagues' book, *Progress without Punishment*. Immodest though this suggestion may seem, it is a good book on the topic of strategies for teaching and for addressing behavior problems in a positive fashion, and written for people who are not behavior psychologists. Many of the strategies included as positive behavior practice have relevance to the difficulties faced by people with movement differences. It is recommended that the reader review these strategies in the light of the information contained in this present book. Here we will be able only to summarize a few of the salient points. We will try to tie successful strategies to what we are learning about movement differences.

We will use the word prompts in this section because it is familiar to many readers as a form of help given to people to bring about a correct response. Technically, there is little difference between an accommodation (discussed in an upcoming section) and a prompt; but there is a subtle theoretical and philosophical difference in the way we use these terms. Prompts are ways that parents, teachers, colleagues, caregivers and others support people to initiate or inhibit behaviors. Accommodations attempt to create an environment that supports peoples' choices to perform or inhibit their own behaviors. As you will see, we believe the notion of prompting is also a good one, but typically it implies external control of a person's behavior. We want to remind ourselves of the importance of using prompts as cooperative not controlling efforts.

Understanding the downside (and power) of verbal cues in teaching technology

For those of you who have learned a new dance, like "Line Dancing" or a tap-dance step, you have felt the lack of coordination and clumsiness that accompanies that new learning. When you have to think about each step you take, you are relying on voluntary movements. Your instructor may give you verbal cues to initially teach you the steps, but eventually you may say these cues silently to yourself and learn to move without thinking about the steps. For many people with symptoms of sensory and movement differences, the leap from following verbal (spoken) instructions to going through those instructions silently never happens. Instead the sequence continues to require two people with one person saying something before each step in order to accomplish the movements. The other person and the verbal instructions have become an integral part of the automatic movement sequence and cannot be easily faded from it.

For reasons we still do not quite understand, verbal (spoken) cues are particularly tricky in at least two ways. One, spoken cues are so routine and natural we often put them in without realizing. Many people have learned most of their skills through an adult telling them each step of a skill sequence. We think of spoken cues as the most natural way of teaching. When we do not know anything else about teaching technology, we tend to fall back on our most common cultural teaching technique, telling someone what to do. Unfortunately, spoken cues seem to be particularly hard to get rid of or to fade use. When spoken cues become part of a skill that should eventually become a solitary, independent skill we feel frustrated. The teaching interaction that was meant to lead to independence has instead become a social routine. We have had hundreds of parents, supporters and caregivers in the English-speaking world report that the people they support are "hooked on prompts," that is, they are able to complete a task but must stop and wait for step-by-step spoken directions. For example, a person can dress himself completely as long as his supporter says, "Pick up the shirt," or "And what's next?" for every step or combination of steps.

In one particularly telling example, a teacher and child we know well had gotten inadvertently into this kind of a pattern. The teacher told the little girl every morning to put her locker key on its hook. The teacher did not realize she herself had become part of the routine, but one morning when she was busy taking care of an emergency the child came in and stood next to the rack, key in hand, for fifteen minutes. Finally, in exasperation, this little one who almost never spoke called out, "Say, 'Put the key on the hook!' "

Other types of cues may also inadvertently become incorporated into the automatic movement sequences being taught. In teaching the morning "settling-in" routine, a teacher asks the child to put his lunch box on a shelf and the child does not respond. The teacher repeats and repeats, pointing and (typically) getting louder. Finally, he brings the child over to the shelf, touches it and says, "Here, put it here!" This student who may learn best through literal repetition of interactional sequences may unintentionally learn to touch the shelf as the teacher did or to store the lunch box this time and every subsequent time, by going through the same interaction with the teacher.

Unfortunately, our teaching strategies sometimes lead to assumptions about the student's intentions, motivation or capacity to learn. In the process of teaching without understanding the student's experience, we miss the possibility that the student may long to do what is being asked of him, but need a more thoughtful teaching strategy for the actions to become automatic movement sequences. The student is doing exactly what he was taught to do. So, we say, "Be careful what you teach, he might learn it!"

Understanding and using the discrete trial format

We start with the assumption that some people have sensory and movement differences that sometimes make it difficult to do, say or learn what they want to when they want to. Given our emerging understanding of the characteristics of sensory and movement differences, we are also beginning to understand why certain teaching strategies have worked so well and others have proved to be inadequate. Our discussion will focus on one particularly useful strategy called "discrete trial format" (DTF). It has a long history in the behavioral literature and was successfully applied to work with children with autism in the 1970s. Basically, the word "discrete" is most important here, meaning that every effort is made to make the component parts of the teaching interaction as "separate and distinct" as possible.

In the previous section we discussed voluntary and automatic movements. For people with symptoms of sensory and movement difference, both types of movement may present challenges. However, experience has shown us that once a person is able to incorporate automatic movement into his repertoire he is often able to function more independently in specific skill areas. Although it may take a great deal of systematic teaching, the automatic movement sequences may become basic skills upon which he can build more elaborate skill sequences. *The discrete trial format is designed to build those automatic sequences or perceptual motor habits that become the basis for building functional skills.* The cues, the sequences of movements and the outcome change little from one teaching session to the next. Therefore, it becomes possible for the individual to eventually perform the sequence without thinking about each movement.

The discrete trial format is a teaching strategy that we have seen used to help many hundreds of people on the autism spectrum or with developmental differences to achieve certain goals. The value of the discrete trial is not confined to recent professionally marketed and distributed programs of massed trials of artificial tasks for dozens of hours a week.

The values and goals of the best discrete trial use have to do with learning ordinary everyday tasks at home, school or work that people wish to do fairly automatically—from shoe tying to sorting papers. Having a large repertoire of such automatic movement sequences makes life easier for anyone. First person stories from people who have sensory and movement differences such as Parkinsonism have stressed the importance of being able to independently participate in these basic tasks.

It is probably safe to assume that most people would like to be offered respectful assistance in learning such sequences.

The discrete trial format requires that any new learning be approached in as thoughtful and systematic a fashion as possible. It is a powerful technique and should be used with care. First make sure that you are teaching something that is useful, meaningful and relevant to the child or adult; something she might actually want to learn. It takes a great deal of effort for some people to participate in these activities. Do not ask an individual to make that effort for a task that is disrespectful busywork.

Second, try to take the learner's perspective. Exactly what is it this person wants to be able to do at the end of this effort? In discrete trial terms this means specifying the response. Be as clear as possible about what is to be a "correct" response for this occasion. These are individual decisions. Setting the table, for example, might mean putting one or two mats, plates, glasses and spoons down for a parent and child, or setting up for a three-course dinner for a house full of guests.

Third, decide what kind of assistance you are going to give the person. Assistance (usually referred to in the literature as a prompt) should be given BEFORE the person makes a mistake. This is very important if you are going to avoid developing long chains of irrelevant behavior before the correct one. Thus far, assume that Mike, in our example below, has learned no part of this task. The sequence might look like this:

> You: "OK, Mike, it's time to eat. I'll help you put these
> items where they belong. Let's set the table."

> Mike stands there. You physically assist Mike to put each
> item where it belongs. DON'T TALK as you do this. When
> you are finished, congratulate Mike on his new skill. If
> Mike makes a mistake, say in a clear but neutral tone:
> "Sorry, Mike, it doesn't belong there. Let's start again."

Then you begin again. You want each step in his new skill to be "connected" to the whole sequence.

Some helpful hints:

1. Avoid unnecessarily talking when teaching tasks that don't require talking. Explain to the learner what you're going to do and then stop talking until the task is done.

2. Pick a prompt (a form of assistance) that will bring about a correct response. Often this is a full physical prompt. If physically touching the learner is acceptable to her, and does not make either of you look ridiculous, use it. It has the advantage of being easy to fade out as the learner starts to be able to initiate and execute the task properly, she may begin to rely on her "motor memory" of the skill.

3. If the person's preference or situation does not allow for a physical prompt, use another form of assistance that can bring about correct actions and is able to be faded. Do not use a verbal (spoken) prompt. The book *Progress without Punishment* gives many examples of other prompts that do not require talking. In the present case, you could use the materials as a prompt. A plastic mat with outlines of utensils could indicate where each of the items goes, or the table might have a properly placed setting that the learner can use as a model. You could gradually fade the lines and items in the model until an ordinary, unlined mat on an empty table is used.

4. Don't talk until the correct actions are complete. When the task is done use conversation to socialize. Remember, very few of us want someone jabbering in our ear when we are trying to learn something new or difficult.

5. If at all possible, start all over again when an error occurs. Remember, you want each action to be tied to the complete sequence. If it is not feasible or reasonable to go back to the starting point, find a step that seems a natural break in the sequence.

We think you will find this teaching strategy useful. We cannot say exactly how it works or why it works so well. We know it has helped hundreds of teachers and parents teach useful skills. We can speculate that it allows individuals on the autism spectrum/developmentally disabled to smoothly perform some basic skills, without interruption and without having to rely unnecessarily on others. As long as the tasks are reasonable and we are working *with* not *on* the person, we are comfortable saying: Try it, you'll like it!

Our reading list includes other useful teaching strategies for communication and social behaviors, such as waiting an unusually long time for a response. We think that ultimately all such successful strategies will be thought of as accommodations. In the next section we will address these strategies, these accommodations, as we have learned about them from people with sensory and movement differences.

IV. Accommodations

A bit more history

In 1932 Aleksander Romanovich Luria, a brilliant Russian psychologist and neurologist, wrote a book about his work on the control of behavior called *The Nature of Human Conflicts*. With crude equipment for measuring brain activity, consisting mostly of machinery like the electroencephalograph (EEG), Luria and his colleagues began to explore and develop a new area of human research, that of neuropsychology. They were interested in the role of *willpower* in overcoming difficulties that people with neurological differences experienced in controlling their behavior. Their interest stemmed from the fact that many researchers before them had described control in terms of willpower, suggesting that when people have difficulties, which they cannot overcome, lack of "will" was at the root of their problems. Luria believed that the concept of willpower in such circumstances was a myth. He wrote, "... the human cannot by direct force control his behavior any more than a shadow can carry stones." Not direct means, such as force of will, but indirect means were found to be the most effective. The experiments successfully taught people ways to "accommodate" to their neurological differences. People learned to give themselves signals that might aid them in controlling movements. For example, they might blink their eyes rhythmically in order to assist themselves to initiate and sustain a finger-tapping movement.

Luria wrote of the need for people with difficulties in movement control to develop substitutions for the normal methods of motivating movement that are inaccessible because of neurological differences. Years later Oliver Sacks met Luria. In his landmark book, *Awakenings*, from which we draw many examples, Sacks credits Luria for his understanding of the importance of accommodating rather than battling such problems by force of will. Sacks likens the process of findings and developing these accommodating strategies to a sailor successfully navigating through a storm:

> Neither defiance nor denial is of the least use here: one takes arms by learning how to negotiate or navigate a sea of troubles, by becoming a mariner in the seas of one's self. ... Accommodation is concerned with weathering the storm.

In his work with people who had post-encephalitic Parkinsonism, Sacks was intrigued by the notion that some individuals were able, temporarily, to overcome movement difficulties through finding a balance or a way around a problem. Direct attempts to stop the difficulty or to make themselves move were rarely effective. Yet many had devised their own tricks or accommodations to handle their differences. Sacks understood, as Luria did, that no amount of willpower was going to affect the tremendous challenges faced by these individuals. But he was enormously impressed by the ingenuity they showed in creating and implementing their own indirect means of accommodating to their neurological differences. He devoted a chapter to accommodations in *Awakenings* and they appear throughout the feature film that starred Robin Williams and Robert De Niro. Painting the squares on the floor for Lucy, who had lost her visual rhythm, is one you may recall. If you have not seen it, or even if you have, it is worth watching again to better understand this topic.

How we define accommodations

Accommodations are the personalized strategies that assist in temporarily overcoming differences in sensation and movement that are problematic to a person. Accommodations include the use of gesture, touch, rhythm, rituals, visualization, music, repetitive movements and other strategies to temporarily overcome difficulties starting, executing, stopping, combining and switching actions, postures, thoughts, speech, language and emotions. An accommodation assists the individual by activating mechanisms for control, regulation or change of movement. An accommodation may be performed alone by the individual with a sensory and movement difference or may involve another person; it may also include materials or equipment.

The person (or their supporter) may discover an accommodation accidentally or through repeated experiments. In *Awakenings*, Sacks writes that one of his patients described to him how she seemed to need to be "re-musiked" at times. Her accommodation involved thinking about specific music, songs—the type she loved to dance to—in order to establish a rhythm with which she could move. A patient of Luria's, Ivan, had a tree painted on the wall near his bed so that he could arise in the morning by imagining himself climbing the tree.

Sacks also noted the importance of relationship in supporting people to accommodate to sensory and movement difficulties. He wrote of some of his patients being able to move if certain staff moved with them. They could walk beside a particular person or persons, but not with others or alone. He wrote that people were sometimes able to move smoothly and rhythmically with another person when they might otherwise be akinetic, "stuck" or frozen in movement, or the opposite of stuck, moving with increasing speed in festination. One of Sacks's patients described this type of accommodation. "When you walk with me," she said, "I feel in myself your own power of walking." The touch of another person may have the power to assist in starting, stopping or switching movements. Sacks described the assistance of another person as not only the stimulation of the tactile sense or the visual image of another person moving which assisted a person to accommodate to movement difficulties. He describes this special relationship as an art:

> The art of handling Parkinsonian patients, learned by sensitive nurses and friends—assisting them by the merest intimation or touch, or by wordless, touchless moving-together, in an intuitive kinetic sympathy of attunement—this is a genuine art, which can be exercised by a man or a horse or a dog, but can never be simulated by any mechanical feedback; for it is only an ever-changing,

melodic, and living play of forces which can recall living beings into their own living being.

   Some people are more aware of the movement difficulties that challenge them and although awareness alone is not enough to create an accommodation, it is a step in the right direction. With awareness comes a greater ability to analyze a situation and to problem-solve various ways of accommodating. Sacks described the experience of a woman who could not regulate the speed at which she moved. She was either motionless or running. This presented great difficulties for everyday living activities. Through ingenuity and analysis of the situation, she devised an accommodation for moving about in her apartment which included calculating the angle at which she would bounce off the wall in order to arrive at her desired destination! The following section details many other accommodations, and discusses how some accommodations were developed.

   The medical literature has more recently begun to explore the power of accommodations. This literature refers to accommodations by the words: sensory tricks; forced tricks; or the French expression "gests antagoniste." The focus of research has been for people with the movement disorder dystonia, and more specifically, cervical dystonia. The research on the use of touch has been very promising as an accommodation for helping people to release from a dystonic contraction. One piece of research found that consistent use of touch to accommodate a dystonic episode was in some cases as effective or more effective than an increase in medication. More research on accommodations would be very helpful as evidence-based techniques carry more credibility than techniques that are shared through personal stories. A stumbling block to research on accommodations is that for the most part they are not products, and in very few cases does anyone make a profit from distributing an accommodation. The only profit to be made on most accommodations is the relief of the person with the symptoms of sensory and movement differences.

   Our Wisconsin colleagues, Kate McGinnity, Sharon Hammer, and Lisa Ladson, have compiled a book that details some promising practices utilizing visual supports and technology to get around difficulties. *Lights! Camera! Autism!* (CBR Press 2011) offers strategies that can easily be described as accommodations since the intention of the supports is not to cure anyone of a problem, but to provide a means for getting around a difficulty. The authors describe their book:

> *Lights! Camera! Autism!* is a book about using video technology to support individuals with autism spectrum disorder. We define video technology broadly, to include PowerPoint presentations, SMART boards, iPads, iPods, iPhones, and all manner of electronic devices and applications for these and similar devices. The match of autism neurology and technology is discussed and explained. The book is filled with examples and stories from our classrooms and consulting work and includes a DVD supplement. Most importantly, we are clear in our respect for individuals with autism and the value of "collaborating with" instead of "doing to."

Developing accommodations: proceed with caution

Sacks discussed the uniqueness of expression of the post-encephalitic Parkinsonism in each of his patients. The symptoms were never ever the same from person to person. Each person had unique ways of expressing the difficulties he experienced with organizing and regulating movement, sensation, postures, speech, thought, awareness and emotion. The same was true for each person's way of accommodating to these challenges. Sacks wrote:

> I know of no simple way, no set of criteria, which allows one to predict whether a satisfactory coming to terms of this sort will occur. Certainly the severity of the original Parkinsonism or post-encephalitic illness is not itself a good index. ... One must allow the possibility of an almost limitless repertoire of functional reorganizations and accommodations of all types ...

As we proceed in this section it is of the utmost importance that the reader bear this uniqueness in mind. One person's accommodations to difficulties associated with sensory and movement differences may create even more severe difficulties when applied to another person.

What follows could be viewed as a distillation of the stories of many different people. Some come from published first-person accounts of individuals who have labels such as Parkinsonism, Tourette syndrome, autism or other developmental disability. Many of the accommodation stories come from unpublished sources—individual people and those who support them have been generous in sharing their experiences in accommodating to their sensory and movement differences.

In order to bring some organization to our thinking about accommodations, we have created some categories and charts. We do not use these artificial categories as a cookbook (e.g., "Hmmm, let me see. Difficulties switching attention. Ah yes! We need to use the tactile category!"). Rather, we use them to stimulate creative thinking for considering a range of possibilities for personalized accommodations. It is for this purpose that we share them with you.

Experience with accommodation

In section II, Figure 1.3 is a simple chart to aid in understanding some dynamics of movement and the types of personal experience that may be affected by differences in sensation and movement. The degree of severity of symptoms of a sensory and movement difference may vary moment-to-moment depending on the environment and the physical or emotional state of the individual. Ordinary sensory perception and movement require a delicate balance of the forces of activation and inhibition and results in the effective regulation of movement. If the force of activation is too great, we may see an excess of force or a flurry of movement. If the force of inhibition is too great, we may see a lack of movement or attention or possibly movements that are extremely slow and labored.

When we are feeling comfortable and stable, the balance between forces of activation and inhibition is usually not too difficult to achieve. It is something that comes naturally. For a person with sensory and movement differences, the natural, unconscious aspect of balancing may be lost at times.

In order to think about the balancing task it may help to draw upon common experience. Imagine, for example, that you are pulling a cork out of a champagne bottle. If you exert a great deal of force on the cork by pushing or pulling straight away from the bottle (activation), the force may result in splashing champagne on the ceiling (disturbance). Those with more than one champagne bottle opening experience have learned to balance the activation force with a dash of inhibition. That is, you cover the cork with towel and twist the cork slowly as you pull it gently from the bottle. It is the balance of activation and inhibition that makes for a successful uncorking. Incidentally, a similar balance is needed in searching for that coveted human quality of moderation, especially when drinking the champagne!

Accommodations are the things that people use to find the balance they need to regulate movement when the natural, unconscious mechanisms are not enough. Some of the following positive examples may help to demonstrate the range of accommodations that may be brought to a variety of sensory and movement difficulties.

Touch and rhythm help Doug to initiate

Doug tries to start talking. He gives eye to eye gaze, a tense, broad smile and begins vocalizing with his jaw clenched tightly shut. His vocalizations are rhythmic and continuous. Sometimes he also rocks forward and backward, foot to foot. He reaches out to people with one hand. If he touches a person he is sometimes able to talk. His speech comes rushing out like a dam that has burst. After noting this accommodation, one sensitive staff person also notes that if he nods his head in time with Doug's rocking and vocalizations this may also accommodate Doug's difficulty starting speech.

Visualization helps Asham to start

Asham has difficulty coordinating his perceptions, actions and motivations to begin getting dressed in the morning. He is able to start the task independently when he uses visualization. Asham pictures himself fully dressed and sitting at the breakfast table. Without thinking further about it, he finds himself dressed and ready for the day.

Following an established sequence helps Raymond start, stop, combine and switch

Getting through the complex sequence of actions necessary for going for a walk was difficult for Raymond. Gathering the necessary items (shoes, coat, keys), putting them where they belonged (feet, body, pocket) and passing purposely through the house (through doorways, over patterned carpet, past the hardwood floor) presented major challenges to his ability to start, stop, switch and execute movements. Once out the door there were endless possibilities for distracting stimuli. Would the car be in the driveway? In which direction should he walk? What would he encounter on the walk? Would he be able to stop walking in a direction to turn back for home when he was tired? At times the event presented so many barriers that he thought it best to stay in the house even though he felt better after exercising.

Raymond and a friend worked out a sequence for minimizing the number of adjustments that were necessary for him to prepare for and take a walk. The items that he needed were always kept in the same place. He gathered and used them in a sequence that varied little from one time to the next. He passed through the house using the same route each time. Once outside, he always went in the same direction. "The Walk" route was laid out and followed exactly each time. The accommodation of an established sequence assisted Raymond with the numerous transitions. The end of one part or the presence of a certain object signaled or cued the next part. The rhythm and sequence of events allowed Raymond to balance and regulate the actions, thoughts, memories and motivations for proceeding smoothly. Things went so well that Raymond was soon using variations on the accommodation theme. He established the "summer walk" (sun hat, no coat), the "winter walk" (coat, gloves, hat and boots), the "rain walk" (add an umbrella) and even several variations for the route (long walk, stop-at-the-store walk).

Writing things down helps Christine to stop and switch

When Christine saw things that were broken she felt compelled to talk about them, and had difficulty stopping and switching her attention and speech from that topic to another. She would begin by commenting on the broken item and, if nothing was done about it, she eventually found herself out of control or in a rage. This difficulty presented itself frequently, as there are many things in a big city that need repair (doorbells, burned-out light bulbs, dented cars, etc.) and they cannot be fixed immediately. Christine could not switch her attention, speech and emotions away from things that were broken. Instead, her attention, speech and emotions grew more intense. Although she understood that others found her reaction to be unreasonable, it seemed impossible for her to stop this reaction and switch to other concerns.

An observant support worker noticed that Christine used a journal to chronicle the day's events. She took comfort in writing down details on things that interested her: the number of people at the supermarket today, the weather in major cities. Working together, Christine and the support worker developed an accommodation to help her begin to address her challenges with things that are broken in her community. She began to inventory the broken items found each day in a small notebook that she carried in her purse. When she saw something in need of repair, she wrote it down in her notebook. If an item appeared for several days, she might share her concern with others in writing. For example, she contacted the city maintenance department regarding burned-out streetlights, and put in a maintenance request at work regarding a broken door latch. Although there continued to be times that Christine could not stop and switch, she most often found that writing it down helped her to accommodate to this challenge.

People use accommodations without permission!

In the examples above, people used accommodations that were fairly clear. The people around them had noticed the beneficial effects of touch, rhythm, sequences, visualization and written language. The accommodations were recognized and accepted by others.

However, it is not always possible to see an accommodation, or to know that a person is using one. Donna Williams, whose insightful books can be found in our reading list, refers to these as her "tricks," because she often needs them to trick or trigger herself into action. Sometimes the person using the accommodation may not be able to let others know what they are doing, and often, it is none of our business. A problem may arise when a situation changes a person's access to an accommodation. Consider Raymond, whose accommodation of using the rhythm and sequence of events to get around and to exercise might no longer work if he were to move to a new home. It may take him a considerable amount of effort to re-establish his former level of competency in a new setting, with new rooms, new floors and new places to keep the objects he needs.

Jonathan had several sleepless nights when he moved to a new house. For ten years, he had been able to organize his body posture, thoughts and emotions in order to prepare for sleep. Each night he followed the same sequence of events and this sequence became an effective accommodation for settling himself for the night. An important part of his sequence before getting into bed was to set the dining room table for breakfast. If by chance the table were not set, he would toss and turn until he was allowed to get out of bed to set the breakfast table. This sequence (and thus his accommodation) was not available in his new home. The adjustment to be made was in preparing for sleep without the old dining room table set for breakfast. The old accommodation was not repeated in the new house. He uses a new accommodation now. No one knows what the new accommodation is.

Another type of difficulty may arise when a person uses one socially unacceptable behavior to accommodate another. This can be a major source of frustration for everyone. In psychological or behavioral terms, this might be called symptom substitution. The advantage in viewing the new behavior as an accommodation is that it may be helpful in getting to the real root of the problem, rather than seeking to assist the person in getting rid of behavior.

Franco had a reputation for being aggressive toward others. The aggression had excluded him from many opportunities because of the severity of the problem. For several years, he lived in an institution and his aggressive behaviors resulted in restraints. The rate of aggressive behaviors remained relatively unchanged. After many years of loneliness, disappointment and frustration, Franco had an opportunity to move into a home with people who were supportive and caring. His rate of aggressive behavior immediately decreased dramatically. However, at the same time he developed a problem with soiling himself. Through detailed observations of the timing of soiling and by Franco effectively using augmentative communication, supporters were able to understand that Franco had substituted soiling for aggression. They were able to work together to develop other accommodations, such as adequately preparing Franco for new experiences and offering sympathetic reassurance when he was feeling frightened. If, instead, the support workers had attempted to focus their support efforts on decreasing the frequency of soiling, there may have been an increase in the aggressive behavior or some other problem.

As Sacks, Luria and countless individuals who experience sensory and movement difficulties have reported, there are as many accommodations as there are people and situations to use them. Here we can only begin to report on them, emphasizing that they are always unique and often complex. Sometimes it is critical for us, as outsiders, to understand them, sometimes not. But understanding will require us to tune in and be sensitive to individuals in ways that may be new and different for us. The rewards, of course, are limitless, because such tuning in allows us an unparalleled opportunity for deeper relationships with very remarkable people.

Accommodations are developed in many ways. While awareness of the nature of the difficulty is useful for individuals in beginning to create accommodations, sometimes this is not easy. For example, as obvious as a tic may seem to an observer, a first-person account by J. Bliss, a mature adult who has Tourette syndrome, emphasizes the extensive self-analysis which he needed to perform in order to be able to recognize and feel the moment just before a tic, when an accommodation could best interrupt it. Other individuals report a lack of awareness of an episode of sensory and movement disturbance, only becoming aware when others call their attention to it. For those who are unaware of the occurrence, accommodating will likely include recognition of the antecedents to difficulty or the early signs of a change.

In the following section we have listed a number of accommodations that people on the autism spectrum, their parents, teachers and/or staff have found to be effective for temporarily getting around unusual sensory and movement differences. We share them in the hope that they will spark interest in this topic and ideas to help others. We stress the need to personalize all accommodations. Consider the need for many accommodations—personalized for a variety of environments, and emotional and physical states. Remember, this is *not* a cookbook!

Accommodations that are related to communication

Often when we think of accommodating to sensory and movement differences our thoughts run immediately to helping a person "get rid" of problem behaviors. The following examples are included to demonstrate some of the ways in which people have used accommodations to improve their ability to communicate more effectively:

Staying near and developing relationships:

- A hand touching William's back helps him pay attention during conversation.
- Tickling Ronald's arm helps him stay with you while he listens.
- Reading aloud to Margaret keeps her in the room.
- Whispering to Jose keeps him beside you.
- Singing to Brenda helps her to look at you.
- A touch to John's shoulder before you speak helps him to attend to you.
- Coming close enough for Trevor to smell you helps him to recognize you.

Using symbols:

- A touch to Linda's elbow helps her to use sign language.
- Two fingers on Jason's wrist helps him to use handwriting.
- Scratching Martin's back while he types helps him to express opinions, emotions and preferences.
- Support to Chang's wrist helps him to point to Picture Communication Symbols.
- A hand on Melanie's shoulder helps her to type words to clarify unintelligible speech.
- Typing or writing your questions helps Donna to respond to you.
- Writing down her repetitive thoughts helps Christine to avoid talking about them.

Using speech:

- Typing with support helps Dylan to speak while typing.
- Touching another person helps Andre to initiate speaking.
- Singing helps Rosa to say new words.
- After typing with support Aston is able to continue the topic by speaking.
- Touching Glen's throat helps him to initiate vocalizations.
- Echoing your words helps Barry to add some of his own.
- Reciting poems helps Chris to express his feelings.
- Associating words with particular circumstances helps Mario use delayed echolalia to get what he wants.

Categories of Accommodations

The following categories of accommodations are quite arbitrary, but the reader may find them useful in stimulating thought in relation to a friend or relative.

Accommodation using rhythm or tempo:

- Moving with another person, dancing together.
- Staying in step with another person.
- Marching chants.
- Music: performing a task to a certain tune.
- Reading aloud.
- Reciting a poem.
- Singing.
- Finding something rhythmical in the environment: the sound of a clock ticking.
- Deliberate pacing of movement: counting steps.
- Tapping out rhythms on the wrist or arm.

Emotional accommodations:

- Expressions of confidence, pep talks.
- Affirmations: sayings that promote positive images and emotions.

- Humor: using a joke to break an anxious mood.
- Personal space: establishing a distance consistent with mood and relationship.
- Associations with certain emotional images: memories, visual images.
- Expressing a paradoxical emotion: smiling at someone who is unhappy.
- Eye gaze or lack of eye gaze: to accentuate or dissipate focus of attention.
- Quiet talking on an unrelated topic.
- Social stories that elicit feelings of familiarity and comfort.
- Learning how to recognize and respond to emotions differentially.
- Emotional thermometer to rate feelings of emotional comfort or discomfort.

Visual accommodations:

- Placement of objects: using objects to cue an automatic movement sequence.
- Movement of objects: placing the person's favorite piece of string near your face to help the person attend.
- Positions of people: looking toward the destination, standing near the next activity.
- Use of written language: providing a written or pictorial list of the steps in a task, writing down the key word to name the topic of conversation, writing down the motivator for participating.
- Use of gesture: gesturing to indicate the next step or a forgotten detail, using an assigned word as a cue, using a certain facial expression.
- Watching something move: rolling a ball on the floor, dropping a piece of paper, watching a video of moving water, focusing on the movements of animals or people around you.
- Following lines along a wall, a pattern on the floor or on the ground.
- Sitting very still while waiting for a person to respond may help her to organize her thoughts and speech.

- Using tinted or colored lenses in eyeglasses may increase a person's ability to see details more clearly. Other types of visual accommodations such as prism lenses may also be effective.
- Wearing a peaked hat may help a person to see more clearly by blocking out overhead light.

Verbal or auditory accommodations:

- Spoken instructions: that name the next movement, "on your mark … ," saying words silently to yourself, listening to a tape recording of the instructions.
- Giving a specific direction: to engage in the behaviors one more time, to perform an action incompatible with a dangerous or troublesome action.
- Specific words or "catch phrases": that cue initiation or completion of behavior, movement or emotion.
- Calling a person's name.
- References to the next activity rather than naming a specific physical act needed to get there.
- Remaining silent, relaxed may help some people to initiate.
- Using sentence completion: to cue words or actions.
- A specific person's voice: in person, on tape, or remembered silently.
- Counting.
- Wearing headphones or earplugs may help block out unexpected sounds, specific sounds and excess noise that can cause a person anxiety.

Tactile accommodations:

- A touch on the arm, wrist, shoulder, back, or to the body part which needs to move or stop moving.
- Keeping in contact with another person.
- Backward pressure that opposes the desired movement and stabilizes the arm for assisting with difficult actions, like brushing teeth or using augmentative communication.

- Deep pressure: the "Squeeze Machine"; hugs; wrapping up tightly in a blanket.
- Massage.
- Wearing weighted clothing may help a person to feel his own body and to remain calm.
- Using a weighted blanket or lap pillow may offer enough feedback to allow a person to refrain from constant movement for a time.

Use of an object:

- To touch, squeeze or manipulate.
- Holding an object in front of oneself may give a person something to move toward.
- Carrying an object may provide a consistent "place marker" and help to keep sameness in environments that otherwise contain plenty of variability.

Accommodations using smell:

- Sniffing an object or person: in order to identify a person or object.
- Seeking certain smells: establishing an association between relaxation and scent, purposely eliciting certain memories by smell.
- Initiating movement or action: smell of cooking brings person to kitchen; smell of outdoors helps person to walk; smell of cleaning fluids elicits house cleaning.

Cognitive accommodations:

- Imagination: pretending certain circumstances builds confidence.
- Redirection of attention: choosing a different cue to attend to; distraction; focus attention on familiar object, person or place.
- Auditory imagery: remembering and silently repeating sequences of words, tunes, instructions, praise or encouragement.
- Sound cues: establishing meaning or an automatic response to a particular sound.

- Visual imagery: use of visualization and conditioning in order to cognitively rehearse success in difficult situations; choice of images that call up certain rhythms or emotions.
- Intellectual stimulation: learning or studying new material in order to provide oneself with alternatives to repetitive thoughts or to elaborate on interests.
- Calling up memories: using past experiences to bolster confidence or assist in problem-solving a new situation.
- Imagining an object or hurdle to step over may help a person to initiate movement.

Kinetic accommodations:

- Automatic movements: learning a sequence of movements so thoroughly that performing a task becomes automatic; choosing automatic movements such as riding an exercise bike or running in place as a means of self-control; establishing a sequence of actions, activities or movements to follow when early signs of distress are apparent.
- Movement of a single body part: movement of fingers, eyes, toes, etc., in order to initiate movement in other body parts, or whole body movement.
- Jumping on a trampoline or other bouncer helps to organize and regulate the body.
- Predictable sequences: always following the same path; doing things in the same order; following a schedule; establishing a procedure for changes in schedule; eating the least favorite food first and most favorite last.
- Using indirect sequences: using a series of unrelated actions to lead up to the desired movement, such as touching the doorframe to get through the door.

Recognizing accommodations in everyday life

Many accommodations are difficult to recognize. Sometimes that is just fine. Other times the actions of a person using an accommodation may even appear to be unusual or bizarre to an observer. This may be in part because the context of the behavior or the intention of the person is not clear to us or others.

For example, if we were to observe the warm-up and wind-up of a baseball pitcher without knowing that he was preparing to pitch a ball, we would all wonder what his intention was. He has a great deal of concentration on one hand, but, at the same time, engages in bizarre and unusual sequences of seemingly purposeless behaviors—touching his cap, hitching up his pants and peering over his left shoulder! Technically these are not required for the motor sequence of throwing a ball, but they obviously are useful, and perhaps necessary for these ballplayers in ways that they alone know.

Similarly, for an individual with sensory and movement differences, the personal context and intention may be unknown to a supporter or an outside observer. We tend, therefore, to rely on the known context and may see the unusual behavior as purposeless, silly or bizarre.

It is often not easy to recognize an individual's use of an accommodation. We are accustomed to judging and evaluating behavior against standards of what is normal and labeling other behavior deviant, regardless of the purpose it may serve for the individual. Labels such as "self-stimulation" or "perseverating" help us to dismiss behavior as merely the result of being self-centered or not very smart. In order to view behavior differently, it is necessary to give up some of the labels that we use and begin to observe more closely the timing and results of behavior.

For example, earlier we referred to a woman who uses music as an accommodation to keep her rhythm and her ability to move. Many people on the autism spectrum or with other developmental labels have been described as having inappropriate humming or singing. At times, we have seen behavior programs designed in order to eliminate a person's humming or singing. It may be the case that the person does not wish to be humming and is relatively unconscious of its occurrence. It may be that the person is using humming or singing as an accommodation in order to adjust herself to the demands of a situation or an interaction. It is often not possible to tell the difference merely by judging the behavior as annoying and deciding the behavior should be eliminated.

A man named Kanwal, who had provided us with many insights about sensory and movement differences, described in poetry a daydream which he has had while "stuck" or frozen in movement. He uses this kind of imagery at these times as an accommodation to help himself start moving again. To an outside observer this young man who does not speak might seem to be "non-compliant," non-responsive or engaged in self-stimulatory behavior, as he sits motionless except for a subtle flicking of his shoelaces. We cannot see the visual imagery he is using to get himself reoriented to the time, space and rhythm of his companions.

> Steel gray
> Soot falling lending gloom to town
> Sleet moves in like fog to wash with emotions, covering all
> Sleet melts to light
> Light brings life meeting life
> Kanwal stands leaning on Kanwal
> > (Searha 1993)

In a similar fashion, Donna Williams has described how she "tricks" herself into communicating fluently. These are internal, personal accommodations that help her deal with her differences. She gives the following examples of ways she keeps her exposure anxiety in control. She tells herself things that lessen her nervousness about speaking directly with another person.

- What is being said is of no emotional importance—it is just "babbling," or stating hard facts or trivia.
- That the listener will not be able to reach her, the speaker, via words.
- That her speech is not aimed at the listener but at an inanimate object.
- That it is not speech at all but a song she is singing.

Accommodations that involve another person may be recognized, but not always interpreted correctly. For example, a parent may notice that his daughter is able to mow the lawn as long as he walks beside her. The young woman's failure to mow the lawn independently could be described as reflecting a lack of motivation, a lack of knowledge, or as demonstrating how she is "cue dependent." A different perspective on the same behavior may be that moving together with another person is an accommodation that allows the young woman to initiate, regulate and sustain movement.

In order to assist his daughter, the father may need to help her discover another accommodation that could serve the same purpose. For example, the rhythm of music on an iPod or other MP3 player may help her to initiate, regulate and sustain movement well enough to be able to mow the lawn without dad accompanying her. Another type of accommodation may address the visual perceptual aspect of walking along in straight lines. Innovations come from making sensitive guesses about the nature of the type of assistance the accommodation may be providing. A difference in analysis may produce a different approach to problem-solving a situation. Discovering competence that may not be observable is the best kind of supportive exploration. In the end, Dad may also decide this is an activity he enjoys doing with his daughter.

The accommodating functions of behavior

The notion that some problem behaviors may serve a function for the individual is certainly not new. Anne and colleague Gary LaVigna addressed the topic in their book *Alternatives to Punishment: Solving Behavior Problems with Nonaversive Strategies*. Chapter Three of that book focuses on how to implement a functional analysis of behavior. The authors have drawn up a table to use as a tool for identifying the possible communicative functions of problem behaviors. The table lists four major categories for possible interactive functions of behaviors: Attention, Negation, Comment, and Feeling. These have been studied and written about fairly extensively. Following the interactive functions of behavior, possible non-interactive functions of behavior are considered. Self-regulation, rehearsal, habit, and relaxation or tension release are proposed as functions of behavior that may reflect a person's own attempts to create an internal balance. These non-interactive functions have not been so well-documented.

With an emerging understanding of symptoms of sensory and movement difference we see that self-regulation, rehearsal, habit and relaxation are critical to maturity. Self-regulation is what helps an adult to control her own behavior. Rather than the reliance on the external controls of childhood, adults pretty much control themselves. For people who have sensory and movement differences, learning internal control and self-regulation early in life might be of considerable benefit in organizing and regulating actions, thoughts, emotions, etc. Self-regulation involves controlling ourselves to stop doing something as well as to do something even if we do not want to. Rehearsal (actually doing something, visualizing doing something, or listening to a social story that describes doing something) is a culturally preferred technique for improving performance. Habit and tension release can involve automatic movement sequences, rehearsal or sensory activities that provide a balance in a person's life. It is probably not possible to clearly differentiate these terms from each other because they are so interrelated. Sometimes it seems that habit is something we do not think about. Tension release may be more deliberate but, as you see in our examples, most of the things we do to get through ordinary as well as extraordinary days include a little of each. What is important here is to recognize that people with sensory and movement differences may be doing things that look unusual to us, but the function of the behavior may be just as ordinary as the accommodations that help each of us to organize our own sensory input, movements and experiences.

Most accommodations fall into this non-interactive category. A person may use accommodation in order to prepare for interactions and the actions, postures, speech, thoughts, memories, perceptions and emotions necessary for those interactions. The accommodations themselves are not intended as interactions and can be confusing to an observer. When Rita passes through a doorway she may have difficulty with the transition between one room and the next. Each time she passes through a doorframe she touches the edges of the frame, sliding her fingers across the entire surface, twirls around once and moves on to the next room. It may be that Rita has used touching the doorframe and twirling in order to assist her in that transition. There may be an accommodating function to this habitual or ritualistic behavior which may not be intended as an interaction nor as a recreational activity, but as a symbol of creating a physical, perceptual or emotional balance in order to move across a threshold.

An understanding of accommodations may come from first-person reporting of an individual's view of his or her experience, or it may be a best guess based on knowledge of an individual in many situations. For example, if experience tells us that a touch to Raul's back helps him to respond more quickly or more accurately, we may assume that touch is an effective accommodation. Developing a theory of accommodations may help us to consider that there are events that affect behavior that are not readily observable.

We do not propose that a theory of accommodations should entirely replace the ABC method of analysis. Rather, an analysis that includes possible accommodations will consider aspects of intention that may be internal and not easily observed by an interactional partner or a mediator. In assisting a person who has challenging behaviors, it may be useful to identify the possible communicative functions of a behavior, and consider that there may also be an accommodating function for the person in performing an action.

These analyses may allow a person and his supporters to better understand the range of reasons why a behavior persists. Decisions about whether to recommend a change in a behavior depend on many factors. Identification of a behavior as an accommodation does not also mean that it is the most effective way for a person to get around a difficulty. It may, however, be a starting point for further discussions.

Accommodations within relationships

Accommodations are often developed within a special relationship that a person may have with a parent, friend, teacher or personal assistant. Accommodations may be a natural byproduct of listening to each other. Unfortunately, we often forget to pass on important information about the effectiveness of some accommodations that develop within relationships. These accommodations sometimes go unacknowledged as having a key role in self-regulation.

An experienced support worker described her early work with a young man with challenging behaviors in such a way. She had been implementing a behavior management program in order to assist him in taking a walk in his neighborhood. The program called for preparing the young man for events and landmarks that they would encounter on the walk so that he would not be surprised or panicked by them. She and the young man developed a routine in which she would rhythmically chant the information rather than speaking in her usual way. The rhythm of the chant matched the rhythm of their walking. This partnership was highly successful and walks in the neighborhood became a pleasure. The problem arose when a different support staff followed the prescribed program and accompanied the young man. He followed the behavior management program of preparation as it was written (that is, without chanting). It was apparent that although the first support worker had thought that the chanting was merely something fun that they did together, it was in fact an integral part of the success that the young man experienced.

Often these important accommodations that are added to a behavior program are not recognized as essential and are not reported to others. Another example of accidental discovery of an accommodation is detailed in Margaret and David Eastham's book, *Silent Words, Forever Friends* (Oliver Pate 1992). In working together on literacy and communication development, this mother and her non-speaking son stumbled upon a method of accommodating David's difficulty with writing to communicate. When his mother touched his hand or later in their work, touched his shoulder, David was able to write or type to express his thoughts and feelings. David wrote many poems before his untimely death in 1988 at age twenty-five. The accommodation that they (and others) discovered has since gained fame and notoriety as facilitated communication. When viewed as an accommodation, the important components seem to be the touch of another person, moving in rhythm with another person and the emotional support of the relationship.

Accommodations that may have helped a person to regain balance and control over sensation or movement may not be effective in every situation or may lose their effectiveness over time. But the individual may continue to use the accommodating behavior even though it is no longer working. People providing support may become frustrated that an accommodation that had worked so well at one time or in one situation, may not be of use in another. For this reason, many people report that they have a variety of accommodations on which to draw.

When Tony is experiencing movement difficulties he stops moving. He may look directly at you and he may begin to cry softly. Support staff and Tony have a "menu" of accommodations to assist him at these times which include: calling his name; repeating the last phrase spoken; touching Tony's arm; whistling a tune; telling him a short story; creating an image for Tony, such as, "See yourself in the grocery store pushing the cart"; reading to Tony from one of his books; giving Tony emotional support and encouragement, such as, "You can do it, keep going, Tony, that's it."

Who uses accommodations?

By now we trust that you have recognized that everyone uses accommodations of one kind or another to get around difficulties in action, speech, language, memory, perception or emotion. Many accommodations are so commonplace that we do not think of them as aids, but rather "the way we do" something. Some accommodations get built into our culture. For example, many radio stations play restful music in the late evening and lively music around 6:00 A.M. On a personal level we may prefer to read awhile before falling to sleep, and have an alarm clock to wake us again in the morning. Of course, people with sensory and movement differences also may take advantage of the accommodations that are common to many others.

More sophisticated examples of accommodations include imagery techniques that athletes and business professionals have learned to increase their ability and to enhance their performance in a stressful situation. The pole-vaulter visualizes success in vaulting over a barrier of increased height. In his mind he sees the event in detail including successfully vaulting with ease and grace to a new height. Some athletes even include the cheering crowd as a part of their visualizations. Imagery can be thought of as an accommodation that temporarily overcomes challenges to physical, behavioral or emotional performance. One of the best resources for implementing a visualization program for people with learning and movement differences is a book and video by June Groden and Joe Cautela, *Breaking the Barriers II: Imagery procedures for people with special needs* (Research Press 1991).

More common examples of accommodations used by people include: getting out of bed after smelling freshly brewed coffee; using the rhythm of music to develop a relationship with someone through dancing; exercising in order to take your mind off something; snapping your fingers in order to call up a forgotten word; adjusting the speed and movement of your tongue, lips and jaw in order to talk clearly after dental work; physically retracing your steps in order to remember what you were intending to do; and putting important information into a rhyme in order to be able to remember it later. Clearly, the list is endless, as accommodations are constantly developed to meet the needs of changing circumstances. It is our hope that by bringing this perspective to the individual need of people we support a new chapter will be be written in the history of human diversity.

Some parting thoughts

> No theory can be thoroughly correct in each detail. But it can be right in the sense that it's not wrong. Does it bother me that I have critics? No. It *would* bother me if someone said, "You've asked the wrong question." *Oh, boy*, that would bother me! (Edelman 1994)

Some seventy years ago Dr. Leo Kanner originally applied the adjective "autistic" to the unusual behaviors he saw in a group of his young patients. He later used a German proverb to describe his experience of presenting a new conceptualization to our field: "He who builds a house by the side of the road has many masters."

As we built this book, this attempt to take a different approach to understanding the experience of being and being with people on the autism spectrum or other developmental differences, we often thought of and tried to anticipate those masters. Given the chaos in the field at the moment, our masters will likely fall into two equally problematic groups: Unloving critics and uncritical lovers. The risk for our lovers in that they will think that the ideas herein are new kinds of answers rather than new kinds of questions. To them we say, don't follow us, join us in this journey. We hope that these ideas have lighted up new roads to follow.

Our critics will have an easier time. They will rightly point out our errors and our inconsistencies. This being a human effort, we will surely have erred. As a work in progress, inconsistencies, unfinished thoughts, incomplete connections are inevitable. We apologize in advance if the limits of our abilities to explain have diminished in any way the importance of the exploration.

We thought about those who will misunderstand and misrepresent our position, particularly on the topics of the existence of a thing called "retardation" and the contribution of "symptoms of sensory and movement disturbances" to severe disabilities like autism or developmental disability. We have already heard valued colleagues say: "They think movement explains everything. What about _____ problems?" We are not suggesting that what we present here explains everything. We have been particularly careful to say that supporting an individual to accommodate a sensory or movement difficulty does not mean that the person will necessarily reveal genius, or even ordinary ability. We are not minimizing human difference; we are saying that it is more complex than our categories. Symptoms of sensory and movement differences once were seen to contribute to what is now known as autism and then were forgotten. Until they are taken into account, one cannot begin to know what a person with such a label knows or experiences. We believe that the concept of sensory and movement difference may prove more useful to our understanding of labeled people than categorical labels and syndromes. We hope that we have contributed to that understanding.

We cannot overemphasize these caveats about our conceptualization of the role of sensory and movement difference and disturbance in the life experience of these labeled people. Our knowledge is limited. We look forward to learning much more from others, including our critics, wherever we meet on this journey.

Having said all that, we leave you with some final thoughts about sensory and movement difference and about diversity. The late Moshe Feldenkrais said it best: All of life is movement. As new technologies in neuroscience have begun to reveal, neuromolecular movements before birth create a unique brain in every baby, even in identical twins. Recent advances in knowledge about child development through biodynamic systems models of researchers such as the late Esther Thelen and her colleagues support the notion that once a baby is conceived, patterns are shaped with every experience, every interaction so that each baby follows a unique course. Genetics provide the species-specific constraints on development but do not cause it.

Advances in understanding of genetics are showing us that even the extra chromosome in Down syndrome does not cause any particular characteristic associated with that seemingly clear label. Each characteristic of that syndrome is found in the general population—though amplified in these babies because of the chromosomal irregularities. That means that even where we can see the difference in a gene we cannot guarantee that it will produce any given physical characteristic. Those characteristics depend on the intrauterine environmental experiences of the developing fetus. If we cannot be sure of what physical symptoms that baby will have from counting his chromosomes, how then can we continue to think that we can predict what his ability or life experience will be based on our ability to count his chromosomes? What about all the rest of the "different" babies where the only "symptom" they have in common is the inability to perform on our "predictive tests" or a score on an autism checklist? How long will we continue to pretend that putting a person in a disability category tells us any more than the most superficial information about her?

Development can no longer be thought of as just following either a "normal" or an "abnormal" course in any way that is conceptually or therapeutically meaningful. Movement on every level of interaction, environmental, intrapersonal and interpersonal (action, posture, speech, perception, emotion, thought and memory), from conception to birth, contributes to diversity of development that is uniquely human.

As we begin to understand difference and diversity, new scientific knowledge will help us move beyond the categories to an appreciation of human uniqueness. This effort needs the contribution of people from every conceptual, scientific and theoretical position. We have too much to learn about and from people who are "differently able" to continue to be bogged down in what we think we already know. Let us have the humility to say how little we know and the courage to be wrong as we begin to ask better questions. The words of Kanwal Searha, a person labeled autistic/ mentally retarded, can advise us: "Keep trying to learn but never expect to know!"

Works Cited

Abrams, R., and M. A. Taylor, eds. 1976. Catatonia: A prospective clinical study. *Archives of General Psychiatry* 33: 579-581.

American Psychiatric Association. 2000. *Diagnostic and statistical manual of mental disorders* (4th ed., text rev.). Washington, DC: Author.

Ayers, A.J. 1979. *Sensory Integration and the Child*. Los Angeles: Western Psychological Services.

Bauman, M. L., and T. L. Kemper, eds. 1994. *The Neurobiology of Autism*. Baltimore and London: Johns Hopkins University Press.

Beukelman, D., and P. Mirenda. 1998. *Augmentative and Alternative Communication: Management of severe communication disorders in children and adults*, 2nd ed. Baltimore: Paul Brookes.

Biklen, D. 1990. Communication unbound: autism and praxis. *Harvard Educational Review* 60 (3): 291-314.

Biklen, D., and D. Cardinal, eds. 1997. *Contested Words, Contested Science: Unraveling the facilitated communication controversy*. New York: Teachers College Press.

Biklen, D., and J. Duchan. 1994. "I Am Intelligent": The social construction of mental retardation. *Journal of the Association for Persons with Severe Handicaps* 19 (3): 173-184.

Blatt, B., A. Ozolins, and J. McNally. 1978. *The Family Papers: Documentation from the hidden world of mental retardation*. Glen Ridge, NJ: Exceptional Press.

Bleuler, E. [1911] 1950. *Dementia Praecox or the Group of Schizophrenias*. Trans. J. Zinkin. New York: International Universities Press.

Bliss, J. 1980. Sensory experiences of Gilles de la Tourette syndrome. *Archives of General Psychiatry* 37: 1343-1347.

Bogdan, R., and S. Taylor. 1982. *Inside Out: The social meaning of mental retardation*. Toronto: University of Toronto Press.

Cardinal, D., D. Hanson, and J. Wakeham. 1996. An investigation of authorship in facilitated communication. *Mental Retardation* 34 (4): 231-242.

Cautela, J. R., and J. Groden. 1981. *Relaxation: A comprehensive manual for adults, children, and children with special needs*. Champaign, IL: Research Press.

Cesaroni, L., and M. Garber. 1991. Exploring the experience of autism through firsthand accounts. *Journal of Autism and Developmental Disorders* 21 (3): 303-312.

Cole, M. 1996. *Cultural Psychology: A once and future discipline*. Cambridge, MA: The Belknap Press, Harvard University.

Donnellan, A. M. 1999. Invented knowledge and autism: Highlighting our strengths and expanding the conversation. *Journal of the Association for Persons with Severe Handicaps* 24 (3): 230-236.

Donnellan, A. M., and B. Kilman. 1986. Behavioral approaches to social skill development: Strengths, limitations and alternatives. In *Social Behavior and Autism*, eds. E. Schopler and G. Mesibov, 213-235. New York: Plenum.

Donnellan, A. M., G. W. LaVigna, N. Negri-Schoultz, and L. Fassbender. 1988. *Progress Without Punishment*. New York: Teachers College Press.

Donnellan, A. M., P. L. Mirenda, R. A. Mesaros, and L. L. Fassbender. 1984. Analyzing the communicative functions of aberrant behavior. *Journal of the Association for Persons with Severe Handicaps* 9 (3): 201-212.

Donnellan, A. M., L. A. Sabin, and L. A. Majure. 1992. Facilitated communication: Beyond the quandary to the questions. *Topics in Language Disorders* 12: 69-82.

Eastham, M. 1992. *Silent Words, Forever Friends*. Ottawa: Oliver Pate.

Edelman, G. M. 1992. *Bright Air, Brilliant Fire*. New York: Basic Books.

Edgerton, R. 1967. *The Cloak of Competence*. Berkeley: University of California Press.

Editorial. 1942. Euthanasia. *American Journal of Psychiatry* 99: 141-143.

Gardner, H. 1993. *Multiple Intelligences: The theory in practice*. New York: Basic Books.

Goddard, H. H. 1912. Mental tests and the immigrant. *Journal of Delinquency* 2: 243-277.

Gould, S. J. 1981. *The Mismeasure of Man*. New York: W.W. Norton.

Grandin, T., and M. Scariano. 1986. *Emergence: Labeled autistic*. Novato, CA: Arena Press.

Groden, J., J. Cautela, and G. Groden, producer. 1989. *Breaking the Barriers: Relaxation techniques for people with special needs*. Videotape and guide. Champaign, IL: Research Press.

Groden, J., J. R. Cautela, P. LeVasseur, G. Groden, and M. Bausman. 1991. *Imagery Procedures for People with Special Needs: Breaking the barriers II*. Videotape and guide. Champaign, IL: Research Press.

Horwood, W. 1988. *Skallagrigg*. London: Penguin.

Joliffe, T., R. Lansdown, and C. Robinson. 1992. Autism: a personal account. *Communication* 26 (3): 12-19.

Kahlbaum, K. [1874] 1973. *Catatonia*. Translated by Y. Levij and T. Pridan. Baltimore: Johns Hopkins University Press.

Kuhn, T. S. 1970. *The Structure of Scientific Revolutions*. Chicago: University of Chicago Press.

LaVigna, G., and A. M. Donnellan. 1986. *Alternatives to Punishment: Solving behavior problems with non-aversive strategies*. New York: Irvington Publishers.

Leary, M. R., and D. A. Hill. 1996. Moving on: Autism and movement disturbance. *Intellectual and Developmental Disability* (formerly *Mental Retardation*) 34 (1): 39-53.

Lovett, H. 1996. *Learning to Listen: Positive approaches and people with difficult behavior*. Baltimore, MD: Brookes.

Lund, C. E., A. M. Mortimer, D. Rogers, and P. J. McKenna. 1991. Motor, volitional and behavioral disorders in schizophrenia 1: Assessment using the modified Rogers scale. *British Journal of Psychiatry* 158: 323-336.

Luria, A. R. [1932] 1976. *The Nature of Human Conflicts: Or emotion, conflict and will*. New York: Liveright.

Luria, A. R. 1979. *The Making of Mind: A personal account of Soviet psychology*, eds. M. Cole and S. Cole. Cambridge, MA: Harvard University.

Marcus, E., and M. Shevin. 1997. Sorting it out under fire: Our journey. In *Contested Words, Contested Science: Unraveling the facilitated communication controversy*, eds. D. Biklen, and D. Cardinal.

McGoon, D. C. 1990. *The Parkinson's Handbook*. New York: W.W. Norton.

McKinlay, I. 1989. Autism: The paediatric neurologist's tale. *British Journal of Disorders of Communication* 24: 201-207.

Mirenda, P., and A. M. Donnellan. 1986. The effects of adult interaction styles on conversation behavior in adolescents with handicaps. *Language, Speech, & Hearing Services in Schools* 17: 126-141.

Realmuto, G. M., and G. J. August. 1991. Catatonia in autistic disorder: A sign of co-morbidity or variable expression? *Journal of Autism and Developmental Disorders* 21 (4): 517-528.

Rogers, D., C. Karki, C. Bartlett, and P. Pocock. 1991. The motor disorders of mental handicap: an overlap with motor disorders of severe psychiatric illness. *British Journal of Psychiatry* 158: 97-102.

Rogers, D. 1992. *Motor Disorder in Psychiatry: Towards a neurological psychiatry*. Chichester, England: John Wiley & Sons.

Sacks, O. 1990. *Awakenings*, 6th ed. New York: Harper Perennial.

Shapiro, B. 1994. The environmental basis of the Down syndrome phenotype. *Developmental Medicine and Child Neurology* 36: 84-90.

Sheehan, C. M., and R. Matuozzi. 1996. Validation of facilitated communication. *Mental Retardation* 34 (2): 94-107.

Smith, J. D. 1985. *Minds Made Feeble*. Rockville, MD: Aspen.

Stup, S. 2011. Interview with author Sarah Stup by Jennifer Keats Curtis. Marylandlife.com. Website article. http://www.marylandlife.com/blogs/around-maryland/interview-with-author-sarah-stup.

Thelen, E. 1995. Motor development: A new synthesis. *American Psychologist* 50 (2): 79-95.

Thelen, E., and L. B. Smith. 1994. *A Dynamic Systems Approach to Development and Cognition*. London: MIT Press.

Tourette Syndrome Association, Inc. 1995. *Twitch and Shout.* Videotape. Bayside, NY.

Vasquez, C. 1994. Brief report: A multi-task controlled evaluation of facilitated communication. *Journal of Autism and Developmental Disability* 24 (3): 369-379.

Vygotsky, L. S. 1993. Fundamentals of defectology. In *Collected Works, vol. 2*, trans. J. Knox and C. Stevens. New York: Plenum.

Weiss, M., S. Wagner, and M. Bauman. 1996. A case of validated facilitated communication. *Mental Retardation* 34 (4) 220-230.

Williams, D. 1992. *Nobody Nowhere.* London: Doubleday.

Williams, D. 1994. *Somebody Somewhere.* New York: Times Books.

Williams, D. 1996. *Autism: An inside out approach.* Bristol, PA: Jessica Kingsley.

Wing, L., and A. Attwood. 1987. Syndromes of autism and atypical development. In *Handbook of Autism and Pervasive Developmental Disorders*, eds. D. Cohen and A. Donnellan, 3-19. New York: Wiley.

Yack, E., S. Sutton, and P. Aquilla. 1998. *Building Bridges through Sensory Integration.* 132 Queens Drive, Weston, ONT, M9N2H6.

Additional References on Sensory Movement Symptoms

Ahuja, Niraj. 2000. Organic catatonia: A review. *Indian Journal of Psychiatry* 42 (4): 327-346.

Baggs, A. 2007. *I knew moving took effort, but ...* Retrieved January 15, 2009 from Ballastexistenz. http://ballastexistenz.autistics.org/?p=379.

Barrow, W. J., M. Jaworski, and P. J. Accardo. 2011. Persistent toe-walking in autism. *Journal of Child Neurology* 26 (5): 619-621.

Barry, S., G. Baird, K. Lascelles, P. Bunton, and T. Hedderly. 2011. Neurodevelopmental movement disorders—an update on childhood motor stereotypes. *Developmental Medicine & Child Neurology* 53 (11): 969-1065. doi: 10.1111/j.1469-8749.2011.04058.x.

Bentham, P., G. Bates, V. Murali, and F. Zaw. 1999. Catatonia, autism, and ECT. *Developmental Medicine & Child Neurology* 41 (12): 843-845. doi: 10.1111/j.1469-8749.1999.tb00552.x.

Bhat, A. N., R. J. Landa, and J. C. Galloway. 2011. Current perspectives on motor functioning in infants, children and adults with autism spectrum disorders. *Physical Therapy* 91 (7): 1116-1129.

Bliss, J. 1980. Sensory experience of Gilles de la Tourette syndrome. *Archives of General Psychiatry* 37 (12): 1343-1347.

Bober, P. 2000. Movement differences in young children with autism: A study of home videotapes. Master's thesis, University of Wisconsin, Madison.

Boria, S., M. Fabbri-Destro, L. Cattaneo, L. Sparaci, C. Sinigaglia, E. Santelli, G. Cossu, and G. Rizzolatti. 2009. Intentional understanding in autism. *PloS (public library of science) One* 4 (5): e5596. doi: 10.1371/journal.pone.0005596.

Brasic, J. R., J. Y. Barnett, M. V. Will, R. H. Nadrich, B. B. Sheitman, R. Ahmad, M. Mendonca, D. Kaplan, and C. Brathwaite. 2000. Dyskinesias differentiate autistic disorder from catatonia. *CNS Spectrums* 5 (12): 19-22.

Brasic, J. R., and J. G. Gianutsos. 2000. Neuromotor assessment and autistic disorder. *Autism* 4 (3): 287-298.

Brasic, J. R. 2007. Catatonia. *Medscape*. http://emedicine.medscape.com/article/1154851-overview.

Calhoun, M., M. Longworth, and V. L. Chester. 2010. Gait patterns in children with autism. *Clinical Biomechanics* 26 (2): 200-206. doi: 10.1016/j.clinbiomech.2010.09.013.

Cattaneo, L., M. Fabbri-Destro, S. Boria, C. Pieraccini, A. Monti, G. Cossu, and G. Rizzolatti. 2007. Impairment of actions chains in autism and its possible role in intention understanding. *Proceedings of the National Academy of Sciences of the United States of America* 104 (45): 17825-17830.

Chaplin, R. 2000. Possible causes of catatonia in autistic spectrum disorders. *British Journal of Psychiatry* 177: 180-181. doi: 10.1192/bjp.177.2.180.

Comings, D. E., and B. G. Comings. 1991. Clinical and genetic relationships between autistic-pervasive developmental disorder and Tourette syndrome: A study of 19 cases. *American Journal of Medical Genetics* 39: 180-191.

Damasio, A. R., and R. G. Maurer. 1978. A neurological model for childhood autism. *Archives of Neurology* 35: 777-786.

David, F. J., G. T. Baranek, C. A. Giuliani, V. S. Mercer, M. D. Poe, and D. E. Thorpe. 2009. A pilot study: Coordination of precision grip in children and adolescents with high functioning autism. *Pediatric Physical Therapy: The official publication of the section on pediatrics of the American Physical Therapy Association* 21 (2): 205-211.

De Jong, M., and M. Punt, E. De Groot, R. B. Minderaa, and M. Hadders-Algra. 2011. Minor neurological dysfunction in children with autism spectrum disorder. *Developmental Medicine and Child Neurology* 53 (7): 641-646.

Dewey, D., M. Cantell, and S. G. Crawford. 2007. Motor and gestural performance in children with autism spectrum disorders, developmental coordination disorder, and/or attention deficit hyperactivity disorder. *Journal of International Neuropsychological Soc* 13 (2): 246-256.

Dhossche, D. M. 2004. Autism as early expression of catatonia. *Medical Science Monitor* 10 (3): RA31-RA39. Epub: March 1, 2004.

Dhossche, D. M., A. Shah, and L. Wing. 2006. Blueprints for the assessment, treatment, and future study of catatonia in autism spectrum disorders. *International Review of Neurobiology* 72: 267-284.

Dickie, V. A., G. T. Baranek, B. Schultz, L. R. Watson, and C. S. McComish. 2009. Parent reports of sensory experiences of preschool children with and without autism: A qualitative study. *The American Journal of Occupational Therapy: Official publication of the American Occupational Therapy Association* 63 (2): 172-181.

Donnellan, A. M., D. A. Hill, and M. R. Leary. 2010. Rethinking autism: Implications of sensory and movement differences. *Disability Studies Quarterly*, Autism and the concept of neurodiversity, 30 (1). http://dsq-sds.org/article/view/1060/1225.

Donnellan, A. M., and M. R. Leary. 1995. *Movement Differences and Diversity in Autism/Mental Retardation*. Madison, WI: DRI Press.

Donnellan, A. M., M. Leary, and J. Robledo. 2006. I can't get started: Stress and the role of movement differences for individuals with the autism label. In *Stress and Coping in Autism*, eds. G. Baron, J. Groden, G. Groden, and L. Lipsitt, 205-245. Oxford: Oxford University Press.

Dowd, A. M., J. L. McGinley, J. R. Taffe, and N. J. Rinehard. 2011. Do planning and visual integration on difficulties underpin motor dysfunction in autism? A kinetic study of young children with autism. *Journal of Autism and Developmental Disorder*, November 22. PubMed. PMID: 22105140.

Dowell, L. R., E. M. Mahone, and S. H. Mostofsky. Associations of postural knowledge and basic motor skill with dyspraxia in autism: Implication for abnormalities in distributed connectivity and motor learning. *Neuropsychology* 23 (5): 563-570.

Dziuk, M. A., J. C. G. Larson, A. Apostu, E. M. Mahone, M. B. Denckla, and S. H. Mostofsky. 2007. Dyspraxia in autism: Association with motor, social, and communicative deficits. *Developmental Medicine & Child Neurology* 49 (10): 734-739.

Esposito, G., and P. Venuti. 2008. Analysis of toddlers' gait after six months of independent walking to identify autism: A preliminary study. *Perceptual and Motor Skills* 106 (1): 259-269.

Esposito, G., P. Venuti, S. Maestro, and F. Muratori. 2008. An exploration of symmetry in early autism spectrum disorders: Analysis of lying. *Brain & Development* 31 (2): 131-138.

Esposito, G., P. Venuti, F. Apicella, and F. Muratori. 2011. Analysis of unsupported gait in toddlers with autism. *Brain Development* 33 (5): 367-373.

Fabbri-Destro, M., L. Cattaneo, S. Boria, and G. Rizzolatti. 2009. Planning actions in autism. *Experimental Brain Research. Experimentelle Himforschung. Expérimentation Cérébrale* 192 (3): 521-525.

Fink, M., M. A. Taylor, and N. Ghaziuddin. 2006. Catatonia in autistic spectrum disorders: a medical treatment algorithm. *International Review of Neurobiology* 72: 233-244.

Fournier, K. A., C. I. Kimberg, K. J. Radonovich, M. D. Tillman, J. W. Chow, M. H. Lewis, J. W. Bodfish, and C. J. Hass. 2010. Decreased static and dynamic postural control in children with autism spectrum disorders. *Gait & Posture* 32 (1): 6-9. doi: 10.1016/j.gaitpost.2010.02.007.

Fournier, K. A., C. J. Haas, S. K. Naik, N. Lodha, and J. H. Cauraugh. 2010. Motor coordination in autism spectrum disorders: A synthesis and meta-analysis. *Journal of Autism and Developmental Disorders* 40 (10): 1227-1240. doi: 10.1007/s10803-010-0981-3.

Freitag, C. M., C. Kleser, M. Schneider, and A. von Gontard. 2007. Quantitative assessment of neuromotor function in adolescents with high functioning autism and Asperger syndrome. *Journal of Autism and Developmental Disorders* 37 (5): 948-959.

Fuentes, C. T., S. H. Mostofsky, and A. J. Bastian. 2010. No proprioceptive deficits in autism despite movement-related sensory and execution impairments. *Journal of Autism and Developmental Disorders* 41: 1352-136. doi: 10.1007/s10803-010-1161-1.

Gal, E., M. J. Dyck, and A. Passmore. 2008. The relationship between stereotyped movements and self-injurious behavior in children with developmental or sensory disabilities. *Research in Developmental Disabilities* 30 (2): 342-352. PubMed. PMID: 18693081.

Gepner, B., D. Mestre. 2002. Brief report: Postural reactivity to fast visual motion differentiates autistic from children with Asperger syndrome. *Journal of Autism and Developmental Disorders* 32 (3): 231-238.

Gernsbacher, M. A. 2004. Language is more than speech: A case study. *Journal of Developmental and Learning Disorders* 8: 81-98.

Gernsbacher, M. A., E. A. Sauer, H. M. Geye, E. K. Schweigert, and H. Hill Goldsmith. 2008. Infant and toddler oral- and manual-motor skills predict later speech fluency in autism. *Journal of Child Psychology and Psychiatry and Allied Disciplines* 49 (1): 43-50. PubMed. PMID: 17979963.

Ghaziuddin, M., P. Quinlan, and N. Ghaziuddin. 2005. Catatonia in autism: a distinct subtype? *Journal of Intellectual Disability Research* 49 (1): 102-105.

Gidley Larson, J. C., and S. H. Mostofsky. 2008. Evidence that the pattern of visuomotor sequence learning is altered in children with autism. *Autism Research: Official journal of the International Society for Autism Research* 1 (6): 341-353.

Glazebrook, C. M., D. Elliott, and P. Szatmari. 2008. How do individuals with autism plan their movements? Journal of Autism and Developmental Disorders 38 (1): 114-126.

Glazebrook, C., D. Gonzalez, S. Hansen, and D. Elliott. 2009. The role of vision for online control of manual aiming movements in persons with autism spectrum disorders. *Autism: The international journal of research and practice* 13 (4): 411-433.

Goldman, S., C. Wang, M. W. Salgado, P. E. Greene, M. Kim, and I. Rapin. 2009. Motor stereotypies in children with autism and other developmental disorders. *Developmental Medicine & Child Neurology* 51 (1): 30-38.

Gowan, E., J. Stanley, and R. C. Miall. 2008. Movement interference in autism-spectrum disorder. *Neuropsychologia* 46 (4): 1060-1068.

Green, D., T. Chapman, A. Pickles, S. Chandler, T. Loucas, E. Simonoff, and G. Baird. 2009. Impairment in movement skills of children with autistic spectrum disorders. *Developmental Medicine & Child Neurology* 51 (4): 311-316.

Hadders-Algra, M. 2008. Reduced variability in motor behavior: An indicator of impaired cerebral connectivity? *Early Human Development* 84 (12): 787-789.

Haswell, C. C., J. Izawa, L. R. Dowell, S. H. Mostofsky, and R. Shadmehr. 2009. Representation of internal models of action in the autistic brain. *Nature Neuroscience* 12 (8): 970-972.

Hill, D. A., and M. R. Leary. 1992. A different perspective on behavior in autism. *Children's Mental Health* 5 (2): 12-16.

Hill, D. A., and M. R. Leary. 1993. *Movement Disturbance: A clue to hidden competencies in persons diagnosed with autism and other developmental disabilities.* Madison, WI: DRI Press.

Hilton, C. L., Y. Zhang, M. R. Whilte, C. L. Klohr, and J. Constantino. 2011. Motor impairment in sibling pairs concordant and discordant for autism spectrum disorders. *Autism.* Published online before pint, October 19, 2011. doi: 10.1177/1362361311423018.

Hollander, E., E. Anagnostou, W. Chaplin, K. Esposito, M. Haznedar, E. Licalzi, S. Wasserman, L. Soorya, and M. Buchsbaum. 2005. Striatal volume on magnetic resonance imaging and repetitive behavior in autism. *Biological Psychiatry* 58: 226-232.

Iverson, J. M., and R. H. Wozniak. 2007. Variation in vocal-motor development in infant siblings of children with autism. *Journal of Autism and Developmental Disorders* 37 (1): 158-170.

Izawa, J., S. Pekny, M. Marko, C. Haswell, R. Shadmehr, and S. Mostofsky. 2012. Motor learning relies on integrated sensory inputs in ADHD, but over-selectivity on proprioception in autism spectrum conditions. *Autism Research.* First published online, February 22. doi: 10.1002/aur.1222.

Jansiewicz, E., M. Goldberg, C. Newschaffer, M. Denckla, R. Landa, and S. Mostofsky. 2006. Motor signs distinguish children with high functioning autism and Asperger's syndrome from controls. Journal of Autism and Developmental Disorders 36 (5): 613-621.

Jasmine, E., M. Couture, P. McKinley, G. Reid, E. Fombonne, and E. Gisel. 2009. Sensori-motor and daily living skills of preschool children with autism spectrum disorders. *Journal of Autism and Developmental Disorders* 39: 231-241.

Jones, V., and M. Prior. 1985. Motor imitation abilities and neurological signs in autistic children. *Journal of Autism and Developmental Disorders* 15: 37-46.

Kakooza-Mwesige, A., L. Wachtel, and D. Dhossche. 2008. Catatonia in autism: Implications across the life span. *European Child & Adolescent Psychiatry* 17 (6): 327-335. doi: 10.1007/s00787-008-0676-x.

Kannabiran, M., and J. McCarthy. 2009. The mental health needs of people with autism spectrum disorders. *Psychiatry* 8 (10): 398-401.

Kayser, M. A. 2008. Inherited metabolic diseases in neurodevelopmental and neurobehavioral disorders. *Seminars in Pediatric Neurology* 15 (3): 127-131.

Kerbeshian, J., and L. Burd. 1986. Asperger's syndrome and Tourette syndrome: The case of the pinball wizard. *The British Journal of Psychiatry: The journal of mental science* 148: 731-736.

Klintwall, L., A. Holm, L. Ericksson, L. H. Carlsson, M. B. Olsson, A. Hedvall, C. Gillberg, and E. Fernell. 2011. Sensory abnormalities in autism. A brief report. *Research in Developmental Disabilities* 32 (2): 795-800.

Kumar, A., N. Sarvananthan, F. Proudlock, M. Thomas, E. Roberts, and I. Gottlob. 2009. Asperger syndrome associated with idiopathic infantile nystagmus—a report of 2 cases. *Strabismus* 17 (2): 63-65. doi: 10.1080/09273970902829154.

Landa, R., and E. Garrett-Mayer. 2006. Development in infants with autism spectrum disorders: A prospective study. *Journal of Child Psychology and Psychiatry, and Allied Disciplines* 47 (6): 629-638.

Lane, A. E., S. J. Dennis, and M. E. Geraghty. 2010. Brief report: Further evidence of sensory subtypes in autism. *Journal of Autism and Developmental Disorders* 41 (6): 826-831. doi: 10.1007/s10803-010-1103-y.

Leary, M. R., and D. A. Hill. 1996. Moving on: Autism and movement disturbance. *Intellectual and Developmental Disabilities* (formerly *Mental Retardation*) 34: 42-48.

Leekam, S. R., C. Nieto, S. J. Libby, L. Wing, and J. Gould. 2007. Describing the sensory abnormalities of children and adults with autism. *Journal of Autism and Developmental Disorders* 37 (5): 894-910.

Leighton, J., G. Bird, T. Charman, and C. Heyes. 2008. Weak imitative performance is not due to a functional "mirroring" deficit in adults with autism spectrum disorders. *Neuropsychologia* 46 (4): 1041-1049.

Longuet, S., C. Ferrel-Chapus, M. J. Orêve, J. M. Chamot, S. Vernazza-Martin. 2011. Emotion, intent and voluntary movement in children with autism. An example: The goal directed locomotion. *Journal of Autism and Developmental Disorders*, October 26. PubMed. PMID: 22038289.

Mandelbaum, D., M. Stevens, E. Rosenberg, M. Wiznitzer, M. Stein-schneider, S. Koray, P. Filipek, and I. Rapin. 2006. Sensory/motor performance in school-age children with autism, developmental language disorder or low IQ. *Developmental Medicine & Child Neurology* 48 (1): 33-39. doi: 10.1017/S0012162206000089.

Manjiviona, J., and M. Prior. 1995. Comparison of Asperger's syndrome and high-functioning autistic children on test of motor impairment. *Journal of Autism and Developmental Disorders* 25 (1): 23-39.

Mari, M., U. Castiello, D. Marks, C. Marraffa, and M. Prior. 2003. The reach-to-grasp movement in children with autism spectrum disorder. *Philosophical Transactions: Biological sciences* 358 (1430): 393-403. PubMed. PMCID: 12639336.

Markram, H., T. Rinaldi, and K. Markram. 2007. The intense world syndrome—An alternative hypothesis for autism. *Frontiers in Neuroscience* 1 (1): 77-96. doi: 10.3389/neuro.01/1.1.006.2007.

Marsh, L. E., and A. F. Hamilton. 2011. Dissociation of mirroring and mentalising systems in autism. *Neuroimage* 56 (3): 1511-1519.

Martineau, J., C. Schmitz, C. Assaiante, R. Blanc, and C. Barthélémy. 2004. Impairment of a cortical even-related desynchronisation during a bimanual load-lifting task in children with autistic disorder. *Neuroscience Letters* 367 (3): 298-303.

Maurer, R., and A. Damasio. 1982. Childhood autism from the point of view of behavioral neurology. *Journal of Autism and Developmental Disorders* 12: 195-205.

Milne, E., S. White, R. Campbell, J. Swettenham, P. Hansen, and F. Ramus. 2006. Motion and form coherence detection in autistic spectrum disorder: Relationship to motor control and 2:4 digit ratio. Journal of Autism and Developmental Disorders 36 (2): 225-237. doi: 10.1007/s10803-005-0052-3.

Ming, X., M. Brimacombe, and G. C. Wagner. 2007. Prevalence of motor impairment in autism spectrum disorders. *Brain and Development* 29 (9): 565-570.

Minshew, N., K. Sung, B. Jones, and J. Furman. 2004. Underdevelopment of the postural control system in autism. *Neurology* 63: 2056-2061.

Morgan, L., A. M. Wetherby, and A. Barber. 2008. Repetitive and stereotyped movements in children with autism spectrum disorders late in the second year of life. *Journal of Child Psychology and Psychiatry, and Allied Disciplines* 49 (8): 826-837.

Mostofsky, S., P. Dubey, V. Jerath, E. Jansiewicz, M. Goldberg, and M. Denckla. 2006. Developmental dyspraxia is not limited to imitation in children with autism spectrum disorders. *Journal of the International Neuropsychologicl Society* 12 (3): 314-326.

Mostofsky, S. H., S. K. Powell, D. J. Simmonds, M. C. Goldberg, B. Caffo, and J. J. Pekar. 2009. Decreased connectivity and cerebellar activity in autism during motor task performance. *Brain* 132 (9): 2413-2425.

Mostofsky, S. H., J. B. Ewen. 2011. Altered connectivity and action model formation in autism is autism. *Neuroscientist* 17 (4): 437-448. doi: 10.1177/1073858410392381.

Muthugovindan, D., and H. Singer. 2009. Motor stereotypy disorders. *Current Opinion in Neurology* 22 (2): 131-136.

Nayate, A., J. Bradshaw, and N. Rinehart. 2005. Autism and Asperger's disorder: Are they movement disorders involving the cerebellum and/or basal ganglia? *Brain Research Bulletin* 67 (4): 327-334. PubMed. PMID: 16182941.

Nayate, A., B. J. Tonge, J. L. Bradshaw, J. L. McGinley, R. Iansek, N. J. Rinehart. 2011. Differentiation of high-functioning autism and Asperger's disorder based on neuromotor behavior. *Journal of Autism and Developmental Disorders*, June. doi: 10.1007/s10803-011-1299-5.

Neal, D. T., and T. L. Chartrand. 2011. Embodied emotion perception: Amplifying and dampening facial feedback modulates emotion perception accuracy. *Social Psychological and Personality Science* 2 (6): 673-678. doi: 10.1177/1948550611406138.

Nobile, M., P. Perego, L. Piccinini, E. Mani, A. Rossi, M. Bellina, and M. Molteni. 2011. Further evidence of complex motor dysfunction in drug naïve children with autism using automatic motion analysis of gait. *Autism* 15 (3): 263-283. PubMed. PMID: 21478224.

Noterdaeme, M., K. Mildenberger, F. Minow, and H. Amorosa. 2002. Evaluation of neuromotor deficits in children with autism and children with a specific speech and language disorder. *European Child & Adolescent Psychiatry* 11 (5): 219-225. PubMed. PMID: 12469239.

Ohta, M., Y. Kano, and Y. Nagai. 2006. Catatonia in individuals with autism spectrum disorders in adolescence and early adulthood: A long-term prospective study. *International Review of Neurobiology* 72: 41-54.

Pan, C., C. Tsai, and C. Chu. 2009. Fundamental movement skills in children diagnosed with autism spectrum disorders and attention deficit hyperactivity disorder. *Journal of Autism and Developmental Disorders* 39 (12): 1694-1705.

Papadopoulos, N., J. McGinley, B. Tonge, J. Bradshaw, K. Saunders, A. Murphy, and N. Rinehart. 2011. Motor proficiency and emotional/behavioral disturbance in autism and Asperger's disorder: Another piece of the neurological puzzle? *Autism*, Sept. 26. PubMed. PMID: 21949004.

Phagava, H., F. Muratori, C. Einspieler, S. Maestro, F. Apicella, A. Guzzetta, H. F. Prechtl, and G. Cioni. 2008. General movements in infants with autism spectrum disorders. *Georgian Medical News* 156 (3): 100-105.

Perego, P., S. Forti, A. Crippa, A. Valli, and G. Reni. 2009. Reach and throw movement analysis with support vector machines in early diagnosis of autism. *Engineering in Medicine and Biology Society*, Sept., annual international conference of the IEEE. PubMed. PMID: 19965210.

Provost, P., B. Lopez, and S. Heimerl. 2007. A comparison of motor delays in young children: Autism spectrum disorder, developmental delay and developmental concerns. *Journal of Autism and Developmental Disorders* 37 (2): 321-328.

Realmuto, G. M., and G. August. 1991. Catatonia in autistic disorder: A sign of co-morbidity or variable expression? *Journal of Autism and Developmental Disorders* 21: 517-528.

Realmuto, G. M., and B. Main. 1982. Coincidence of Tourette's disorder and infantile autism. *Journal of Autism and Developmental Disorders* 12: 367-372.

Richler, J., S. L. Bishop, J. R. Kleinke, and C. Lord. 2007. Restricted and repetitive behaviors in young children with autism spectrum disorders. *Journal of Autism and Developmental Disorders* 37 (1): 73-85.

Rinehart, N., J. Bradshaw, A. Brereton, and B. Tonge. 2001. Movement preparation in high-functioning autism and Asperger's disorder: A serial choice reaction time task involving motor reprogramming. *Journal of Autism and Developmental Disorders* 31 (1): 79-88.

Rinehart, N., B. Tonge, J. Bradshaw, R. Iansek, P. Enticott, and K. Johnson. 2006. Movement related potentials in high-functioning autism and Asperger's disorder. *Developmental Medicine and Child Neurology* 48 (4): 272-277.

Rinehart, N. J., B. J. Tonge, B. I. Iansek, J. McGinley, A. Brereton, P. Enticott, J. L. Bradshaw. 2006. Gait function in newly diagnosed children with autism: Cerebellar and basal ganglia related motor disorder. *Developmental Medicine and Child Neurology* 48 (10): 819-824.

Ringman, J. M., and J. Jankovic. 2000. Occurrence of tics in Asperger's syndrome and autistic disorder. *Journal of Child Neurology* 15 (6): 304-400.

Rutherford, M. D., and K. M. Krysko. 2008. Eye direction, not movement direction, predicts attention shifts in those with autism spectrum. Journal of Autism and Developmental Disorders 38 (10): 1958-1965. PubMed. PMID: 18521729.

Schieveld, J. N. M. 2006. Case reports with a child psychiatric exploration of catatonia, autism, and delirium. *International Review of Neurobiology* 72: 195-206.

Schmitz, C., J. Martineau, C. Barthélémy, and C. Assaiante. 2003. Motor control and children with autism: Deficit of anticipatory function? *Neuroscience Letters* 348 (1): 17-20.

Shah, A., and L. Wing. 2006. Psychological approaches to chronic catatonia-like deterioration in autism spectrum disorders. *International Review of Neurobiology* 72: 245-264.

Singer, H. S. 2009. Motor stereotypies. *Seminars in Pediatric Neurology* 16 (2): 77-81.

Stanley-Cary, C., N. Rinehart, B. Tonge, O. White, and J. Fielding. 2010. Greater disruption to control of voluntary saccades in autistic disorder than Asperger's disorder: Evidence for greater cerebellar involvement in autism? *Cerebellum*, Nov. doi: 10.1007/s12311-010-0229-y.

Staples, K., and G. Reid. 2009. Fundamental movement skills and autism spectrum disorders. *Journal of Autism and Developmental Disorders* 40 (2): 209-217. doi: 10.1007/s10803-009-0854-9.

Stieglitz Ham, H., A. Bartolo, M. Corley, G. Rajendran, A. Szabo, and S. Swanson. 2011. Exploring the relationship between gestural recognition and imitation: Evidence of dyspraxia in autism spectrum disorders. *Journal of Autism and Developmental Disorders* 41: 1-12.

Stoppelbein, L., L. Greening, and A. Kakooza. 2006. The importance of catatonia and stereotypies in autistic spectrum disorders. *International Review of Neurobiology* 72: 103-118.

Sutera, S., J. Pandey, E. L. Esser, M. A. Rosenthal, L. B. Wilson, M. Barton, J. Green, S. Hodgson, D.L. Robins, T. Dumont-Mathieu, and D. Fein. 2007. Predictors of optimal outcome in toddlers diagnosed with autism spectrum disorders. *Journal of Autism and Developmental Disorders* 37 (1): 98-107.

Takaoka, K., and T. Takata. 2007. Catatonia in high-functioning autism spectrum disorders: Case report and review of literature. *Psychological Reports* 101 (3): 961-969.

Tardif, C., F. Laine, M. Rodriguez, and B. Gepner. 2006. Slowing down presentation of facial movements and vocal sounds enhances facial expression recognition and induces facial-vocal imitation in children with autism. *Journal of Autism and Developmental Disorders* 37 (8): 1469-1484.

Teitelbaum, P., O. Teitelbaum, J. Nye, J. Fryman, and R. Maurer. 1998. Movement analysis in infancy may be useful for early diagnosis of autism. *Proceedings of the National Academy of Sciences* 95 (23): 13982-13987. doi: 10.1073/pnas.95.23.13982.

Tickle-Degnen, L., and K. Doyle Lyons. 2004. Practitioners' impressions of patients with Parkinson's disease: The social ecology of the expressive mask. *Social Science and Medicine* 58 (3): 603-614.

Tickle-Degnen, L., L. Zebrowitz, and Hui-ing Ma. 2011. Culture, gender, health care stigma: Practitioners' response to facial masking experienced by people with Parkinson's disease. *Social Science and Medicine* 73: 95-102.

Tomchek, S. D., and W. Dunn. 2007. Sensory processing in children with and without autism: A comparative study using the short sensory profile. *The American Journal of Occupational Therapy: Official publication of the American Occupational Therapy Association* 61 (2): 190-200.

Trevarthen, C., and S. Daniel. 2005. Disorganized rhythm and synchrony: Early signs of autism and Rett syndrome. *Brain and Development* 27 (1): S25-S34. PubMed. PMID: 16182487.

Vanvuchelen, M., H. Roeyers, and W. De Weerdt. 2007. Nature of motor imitation problems in school-aged boys with autism: A motor or a cognitive problem? *Autism* 11 (3): 225-240.

Van Waelvelde, H., A. Oostra, G. Dewitte, C. Van den Broeck, and M. J. Jongmans. 2010. Stability of motor problems in young children with or at risk of autism spectrum disorders, ADHD, and or developmental coordination disorder. *Developmental Medicine and Child Neurology* 52 (8) (e174-e178). doi: 10.1111/j.1469-8749.2009.03606.x.

Vernazza-Martin, S., N. Martin, A. Vernazza, A. Lepellec-Muller, M. Rufo, J. Massion, and C. Assaiante. 2005. Goal directed locomotion and balance control in autistic children. *Journal of Autism and Developmental Disorders* 35 (1): 91-102. PubMed. PMID: 157961125.

Vivanti, G., A. Nadig, S. Ozonoff, and S. J. Rogers. 2008. What do children with autism attend to during imitation tasks? *Journal of Experimental Child Psychology* 101 (3): 186-205.

Walker, H. A., and M. Coleman. 1976. Characteristics of adventitious movements in autistic children. In *The Autistic Syndrome*, ed. M. Coleman, 135-144. Amsterdam: North Holland Publishing Co.

Wing, L., and A. Attwood. 1987. Syndromes of autism and atypical development. In *Handbook of Autism and Pervasive Developmental Disorders*, eds. D. J. Cohen and A. M. Donnellan, 3-19. New York: John Wiley and Sons.

Wing, L., and A. Shah. 2000. Catatonia in autistic spectrum disorders. *British Journal of Psychiatry* 176: 357-362. doi: 10.1192/bjp.176.4.357.

Wing, L., and A. Shah. 2000. Author's reply to R. Chaplin. *British Journal of Psychiatry* 177: 180-181. doi: 10.1192/bjp.177.2.180.

Wing, L., and A. Shah. 2006. A systematic examination of catatonia-like clinical pictures in autism spectrum disorders. *International Review of Neurobiology* 72: 21-39. PubMed. PMID: 16697289.

Useful Readings

I. Writings by and with autistic people

Baggs, A. M. 2004. Books by people with autism spectrum disorders: Commentary and lists. http://www.ont-autism.uoguelph.ca/books-by-ASD-authors.html.

Baggs, A. M. 2008. Amanda's favorite quotes. http://ballastexistenz.autistics.org/?page_id=381.

Baggs, A. M. 2010. Cultural commentary: Up in the clouds and down in the valley: My richness and yours. Disability Studies Quarterly 30 (1). http://dsq-sds.org/article/view/1052/1238.

Biklen, D. 2006. *Autism and the Myth of the Person Alone*. New York: NYU Press.

Biklen, D., and J. Burke. 2006. Presuming competence. *Equity and Excellence in Education* 39 (2): 166-175.

Blackman, L. 1999. *Lucy's Story: Autism and other adventures*. Brisbane, Australia: Book in Hand.

Bloomfield, A. 2011. *Bridges Over Barriers in My Life With Autism.* Guelph, Ontario, Canada: Friends of Andrew Bloomfield and Guelph Services for the Autistic. http://andrewsbridges.blogspot.com/p/who-am-i-about-myself.html.

Bluestone, J. 2005. *The Fabric of Autism: Weaving the threads into a cogent theory.* Seattle: Sapphire Enterprises.

Endow, J. 2006. *Making Lemonade: Hints for autism's helpers.* Cambridge, WI: CBR Press.

Endow, J. 2009. *Outsmarting Explosive Behavior: A visual system of support and intervention for individuals with autism spectrum disorder.* Shawnee Mission, KS: AAPC.

Goddard, P., and D. Goddard. 2012. *I Am Intelligent: From heartbreak to healing—A mother and daughter's journey through autism.* Guilford, CT: Skirt! Books.

Grandin, T. 1995. *Thinking in Pictures: And other reports from my life with autism.* New York: Doubleday.

Grandin, T., and M. Scariano. 1986. *Emergence: Labeled autistic.* Novato, CA: Arena.

Hane, R. E. J., K. Sibley, S. M. Shore, R. Meyer, and P. Schwartz. 2004. *Ask and Tell: Self-advocacy and disclosure for people on the autism spectrum,* ed. Stephen Shore. Shawnee Mission, KS: AAPC.

Harp, Bev. 2008. I am Joe's functioning label. Asperger Square 8. http://aspergersquare8.blogspot.com/2008/03/i-am-joes-functioning-label.html.

Harp, Bev. 2009. A conversation with Martha Leary. Wellsphere. http://stanford.wellsphere.com/autism-autism-spectrum-article/a-conversation-with-martha-leary/704046.

Kapp, Steven. 2011. Navajo and autism: The beauty of harmony. *Disability & Society* 26 (5). doi: 10.1080/09687599.2011.589192.

Kapp, S. K., K. Gillespie-Lynch, L. E. Sherman, and T. Hutman. 2012. Deficit, difference or both? Autism and Neurodiversity. *Developmental Psychology,* Apr. 30, 2012. PubMed. PMID: 22545843.

McKean, T. A. 1994. *Soon Will Come the Light: A view from inside the autism puzzle*. Arlington, TX: Future Horizons.

Mukhopadhyay, T. R. 2000. *Beyond the Silence: My life, the world and autism*. London: National Autistic Society.

Mukhopadhyay, T. R. 2010. Five Poems. *Disability Studies Quarterly* 30 (1). http://dsq-sds.org/article/view/1192/1256.

Murray, D., M. Lesser, and W. Lawson. 2005. Attention, monotropism and the diagnostic criteria for autism. *Autism* 9 (2): 139-156.

Page, T. 2007. Parallel play: A lifetime of restless isolation explained. *The New Yorker*, August 20, 36-41.

Pentzell, N. 2010. Dissed ability: Grappling with stereotypes and the internalized oppression of babyliss. *Disability Studies Quarterly* 30 (1). http://dsq-sds.org/article/view/1054/1241.

Rubin, S., D. Biklen, C. Kasa-Hendrickson, P. Kluth, D. N. Cardinal, and A. Broderick. 2001. Independence, participation and the meaning of intellectual ability. *Disability & Society* 16 (3): 415-429.

Schwarz, P. 2004. Identifying, educating, and empowering allies. *Autism Information Library*. http://archive.autistics.org/library/allies.html.

Shore, S. 2003. *Beyond the wall: Personal experience with autism and Asperger syndrome*, 2nd ed. Shawnee Mission, KS: AAPC.

Shore, S. 2009. Helping your child to help him/her self: Beginning self-advocacy. *AutismAsperger.net*. http:www.autismasperger.net/writings_self_advocacy.htm.

Sinclair, J. 1993. Don't mourn us. *Our Voice: Autism network international* 1 (3). http://www.autreat.com/dont_mourn.html.

Stillman, W. 2008. *The Soul of Autism: Looking beyond labels to unveil spiritual secrets of the heart savants*. Pompton Plains, NJ: New Page Books.

Sullivan, A. 2002. Inertia: From theory to praxis. *Autism Information Library*. http://archive.autistics.org/library/inertia.html.

Williams, D. 1992. *Nobody Nowhere*. New York: Avon.

Williams, D. 1994. *Somebody Somewhere*. New York: Times Books.

Williams, D. 1996. *Autism: An inside-out approach.* London: Jessica Kingsley.

Williams, D. 2003. *Exposure Anxiety—The Invisible Cage: An exploration of self-protection responses in the autism spectrum disorders.* London: Jessica Kingsley.

Williams, D. 2009. Autism and the spectrum It may be broader than we think. *The Voices and Choices of Autism* 1 (1): 12-14.

II. Communication

Bopp, K. D., P. Mirenda, and B. D. Zumbo. 2009. Behavior predictors of language development over 2 years in children with autism spectrum disorders. *Journal of Speech, Language, and Hearing Research* 52 (5): 1106-1120. doi: 10.1044/1092-4388(2009/07-0262).

Broderick, A., and C. Kasa-Hendrickson. 2001. Say just one word at first: The emergence of reliable speech in a student with autism. *Journal of the Association for People with Severe Handicaps* 26: 13-24.

Buchanan, R. 2010. Autism, Apple, iPhone, MacBook & Life. *ATMac: Empowering Disabled Apple Users.* http://atmac.org/autism-apple-iphone-macbook-life.

Cannon, B., and G. Edmond. 2009. A few good words: Using core vocabulary to support nonverbal students. The ASHA Leader 14 (5): 20-22. http://www.asha.org/Publications/leader/2009/090414/f090414c/.

Casenhiser, D. M., S. G. Shanker, J. Stieben. 2011. Learning through interaction in children with autism: Preliminary date from a social-communication-based intervention. *Autism* 15 (5). doi: 10.1177/1362361311422052.

Chiang, H. 2008. Expressive communication of children with autism: The use of challenging behavior. *Journal of Intellectual Disability Research* 52 (11): 966-972.

Chiang, H., and M. Carter. 2008. Spontaneity of communication in individuals with autism. *Journal of Autism and Developmental Disorders* 38 (4): 693-705.

Crown, C. 1991. Coordinated interpersonal timing of vision and voice as a function of interpersonal attraction. *Journal of Language and Social Psychology* 10 (1): 29-46.

Fogel, A. 1993. *Developing Through Relationships: Origins of communication, self and culture.* Chicago: University of Chicago Press.

Damico, J. S., and R. L. Nelson. 2005. Interpreting problematic behavior: Systematic compensatory adaptations as emergent phenomena in autism. *Clinical Linguistics and Phonetics* 19 (5): 405-417.

Ganz, J. B., and R. L. Simpson. 2004. Effects on communicative requesting and speech development of the picture exchange communication system in children with characteristics of autism. *Journal of Autism and Developmental Disorders* 34 (4): 395-409.

Hodgdon, L. 1999. *Solving Behavior Problems in Autism: Improving communication with visual strategies.* Solana Beach, CA: Mayer-Johnson Co.

Kagan, A., S. Black, J. Duchan, N. Simmons-Mackie, and P. Square. 2001. Training volunteers as conversation partners using "Supported Conversation for Adults with Aphasia" (SCA): A controlled trial. *Journal of Speech, Language, and Hearing Research* 44: 624-638.

Kasa-Hendrickson, C., A. A. Broderick, and D. Hanson. 2009. Sorting out speech: Understanding multiple methods of communication for persons with autism and other developmental disabilities. *Journal of Developmental Processes* 4 (2): 116-133.

Landa, R. 2007. Early communication development and intervention for children with autism. *Mental Retardation and Developmental Disabilities Research Reviews* 13 (1): 16-25.

McIntosh, D. 2006. Spontaneous facial mimicry, emotion and contagion. *Polish Psychological Bulletin* 37 (1): 31-42.

Moody, E. J., D. N. McIntosh, L. J. Mann, and K. R. Weisser. 2007. More than mere mimicry: The influence of emotion on rapid facial reaction to faces. *Emotion* 7 (2): 447-457.

Muir, H. 2009. Emotional robots: Will we love them or hate them? *NewScientist*, July 3. http://www.newscientist.com/article/mg20327151.400-emotional-robots-will-we-love-them-or-hate-them.html?full=true.

Murphy, J., and L. Cameron. 2008. The effectiveness of Talking Mats® with people with intellectual disability. *British Journal of Learning Disabilities* 36 (4): 232-241. doi: 10.1111/j.1468-3156.2008.00490.x.

Olney, M. 2001. Communication strategies of adults with severe disabilities: Supporting self-determination. *Rehabilitation Counseling Bulletin* 44 (2): 87-94.

Prizant, B., and J. Duchan. 1981. The functions of immediate echolalia in autistic children. *Journal of Speech and Hearing Disorders* 46: 241-249.

Prizant, B., and P. Rydell. 1984. Analysis of functions of delayed echolalia in autistic children. *Journal of Speech and Hearing Research* 27: 183-192.

Prizant, B., A. Wetherby, and P. Rydell. 2000. Communication intervention issues for children with autism spectrum disorders. In *Autism Spectrum Disorders: A transactional developmental perspective*, eds. A. Wetherby and B. Prizant, 193-224. Baltimore: Brookes.

Rollins, P., I. Wambacq, D. Dowell, L. Mathews, and P. B. Reese. 1998. An intervention technique for children with autistic spectrum disorder: Joint attentional routines. *Journal of Communication Disorders* 31 (2): 181-193.

Roos, E., A. S. McDuffie, S. E. Weismer, and M. A. Gernsbacher. 2008. A comparison of contexts for assessing joint attention in toddlers on the autism spectrum. *Autism* 12 (3): 275-291.

Stiegler, L. 2007. Discovering communicative competencies in a non-speaking child with autism. *Language, Speech and Hearing Services in Schools* 38: 400-413.

Thomas-Stonell, N., B. Oddson, B. Robertson, and P. Rosenbaum. 2009. Predicted and observed outcomes in preschool children following speech and language treatment: Parent and clinician perspectives. *Journal of Communication Disorders* 42 (1): 29-42.

Tickle-Degnen, L., and K. Doyle Lyons. 2004. Practitioners' impressions of patients with Parkinson's disease: The social ecology of the expressive mask. *Social Science and Medicine* 58 (3): 603-614.

Tickle-Degnen, L., L. Zebrowitz, and Hui-ing Ma. 2011. Culture, gender, health care stigma: Practitioners' response to facial masking experienced by people with Parkinson's disease. *Social Science and Medicine* 73: 95-102.

Toth, K., J. Munson, A. N. Meltzoff, and G. Dawson. 2006. Early predictors of communication development in young children with autism spectrum disorder: Joint attention, imitation, and toy play. *Journal of Autism and Development Disorders* 36 (8): 993-1005. PubMed. PMID: 16845578.

Wetherby, A. M. 1986. Ontogeny of communication functions in autism. *Journal of Autism and Developmental Disorders* 16 (3): 295-316.

Winner, M. G., and P. J. Cooke. 2011. Social communication strategies for adolescents with autism. *The ASHA Leader*, January 18. http://www.asha.org/Publications/leader/2011/110118/Social-Communication-Strategies-for-Adolescents-With-Autism/.

Woods, J., and A. Wetherby. 2003. Early identification of and intervention for infants and toddlers who are at risk for autism spectrum disorder. *Language, Speech, and Hearing Services in Schools* 34: 180-193.

Yoder, P., H. Spruytenburg, A. Edwards, and B. Davies. 1995. Effect of verbal routine contexts and expansions on gains in the mean length of utterance in children with developmental delays. *Language, Speech, and Hearing Services in Schools* 26: 21-32.

Yoder, P., and W. L. Stone. 2006. Randomized comparison of two communication interventions for preschoolers with autism spectrum disorders. *Journal of Consulting and Clinical Psychology* 74 (3): 426-435. doi: 10.1037/0022-006X.74.3.426.

III. Augmentative and alternative communication (AAC)

AAC and Autism. http://www.aacandautism.com/parents.

ACC Myths Revealed. 2011. Dynavox. Website. http://www.dynavoxtech.com/implementation-toolkit/learning-paths/list/?id=7.

Adamson, L. B., M. Romski, R. Bakeman, and R. A. Sevcik. 2010. Augmented language intervention and the emergence of symbol-infused joint engagement. *Journal of Speech, Language, and Hearing Research* 53: 1769-1773. doi: 10.1044/1092-4388(2010/09-0208).

Beukelman, D. R., and P. Mirenda. 2005. *Augmentative and Alternative Communication*. Baltimore: Brookes.

Biklen, D. 1990. Communication unbound: Autism and praxis. *Harvard Educational Review* 60 (3): 291-314.

Biklen, D., and D. Cardinal, eds. 1997. *Contested Words, Contested Science: Unraveling the facilitated communication controversy*. New York: Teachers College Press.

Cardinal, D., D. Hanson, and J. Wakeham. 1996. An investigation of authorship in facilitated communication. *Mental Retardation* 34 (4): 231-242.

Chen, G., K. Yoder, B. Ganzei, M. Goodwin, and M. Belmonte. 2012. Harnessing repetitive behaviors to engage attention and learning in a novel therapy for autism: An exploratory analysis. *Frontiers in Educational Psychology* 3:12. doi: 10.3389/fpsyg.2012.00012.

Drager, K., J. Light, and D. McNaughton. 2012. *Augmentative and Alternative Communication*. Video webcast. http://mcn.educ.psu.edu/aacpennstate/webcasts/drager_aac_2011.mov.

Light, J., and K. Drager. Early intervention for young children with autism, cerebral palsy, Down syndrome or other disabilities. http://aackids.psu.edu/index.php/page/show/id/1.

Millar, D. C., J. C. Light, and R. W. Schlosser. 2006. The impact of augmentative and alternative communication intervention on the speech production of individuals with developmental disabilities: A research review. *Journal of Speech, Language and Hearing Research* 49: 248-264.

Mirenda, P. 2001. Autism, augmentative communication, and assistive technology: What do we really know? *Focus on Autism and Other Developmental Disabilities* 16 (3): 141-151. doi: 10.1177/108835760101600302.

Mirenda, P. 2003. Toward functional augmentative and alternative communication for students with autism: Manual signs, graphic symbols, and voice output communication aids. *Language, Speech, and Hearing Services in Schools* 34: 203-216. doi: 10.1044/0161-1461(2003/017).

Mirenda, P. 2003. A back door approach to autism and AAC. *Augmentative and Alternative Communication* 24: 219-233.

Schlosser, R. W., and O. Wendt. 2008. Effects of augmentative and alternative communication intervention on speech production in children with autism: A systematic review. *American Journal of Speech Language Pathology* 17: 212-230.

van der Meer, L., D. Kagohara, D. Achmadi, M. F. O'Reilly, G. E. Lancioni, D. Sutherland, and J. Sigafoos. 2012. Speech-generating devices versus manual signing for children with developmental disabilities. *Research in Developmental Disabilities* 33 (5): 1658-1669.

YAACK: AAC connecting young kids. 1999. Does AAC impede natural speech?—and other fears. http://aac.unl.edu/yaack/b2.html.

IV. Points of view on characteristics of autism

Bauman, M. L., and T. L. Kemper, eds. 1994. *The Neurobiology of Autism.* Baltimore and London: Johns Hopkins University Press.

Biklen, D., and J. F. Duchan. 1994. "I am intelligent": The social construction of mental retardation. *Journal of the Association for Persons with Severe Handicaps* 19 (3): 173-184.

Bogdan, R., and S. Taylor. 1982. *Inside Out: The social meaning of mental retardation.* Toronto: University of Toronto Press.

Boria, S., M. Fabbri-Destro, L. Cattaneo, L. Sparaci, C. Sinigaglia, E. Santelli, G. Cossu, and G. Rizzolatti. 2009. Intention understanding in autism. *PloS One* 4 (5): e5596. doi: 10.1371/journal.pone.0005596.

Broderick, A. A. 2009. Autism, "recovery (to normalcy)," and the politics of hope. *Intellectual and Developmental Disabilities* 47 (4): 263-281. doi: 10.1352/1934-9556-47.4.263.

Cashin, A., and C. Waters. 2006. The undervalued role of over-regulation in autism: Chaos theory as a metaphor and beyond. *Journal of Child and Adolescent Psychiatric Nursing* 19 (4): 224-230.

Davidson, J. 2010. It cuts both ways: A relational approach to access and accommodation for autism. *Social Science and Medicine* 70: 305-312.

Davis, K. 2001. Movement difference: A closer look at the possibilities. *The Reporter* 6 (3): 15-24. Retrieved online: Indiana Resource Center for Autism. http://www.iidc.indiana.edu/?pageId=468.

Davis, K., and M. Dubie. Sensory integration: Tips to consider. Retrieved online: Indiana Resource Center for Autism. http://www.iidc.indiana.edu/?pageId=471.

Donnellan, A. M. 1984. The criterion of the least dangerous assumption. *Behavior Disorders* 9: 141-150.

Donnellan, A., N. Negri-Shoultz, L. Fassbender, and G. LaVigna. 1988. *Progress Without Punishment.* New York: Teachers College Press.

Donnellan, A., and M. Leary. 1995. *Movement Difference and Diversity in Autism/Mental Retardation.* Madison, WI: DRI Press.

Donnellan, A. M., M. Leary, and J. Robledo. 2006. I can't get started: Stress and the role of movement differences for individuals with the autism label. In *Stress and Coping in Autism,* G. Baron, J. Groden, G. Groden, and L. Lipsitt, eds., 205-245. Oxford: Oxford University Press.

Donnellan, A. M., D. A. Hill, and M. R. Leary. 2010. Rethinking autism: Implications of sensory and movement differences. *Disability Studies Quarterly,* Autism and the concept of neurodiversity, 30 (1). http://dsq-sds.org/article/view/1060/1225.

Edelson, M. 2006. Are the majority of children with autism mentally retarded? A systematic evaluation of the data. *Focus on Autism and Other Developmental Disabilities* 21 (2): 66-83.

Edelson, M. G., S. M. Edelson, and S. Jung. 1998. Assessing the intelligence of individuals with autism: A cross-cultural replication of the usefulness of the TONI. *Focus on Autism and Other Developmental Disabilities* 13 (4): 221-227.

Gepner, B., and C. Tardif. 2006. Autism, movement, time and thought. E-motion, mis-sight and other temporo-spatial processing disorders in autism. In *Frontiers in Cognitive Psychology*, M. Vanchevsky, ed., 1-30. New York: Nova Science Publishers.

Green, S., and A. Ben-Sasson. 2010. Anxiety disorders and sensory over-responsivity in children with autism spectrum disorders: Is there a causal relationship? *Journal of Autism and Developmental Disorders* 40: 1495-1504. doi: 10.1007/s10803-010-1007-x.

Jaarsma, P., and S. Welin. 2012. Autism as a natural human variation: Reflections on the claims of the neurodiversity movement. *Health Care Analysis* 20 (1): 20-30. PubMed. PMID: 21311979.

Kaldy, Z., C. Kraper, A. S. Carter, and E. Blaser. 2011. Toddlers with autism spectrum disorder are more successful at visual search than typically developing toddlers. *Developmental Science* 14 (5): 980-988.

Leary, M., and D. Hill. 1996. Moving on: Autism and movement disturbance. *Intellectual and Developmental Disability* (formally *Mental Retardation*) 34 (1): 39-53.

Reynolds, S., R. M. Bendixen, T. Lawrence, and S. J. Lane. 2011. A pilot study examining activity participation, sensory responsiveness and competence in children with high functioning autism spectrum disorder. *Journal of Autism and Developmental Disorders* 41 (11): 1496-1506.

Ruef, M., and A. Turnbull. 2002. The perspectives of individuals with cognitive disabilities and/or autism on their lives and their problem behavior. *Research and Practice for Persons with Severe Disabilities* 27 (2): 125-140.

Vismara, L. A., C. Colombi, and S. J. Rogers. 2009. Can one hour per week of therapy lead to lasting changes in young children with autism? *Autism* 13 (1): 93-115. doi: 10.1177/1362361307098516.

Wikipedia. 2011. Definition and description of tics. http://en.wikipedia.org/wiki/Tic.

V. Aspects of support

Amos, Pat. 2007. It's about relationships: for you, for your child. Uniting journey and goal on the autism spectrum. Youth Advocate Programs, Inc. Website. http://www.yapinc.org/_files/live/Its_About_Relationships.pdf.

Davidson, J. 2010. "It cuts both ways": A relational approach to access and accommodation for autism. *Social Science & Medicine* 70 (2): 305-312.

Des Roches Rosa, S., J. B. Myers, L. Ditz, E. Willingham, and C. Greenburg (eds.). 2011. *Thinking Person's Guide to Autism.* San Francisco: Deadwood City Publishing. Website: http://thinkingautismguide.blogspot.com.

Donnellan, A. M., G. W. LaVigna, N. Negri-Schoultz, and L. Fassbender. 1988. *Progress Without Punishment.* New York: Teachers College Press.

Garcia-Winner, M. 2010. *Social Thinking.* Website. http://www.socialthinking.com/.

Herbert, M., and K. Weintraub. 2012. *The Autism Revolution: Wholebody strategies for making life all it can be.* New York: Ballantine Books.

Hill, D. A., and M. R. Leary. 2009. Casting call for a supporting role. *Journal of Intellectual and Developmental Disability* 47 (6): 469-472.

Hopkins, I. M., M. W. Gower, T. A. Perez, D. S. Smith, F. R. Amthor, F. C. Wimsatt, and F. J. Biasini. 2011. Avatar assistant: Improving social skills in students with ASD through a computer-based intervention. *Journal of Autism and Developmental Disorders* 41 (11): 1543-1555.

Jorgensen, C. M., M. McSheehan, and R. M. Sonnenmeier. 2007. Presumed competence reflected in the educational programs of students with IDD before and after the Beyond Access professional development intervention. *Journal of Intellectual and Developmental Disability* 32 (4): 248-262. PubMed. PMID: 18049970.

Joyce, S. 2011. *Meeting the Challenge: A guide for respectful, effective planning, advocacy and support for people who have puzzling behavior.* London, Ontario, Canada: Realizations Training & Resources.

Kaiser, A., T. Hancock, and J. Nietfelf. 2000. The effects of parent-implemented enhanced Milieu Teaching on the social communication of children who have autism. *Early Education and Development* 11: 423-446.

Kliewer, C., D. Biklen, and C. Kasa-Hendrickson. 2006. Who may be literate? Disability and resistance to the cultural denial of competence. *American Educational Research Journal* 43 (2): 163-192.

Kluth, P. 2003. *You're Going to Love This Kid!: Teaching students with autism in the inclusive classroom*. Baltimore: Paul H. Brookes Publishing Co.

Kluth, P., and K. Chandler-Olcott. 2008. *A Land We Can Share: Teaching literarcy to students with autism*. Baltimore: Paul H. Brookes Publishing Co.

LAMP: Language acquisition through motor planning. 2010. A therapeutic approach based on neurological and motor learning principles. The Center for AAC & Autism. Website. http://www.aacandautism.com/lamp.

Lovett, H. 1996. *Learning to Listen: Positive approaches and people with difficult behavior*. Baltimore: Paul H. Brookes Publishing Co.

McGinnity, K., S. Hammer, and L. Ladson. 2011. *Lights! Camera! Autism!: Using video technology to enhance lives*. Cambridge, WI: CBR Press.

Mount, B., and C. Lyle O'Brien. 2002. *Building New Worlds: A sourcebook for students with disabilities in transition from high school to adult life*. Amenia, New York: Capacity Works.

National Public Radio. 2011. Treating stress, speech disorders with music. *Talk of the Nation*, host Ira Flatow, December 16. http://www.npr.org/2011/12/16/143847285/treating-stress-speech-disorders-with-music.

Notbohm, E. 2005. Ten things every child with autism wishes you knew. *Ellen Notbohm*. Website. http://www.ellennotbohm.com/article-archive/ten-things-every-child-with-autism-wishes-you-knew/.

O'Brien, J., and C. Lyle O'Brien. 1998. *A Little Book About Person Centered Planning*. Toronto, Ontario: Inclusion Press.

Orr, T. J., B. S. Myles, and J. K. Carlson. 1998. The impact of rhythmic entrainment on a person with autism. *Focus on Autism and Other Developmental Disabilities* 13 (3): 163-166.

Owen, A. 1999. Using Laban movement analysis to assess progress in dance therapy. Dance Therapy Collections 2. http://dtaa.org.au/ download/DanceTherapyCollections2.pdf.

Pan, C. 2010. Effects of water exercise swimming program on aquatic skills and social behaviors in children with autism spectrum disorders. *Autism* 14 (1): 9-28.

Panagiotopoulos, C., R. Ronsley, D. Elbe, J. Davidson, and D. H. Smith. 2010. First do no harm: Promoting an evidence-based approach to atypical antipsychotic use in children and adolescents. *Journal of the Canadian Academy of Child and Adolescent Psychiatry* 19 (2): 124-137. PubMed. PMID: 20467549.

Piacentini, J., D. W. Woods, L. Scahill, S. Wilhelm, A. L. Peterson, S. Chang, G. S. Ginsburg, T. Deckersbach, J. Dziura, S. Levi-Pearl, and J. T. Walkup. 2010. Behavior therapy for children with Tourette disorder: A randomized controlled trial. *Journal of the American Medical Association* 303 (19): 1929-1937.

Pitonyak, D. 2002. 10 things you can do to support a person with difficult behaviors. Website. Dimagine.com. http://www.worksupport.com/ documents/10things2.pdf.

Pitonyak, D., and J. O'Brien. 2011. Effective behavior support. Website. Dimagine.com. http://www.worksupport.com/ documents/10things2.pdf.

Robledo, J. A., and A. M. Donnellan. 2008. Properties of supportive relationships from the perspective of academically successful individuals with autism. *Intellectual and Developmental Disabilities* 46 (4): 299-310. PubMed. PMID: 18671444.

Rosenblatt, L. E., S. Gorantla, J. A. Torres, R. S. Yarmush, S. Rao, E. R. Parks, J. W. Denninger, H. Benson, G. L. Fricchione, B. Bernstein, and J. B. Levine. 2011. Relaxation response-based yoga improves functioning in young children with autism: A pilot study. *The Journal of Alternative and Complementary Medicine* 17 (11): 1029-1035. doi: 10.1089/acm.2010.0834.

Snow, J. A. 1994. *What's Really Worth Doing and How To Do It*. Toronto: Inclusion Press.

Snow, J. A. 2011. *Who's Drawing the Lines?* Toronto: Inclusion Press.

Strully, J., and L. Broderick. Thoughts on leadership. Website. *Inclusion Network*. This short article shares thoughts about developing supports for people within humn services and education. http://www.inclusion.com/artleadership.html.

Vismara, L. A., C. Colombi, and S. J. Rogers. 2009. Can one hour per week of therapy lead to lasting changes in young children with autism? *Autism* 13 (1): 93-115.

Wan, C. Y., K. Demaine, L. Zipse, A. Norton, G. Schlaug. 2010. From music making to speaking: Engaging the mirror neuron system in autism. *Brain Research Bulletin* 82 (3-4): 161-168. doi: 10.1016/j. brainresbull.2010.04.010.

Winter-Messiers, M. A. 2007. From tarantulas to toilet brushes: Understanding the special interest areas of children and youth with Asperger syndrome. *Remedial and Special Education* 28 (3): 140-152. doi: 10.1177/07419325070280030301.

Yack, E., P. Aquilla, and S. Sutton. 2003. *Building Bridges through Sensory Integration*, 2nd ed. Las Vegas: Sensory Resources.

Zeidán-Chuliá F., U. K. Gursoy, E. Könönen, and C. Gottfried. 2011. A dental look at the autistic patient through orofacial pain. *Acta Odontologica Scandanavia* 69 (4): 193-200. doi: 10.3109/00016357.2010.549505.

VI. Accommodations

Blepharospasm. (A movement disorder that includes forced closing of eyes.) Website. *Dystonia Ireland*. http://www.dystonia.ie/page.asp?Page=42&Menu=33.

McIntosh, G. C., S. H. Brown, R. R. Rice, and M. H. Thaut. 1997. Rhythmic auditory-motor facilitation of gait patterns in patients with Parkinson's disease. *Journal of Neurology, Neurosurgery & Psychiatry* 62 (1): 22-26. PMCID: PMC486690.

VII. Employment

Kurtz, A., and J. Collins. 2009. Quality employment practices for supporting individuals with autism spectrum disorders. Unpublished training curriculum. University of Maine Center for Community Inclusion and Disability Studies. http://www.ccids.umaine.edu.

Project SEARCH. Website: Project SEARCH provides employability skills training and workplace internships for individuals with significant disabilities, particularly youth transitioning from high school to adult life. http://www.cincinnatichildrens.org/service/p/project-search/default.

Standfier, S. 2009. Adult autism and employment: A guide for vocational rehabilitation professionals. Disability Policy and Studies, School of Health Professions, University of Missouri Health System. http://www.dps.missouri.edu/Autism/Adult%20Autism%20&%20Employment.pdf.

Valuing employment now—real jobs for people with learning disabilities. Department of Health. UK. Website: http://www.dh.gov.uk/en/Publicationsandstatistics/Publications/PublicationsPolicyAndGuidance/DH_101401.

VIII. Self-Regulation

Cautela, J. R. 1983. The self-control triad: Description and clinical applications. *Behavior Modification* 7 (3): 299-315. doi: 10.1177/01454455830073001.

Cautela, J. R., and P. A. Wisocki. 1977. The thought-stopping procedure: Description, applications, and learning theory interpretations. *Psychological Record* 1: 255-264.

Hölzelab, B., J. Carmody, M. Vangela, C. Congletona, S. Yerramsettia, T. Gardab, and S. Lazara. 2011. Mindfulness practice leads to increases in regional brain gray matter density. Psychiatry Research 191 (1): 36-43.

Hölzel, B. K., J. Carmody, K. C. Evans, E. A. Hoge, J. A. Dusek, L. Morgan, R. K. Pitman, S. W. Lazar. 2010. Stress reduction correlates with structural changes in the amygdala. Social Cognitive and Affective Neuroscience 5 (1): 11-17. PubMed. PMCID: PMC2840837.

Lang, R., M. Rispoli, W. Machalicek, P. J. White, S. Kang, N. Pierce, A. Mulloy, T. Fragale, M. O'Reilly, J. Sigafoos, and G. Lancioni. 2009. Treatment of elopement in individuals with developmental disabilities: A systematic review. *Research in Developmental Disabilities* 30 (4): 670-681. PubMed. PMID: 19118975.

Lovett, Herb. 1996. *Learning to Listen: Positive approaches and people with difficult behavior*. Baltimore: Paul H. Brookes.

McGinnity, K., S. Hammer, and L. Ladson. 2011. *Lights! Camera! Autism!: Using video technology to enhance lives*. Cambridge, WI: CBR Press.

Montavalo, F. T., and M. C. G. Torres. 2004. Self-regulated learning: Current and future directions. *Electronic Journal of Research in Educational Psychology* 2 (1): 1-34. http://www.investigacion-psicopedagogica.org/revista/articulos/3/english/Art_3_27.pdf.

Posner, M. I., and M. K. Rothbart. 2000. Developing mechanisms of self-regulation. *Development and Psychopathology* 12 (3): 427-441.

Ryan, R. M., and E. L. Deci. 2000. Self-determination theory and the facilitation of intrinsic motivation, social development and well-being. *American Psychologist* 55 (1): 68-78. PubMed. PMID: 11392867.

Ylvisaker, M., and T. Feeney. 1998. *Collaborative Brain Injury Interventions: Positive everyday routines*. San Diego: Singular.

IX. Films, Websites and Blogs

Albalat, Yola. 2007. *Get Me to Fair Good Erin: Larry O'Bryan's Journey*. DVD. 55 min. Inclusion Distribution. http://www.inclusiononline.co.uk.

Autism Acceptance Project. Website. http://www.taaproject.com.

Autism and Empathy: Dispelling myths and breaking stereotypes. Website. http://www.autismandempathy.com.

Autism Hub: The very best in autism blogging. Weblog. http://autism-hub.com.

Autism National Committee (AutCom). Organization of people labled with autism, family and friends. Website. http://www.autcom.org.

Autism Street. A blog by Cameron's Dad. Weblog. http://www.autismstreet.org/weblog.

Autistic Self Advocacy Network (ASAN). An organization run by and for autistics. Website. http://autisticadvocacy.org.

Autistics.org: The real voice of autism. Information library on autism written by people labled with autism. Website. http://archive.autistics.org.

Awe in Autism. Creative works and stories by and about people with autism. Website. http://aweinautism.org/index.php/home.

Baggs, Amanda. 2007. *In My Language.* 8:36 min. YouTube video. http://www.youtube.com/watch?v=JnylM1hI2jc.

Baggs, Amanda. *Ballastexistenz.* This is a blog by a self-advocate who has participated in several aspects of the disability rights movement including autistic liberation, psychiatric survivor, mainstream disability rights, and developmental disability self-advocacy. It is meant largely for discussion of these issues. Weblog. https://ballastexistenz.wordpress.com.

The Center on Human Policy. "The Center on Human Policy (CHP) is a Syracuse University based policy, research, and advocacy organization involved in the national movement to insure the rights of people with disabilities." Website. http://thechp.syr.edu.

Dionne, Steve. *One Dad's Opinion.* Steve writes from his perspective as the father of a person labeled with autism. Weblog. http://onedadsopinion.blogspot.com.

Goddard, P. *Peyton Goddard.* Peyton's website contains important descriptions of her life, successes and her challenges. Her Valedictorian speech (2002) from Cuyamaca College and presentation summary, "Separate could never be equal," are inspiring. Weblog. http://www.peytongoddard.com/index.html.

Inclusion Press. Producing books and videos to promote inclusion in school, work, and community. Website. http://www.inclusion.com/inclusionpress.html.

Inclusive Solutions. A website dedicated to inclusion for all people. http://www.inclusive-solutions.com/ideas.asp.

KiSara. Mother (Kim) and daughter (Sara) singing duo. "Music and love have been our passports to a life that transcends the challenges of the autism realm." Website. http://heartfeltmusic.net/kisara.

Klar, E. *Estée Klar: The joy of autism.* Estée blogs from her perspective as the mother of an autistic boy. Weblog. http://networkedblogs.com/p25082421.

Knight, J. Weblog. "The personal thoughts and writings of Jamie Knight and his trusty feline companion Lion. Covering Design, Autism, Lego and Technology!" Weblog. http://jamieknight.tumblr.com/.

Kunc, N., and E. Van der Klift. *A Credo for Support.* A short film about giving support. DVD. 5 min. http://www.normemma.com/dvds.htm.

neurodiversity.com. Weblog with news, opinion, letters, readings, and announcements. http://www.neurodiversity.com/main.html.

Ontario Adult Autism Research and Support Network (OAARSN). Website. http://www.ont-autism.uoguelph.ca/index.shtml.

paulakluth.com. Paula Kluth provides practical information promoting inclusive schooling and exploring ways of supporting students with autism and other disabilities. http://www.paulakluth.com.

Pitonyak, D. 2002. 10 things you can do to support a person with difficult behaviors. Website article. Dimagine.com. http://www.worksupport.com/documents/10things2.pdf.

Rubin, S. *Sue Rubin: Living and thoroughly enjoying life in spite of autism.* Website. http://www.sue-rubin.org.

Shore, S. AutismAsperger.net is the web home of Stephen Shore, author of *Beyond the Wall: Personal experiences with autism and Asperger syndrome.* Website. http://www.autismasperger.net.

Snow, K. *Invisible abilities: Revolutionary common sense.* Website article. http://www.disabilityisnatural.com/~k061480m/images/PDF/invabil.pdf.

Square 8. *Square 8: Talk about squares, autism, and the number 8.* Weblog by Bev Harp. http://aspergersquare8.blogspot.com.

Stup, S. 2011. Interview with author Sarah Stup by Jennifer Keats Curtis. Marylandlife.com. Website article. http://www.marylandlife.com/blogs/around-maryland/interview-with-author-sarah-stup.

Venditti, J., dir. 2007. *Billy the Kid.* 85 min. Documentary film about a teen in Maine. DVD. Zeitgeist Films. http://www.billythekiddocumentary.com.

WrongPlanet.net. "The online resource and community for autism and Asperger's." Website. http://www.wrongplanet.net/index.php.

Wurzburg, G., dir. 2004. *Autism is a World.* 40 min. Written by and featuring Sue Rubin. DVD. CNN Productions.

Wurzburg, G., dir. 2011. *Wretches and Jabberers.* 95 min. Warner Bros. DVD. Website: http://wretchesandjabberers.org.

CHAPTER TWO

The Evolution of Facilitated Communication

Don Cardinal
Jodi Robledo

Faced with the choice between changing one's mind and proving that there is no need to do so, almost everyone gets busy on the proof.—John Kenneth Galbraith

A landmark article in the *Harvard Educational Review* (Biklen 1990) began a firestorm of controversy in the United States. Doug Biklen introduced the method of facilitated communication (FC), developed by Rosemary Crossley in Melbourne, Australia. Biklen was often attributed with touting the method as a miracle for people with autism (Green 1994; Kezuka 1997). The reality was much more benign. In fact, in the original 1990 article, "Communication Unbound: Autism and Praxis," the article's abstract characterized the method this way: "People who have been labeled severely autistic can selectively communicate with certain facilitators and in certain circumstances" (291). Clearly far short of a claim of "miracle."

Since the *Harvard Educational Review* piece in 1990, roughly 180 articles related to facilitated communication have been published in professional journals in the United States as well as many books and hundreds of conference proceedings. Nearly three-fourths (72%) of the 180 journal articles were published in or prior to 1996, within seven years of FC's introduction into the American professional community. In contrast, only a small handful of quantitative studies were done on FC this century. The move to validate FC through quantitative inquiry essentially ended around that time, 1996. Clearly then, the quantitative assessment of facilitation was established during our early understanding of FC.

Only about 40 of the 180 articles (22%) related to facilitation can be construed as quantitative (quasi-experimental), or as some phrase it, scientific. In the authors' opinions the majority of these "scientific" studies regarding the efficacy of facilitation exhibit relatively weak methodology that readers can observe for themselves. Very few if any reflect the methodological controls found to be important in assessing the validity of facilitated communication (Biklen and Cardinal 1997). The majority of these studies were either unable to produce any results from the method or identified that the facilitator may have influenced the FC user (Bebko, Perry, and Bryson 1996; Wheeler, Jacobson, Paglieri, and Schwartz 1993). Several of the 40 quantitative articles did find support of FC to varying degrees (Sheenan and Matuozzi 1996; Weiss 1996) including the largest study to date, which had 43 participants across 3800 trials (Cardinal, Hanson, and Wakeham 1996). The Cardinal et al. study concluded that the FC speaker was much more likely to be effective when they had ample opportunity to practice the testing protocol. Previous studies allowed for very little or no practice of the testing protocol prior to being tested for authenticity.

During this concentrated period of research findings on FC, 1990 through 1996, FC drew the sensationalized attention of the popular media as well (e.g., *Frontline*, "Prisoners of Silence," October 19, 1993). In fact, the media likely had more to do with the public-held perception of FC than any other source. Using today's vernacular to describe the effect media had on the general public's perception of FC, one could say it went "viral." Some found FC so counter to their thinking of intelligence of those with autism, that they bombarded the media with stories from false sexual abuse claims when using FC to outright unethical behavior of facilitators faking the facilitation process. While some of these accusations likely were true, many have been discredited (Botash, Babuts, Mitchell, and O'Hara 1994). Regardless, the media, lay persons and even most of the professional community found these explanations of the method easier to believe than the notion that people with autism having higher levels of intelligence than we had previously thought. It is important that the reader understand that while the idea of people with autism possessing high levels of intelligence is not uncommon today, in the early 1990s it was contrary to what many professionals believed and what the majority of our scientific research was reporting. A paradigm shift regarding the academic and social competence of people with autism has occurred over the past twenty years. Today, proclaiming that a person with severe autism can communicate via typing to a high level is likely more palatable to the professional and lay communities than it was in the early 1990s. This is something to celebrate and credit given to all of those professionals and people with autism who have worked so hard to prove, including those who have used FC as their vehicle of proof.

The evolution of FC: Departure points from the early years

While the quantitative assessment of facilitation was primarily established 15 years ago, practitioners, conference presentations and a plethora of naturalistic research studies have continued to delve deeper into the method, trying to improve the strategies, remedy the peril of facilitator influence and allow for people with disabilities to tell their own stories (Biklen and Duchan 1994; Broderick, Kasa-Hendrickson 2001; Crossley 1992; Robledo and Donnellan 2008). All of this has resulted in the evolution of facilitated communication. Facilitation has evolved enough to be able to say clearly and unequivocally that what we called facilitated communication in 1990 is not the exact method used today. While this possesses no real challenge to practitioners or users, since it is they who have made the periodic adjustments to the method over time, it does present a quandary to researchers and those who count on research publications to make informed decisions. The essential question here is, is what we today call FC (or supported typing and pointing) substantially different from the early practice of FC to a degree that relegates the early scientific studies on FC relatively out-of-date?

Fundamental to facilitation's evolution is the issue of physical support from the facilitator. Early accounts, and critiques, of FC focused primarily on the close physical support of the facilitator and the user. Today's use of the method differs in several important ways from the early 1990s approach, particularly in terms of physical support. The first and by far the most compelling difference between FC in the early 90s and 2012 is independence. Once individuals previously thought to have very limited intellectual functioning began to type independently (no one touching them or a simple pincer grasp of the typer's shirt) after learning to type via FC, the question around who is doing the typing vanished, at least for most reasonable people.

It is important to note at this point in the conversation that not everyone who uses facilitation will become independent, at least that is how it appears today. Many use the method to learn to point to words or symbols toward a goal of greater communication skills. Having so many individuals become independent typers and crediting the method with their developed abilities, certainly shows that the method can result in authentic, original communication. So while those who still require physical support are susceptible to facilitator influence, they also benefit from the knowledge that FC is real and can allow smart people with severe communication disorders to reveal their intelligence. This too becomes a point of difference from early FC research. In contrast to the early days of research on FC, those using FC support to point to words and symbols no longer do so absent the knowledge that FC can be an effective method.

An additional difference in terms of physical support is the speed at which a facilitator moves to independence. While it was thought that physical support could be faded over a few years, if then, today it is commonly believed that under ideal conditions physical support can be faded over a much shorter period of time. In fact, for many, the road toward independence begins at the onset of using the method. This is further exemplified by the notion of "least to most" where the facilitator begins with the least amount of physical support possible to support the production of the most communication possible.

Many other changes exist as well. While FC was thought to be less specific to a disability type, today, it is almost entirely focused on those with a diagnosis in the autism spectrum.

Skeptics still remain

Even in the face of the ultimate proof of FC (i.e., independent typers who now emphatically credit FC with their ability to communicate intelligently), some fringe skeptics remain resolute in their counter beliefs despite what they are seeing with their own eyes. Some continue to insist that because a facilitator still has to be near the communicator for maximum performance in speed and accuracy of typing or pointing, they are in some concealed way manipulating the typing of the speaker. Most unbiased observers dismiss such ideas as unfounded and generally inconceivable. After all, if someone is capable enough to work out a code signaling which letters to strike on a keyboard, exactly when they need to do so, then the communicator would certainly be able enough to type the message. Conspiracy accusations are dwindling as more and more individuals who in earlier years would have been diagnosed with intelligence in the severe disability range are typing independently or with very minimal touch (for example, a soft grasp of the communicator's shirt).

A troubling example of misinformed skepticism arose in a 2005 *Washington Post* article by Lisa Barrett Mann. In the article, titled *Oscar Nominee: Documentary or Fiction?*, Mann challenged the authenticity of twenty-six-year-old Sue Rubin's communication in the Oscar-nominated CNN documentary film, *Autism Is a World*. Sue Rubin, who was diagnosed as having an IQ range in the low 30s and is now able to type independent of any physical touch, credited FC with her ability to communicate her thoughts through typing. Rubin's most recent IQ testing added an additional 100 points to the assessment of her intelligence. Same test, same person, but now she can type her own thoughts. Yet, Lisa Barrett Mann felt compelled to question Rubin's ability. At this point, one might ask what someone with an uncooperative body needs to do to prove their intelligence, their humanness? Unfortunately, Sue Rubin has not been the only individual to have their intelligence challenged (and insulted) and Lisa Barrett Mann is not the only author to succumb to stereotype.

What we have learned from past research on FC

While each of us will argue that our past research on the topic is still relevant, it is becoming increasingly clear that some of it has served its purpose, that it formed the basis for our current understanding of FC. After all, without the conclusion of the body of research suggesting that facilitator influence was problematic to the validation of FC, the motivation of some FC speakers may have not been so heightened and even more time may have had to elapse before some became independent typers. Past research has also revealed that the methods we use in studying facilitation can highly influence the outcome of the research (Biklen and Cardinal 1997). We have also learned that the support systems around the individual communicator can have a positive impact on the individual's ability to communicate effectively, even when no physical support is provided.

While the body of quantitative studies unable to authenticate any actual production of words or ideas from their "subjects" contributed little to the understanding of FC, the large amount of studies that chronicle the life stories of those using FC will serve as a historical record for many years to come. In fact, one could easily argue that these studies can be used as an evolutionary roadmap showing the migration of levels of support and the minimizing of the threat of facilitator influence on the speaker.

Future research

Early research questions on facilitated communication have become obsolete, or at least they have substantially changed. We now know that individuals previously thought to have limited intellectual capacity have learned to express their abilities through a supported process. We do not know in advance exactly for whom the method will work and for whom it will not. For those practitioners who are highly trained in the method, their process is to simply try it, not with fanfare or a promise of specific results, but rather as part of their communication evaluation. If facilitation does not seem to be the correct method, then they move on to the next option, possibly returning later (since it tends to allow for greater independence and production than other methods). Researchers certainly can develop studies to shed light on the question of who can benefit most. A follow-up question might be: If one is not ready to type their thoughts, when does one return to assess their readiness, if at all? Another emerging question in this area is how does FC vary in procedure for those who will likely use their communication primarily for pointing to words or symbols? Such methods will certainly vary from those who use facilitation to learn to type their own thoughts independently, but for both groups, equally important. As our research continues into these various forms of learning how to type, the researchers should focus as much on their research methods as on the method of communication they endeavor to measure. Clearly, many of those who were judged by our research as not typing their own words and thoughts, were doing so, as they conclusively proved by eventually typing their own thoughts without the physical support of others. As so respectfully stated by Mirenda and Beukelman (1998, 327): "For them, the controversy has ended."

What to do with the numerous position statements on facilitation

In addition to conducting research to shed light on the questions above, we must also begin to re-evaluate professional position statements on the topic. Now that ample cultural and scholarly evidence exists that the premise of facilitation is well-founded, albeit through trial and error, it is now time to develop professional position statements that reflect this change. This time, instead of naming the method as the point of focus, it is suggested that these professional position statements pay homage to those who have spent the better part of their lives to prove they are smart and that FC helped them to prove their intelligence to others. If nothing else, this group of brave individuals has demonstrated, proven, the original contentions of FC, that it can work for some people, under certain circumstances (much as Rosemary Crossley and Doug Biklen first conjectured). Professional position statements then should at least acknowledge that FC can be effective and that further research is needed to understand whom it most benefits and the best ways to detect and reduce the chance of facilitator influence and protect the "voice" of those struggling to be heard. This responsible approach is the right thing to do.

Let these new position statements honor those individuals with autism who verified their intelligence through FC. Let's conclude those professional positions with the importance of assuming competence in all people, redirecting the onus of learning back to us as professionals. These past twenty years have taught us the fallacy of one-way learning, assuming the professional holds the instructional truth and the "student's" sole purpose is to be evaluated by our truths. FC has taught us to listen better to people with disabilities. To effectively enhance our methods, we have created partnerships among those with disabilities, their families and those of us entrusted to assist them. FC has changed the dynamic of learning for people with autism and other disabilities. Our professional position statements should absolutely reflect this pedagogical metamorphosis and credit all of those who persevered to bring us to this new level of enlightenment. Only then will we be able to say we are in a helping profession.

Editors' note: Just as Cardinal and Robledo completed this review of the evolution of FC, and as this book was being prepared for publication, we became aware of several more papers that supported an underlying premise of this work: Individuals with autism and other developmental special needs are often more competent than their bodies (and our "assessment") allow them to demonstrate. Chen et al. (2012), a group of neuroscientists, studied the process of "Rapid Prompting Method," and showed that this method of supporting typers involved prompts and supports that likely facilitated brain connectivity allowing people to demonstrate unexpected competence and independence. The authors did not directly study authorship but showed the ability of the typers, previously considered severely cognitively impaired, to maintain high levels of correct responding despite the increasing difficulty of the content.

A second study (Hilton et al. 2011) looked at motor problems in families with children labeled "ASD." According to the abstract:

> *Methods*: Motor impairment of sibling pairs from 67 ASD-affected families comprising 29 concordant pairings and 48 discordant pairings were assessed using the Bruininks Oseretsky Test of Motor Proficiency, 2nd Edition, a standardized measure of motor proficiency.

> *Results*: Motor skills were substantially impaired among ASD-affected children and highly correlated with autistic severity and IQ, whereas motor skills in unaffected siblings were essentially normal. Total motor composite scores of at least one standard deviation below the general population mean were seen in 83% of the affected group compared with 6% in the unaffected siblings.

> *Interpretation*: Findings indicate that motor impairment constitutes a core characteristic of ASD (not necessarily an ASD endophenotype), which has distinct implications for taxonomy, diagnosis, and approaches to intervention.

These and many of the other articles found in our bibliography suggest that we have to get beyond the arguments about FC/RPM derived from outdated assumptions about incompetence and look more carefully for competence in all people. The science is reinforced by anecdotal information about the amazing feats performed by people with severe communication difficulties when they have access to tablets and iPads (e.g., *60 Minutes,* "Apps for Autism," October 23, 2011). Perhaps, at last, we are seeing a paradigm shift that will allow us to study how to help people demonstrate their communication, their competence and their complete humanness.—MRL/AMD

Works Cited

Bebko, J. M., A. Perry, and S. Bryson. 1996. Multiple method validation study of facilitated communication: II. Individual differences and subgroup results. *Journal of Autism and Developmental Disorders* 26 (1): 19-42.

Biklen, D. 1990. Communication unbound: Autism and praxis. *Harvard Educational Review* 60 (3): 291-314.

Biklen, D., and D. Cardinal, eds. 1997. *Contested Words, Contested Science: Unraveling the facilitated communication controversy.* New York: Teachers College Press.

Biklen, D., and J. F. Duchan. 1994. "I am intelligent": The social construction of mental retardation. *Journal of the Association for Persons with Severe Handicaps* 19 (3): 173-184.

Botash, A. S., D. Babuts, N. Mitchell, and M. O'Hara. 1994. Evaluation of children who have disclosed sexual abuse via facilitated communication. *Archives of Pediatrics & Adolescent Medicine* 148 (12): 1282-1287.

Brodrick, A., and C. Kasa-Hendrickson. 2001. Say just one word at first: The emergence of reliable speech in a student labeled with autism. *Journal of the Association for Persons with Severe Handicaps 26* (1): 13-24.

Cardinal, D., D. Hanson, and J. Wakeham. 1996. Investigation of authorship in facilitated communication. *Mental Retardation* 34: 231-242.

Chen, G., K. Yoder, B. Ganzei, M. Goodwin, and M. Belmonte. 2012.
Harnessing repetitive behaviors to engage attention and learning
in a novel therapy for autism: An exploratory analysis. *Frontiers in
Educational Psychology* 3:12. doi: 10.3389/fpsyg.2012.00012.

Crossley, R. 1992. Getting the words out: Case studies in facilitated communication training. *Topics in Language Disorders* 12 (4): 46-59.

Frontline. Prisoners of silence. October 19, 1993 (PBS).

Green, G. 1994. Facilitated communication: Mental miracle or sleight of
hand? *Skeptic* 2 (3): 68-76.

Hilton, C. L., Y. Zhang, M. R. Whilte, C. L. Klohr, and J. Constantino.
2011. Motor impairment in sibling pairs concordant and discordant for autism spectrum disorders. *Autism,* October 19, 2011. doi:
10.1177/1362361311423018.

Kezuka, K. 1997. The role of touch in facilitated communication. *Journal
of Autism and Developmental Disorders* 27 (5): 571-593.

Mirenda, P., and D. R. Beukelman. 1998. *Augmentative and Alternative
Communication: Management of severe communication disorders in
children and adults.* Baltimore: Paul H. Brookes.

Robledo, J., and A. Donnellan. 2008. Essential properties of supportive
relationships from the perspective of academically successful individuals with autism. *Intellectual and Developmental Disabilities* 46
(4): 299-310.

Sheenan, C., and R. Matuozzi. 1996. Investigation of the validity of facilitated communication through the disclosure of unknown information. *Mental Retardation* 34 (2): 94-107.

Weiss, M., S. Wagner, and M. Bauman. 1996. A validated case study of
facilitated communication. *Mental Retardation* 34 (4): 220-230.

Wheeler, D. L., J. W. Jacobson, R. A. Paglieri, and A. A. Schwartz. 1993.
Experimental Assessment of facilitated communication. *Mental
Retardation* 31 (1): 49-59.

CHAPTER THREE

Rethinking Autism:
Implications of sensory and movement differences
for understanding and support

Anne M. Donnellan
David A. Hill
Martha R. Leary

*I was intensely preoccupied with the movement of the spin-
ning coin or lid and I saw nothing and heard nothing. I did
it because it shut out sound that hurt my ears. No sound
intruded on my fixation. It was like being deaf. Even a sudden noise didn't startle me out of my world.* (Grandin 1992)

People with autism often move their bodies in ways that are unfamiliar to us. Some people rock, repeatedly touch an object, jump and
finger posture while other people come to a standstill in a doorway, sit
until cued to move or turn away when someone beckons. As professionals trained to see these as *autistic behaviors,* most of us have interpreted
such movements as both volitional and meaningless; or as communicative acts signaling avoidance of interaction and evidence of diminished
cognitive capacity; or as some combination of these, often to be targeted
for reduction. We have taken a socially constructed interpretation of
what we see and have built a "theory" of autism.

This paper challenges the traditional definitions of autism that give
primacy to a triad of deficits in social interaction, communication and
imaginative play (Wing 1981; American Psychiatric Association [DSM-
IV] 2000). The approach is both widely known and essentially unchallenged despite broad acknowledgment that autism is a condition that
reflects some differences in a person's neurology. Typically, the neurological implications have not become part of the description. Over the

past two decades, however, researchers and self-advocates have begun to rethink this socially defined focus. They express concern that children and adults with the autism label may be challenged by unrecognized and significant sensory and movement differences (e.g., Hill and Leary 1993; Williams 1993; Bristol et al. 1996; Donnellan and Leary 1995; Leary and Hill 1996; Filipek et al. 2000; Donnellan 2001; Sullivan 2002; Dhossche 2004; Bluestone 2005; Nayate et al. 2005; Endow 2006; Jansiewicz et al. 2006; Mostofsky et al. 2006; Leekam et al. 2007; Markram, Rinaldi, and Markram 2007; Tomchek and Dunn 2007; Gernsbacher et al. 2008; Goldman et al. 2009).

Researchers and others describe these differences using a variety of terms such as: motor problems; sensory-integration problems; inertia; sensory overload; apraxia; dyspraxia; echolalia; mutism; behavior disorder; catatonia; or clumsiness. To reflect the range and complexity of sensory perception and movement related phenomena, we use the term "sensory and movement differences" as it encompasses the dynamic interaction of sensation and movement (Gibson 1979; Thelen and Smith 1995) while acknowledging that many differences are merely part of the richness of human diversity.

Behavior is highly interpretable. Some behaviors may be communicative, some may be volitional. Some behaviors, however, may not be intentional. Rather, observed behaviors may be artifacts of the difficulties a person may be having in organizing and regulating sensation and movement. Still others may be subtle signals of the desire for relationship or expressions of meaning. Therapeutic and intervention-based approaches, designed to address perceived and identified challenging and problematic behaviors of individuals with autism, tend to oversimplify the complex nature of human interactions in an attempt to delineate and manipulate variables contributing to and sustaining particular behaviors.

As we have *professionalized* interactions with people with autism, we have trained professionals, parents and others to interpret what happens in terms of simple, binary views of behavior (i.e., good/bad or positive/negative), and to see behaviors as controlled by immediate, situational antecedents and consequences. When we focus on these socially constructed expectations for behavior and communication in our fast-paced, super-technological world, we miss opportunities to know and understand people who may experience their existence and interactions in very different ways. Behaviors may not be what they seem (Donnellan, Leary, and Robledo 2006).

Our interest in the topic of sensory and movement differences has grown from reports by many self-advocates with the autism label and their caregivers that disturbances of sensation and movement are a constant concern, frequently constraining ability to communicate, relate to others and participate in life (e.g., Strandt-Conroy 1999; Barron and Barron 1992; Rubin et al. 2001). Organizing and regulating sensory information and movement in order to participate in social relationships may be frustrating for people with such differences. These differences can involve difficulties initiating and executing movements or difficulties with stopping, combining, and switching sensation and movement including speech, thought and emotion (Hill and Leary 1993; Donnellan and Leary 1995; Donnellan, Leary, and Robledo 2006), making social relationships and many other activities very challenging, even overwhelming.

Self-advocates also report that they lack sensation or feedback from their bodies and may feel physically unaware of their facial expressions, position in space and movements (e.g., Blackman 1999; Hale and Hale 1999; Williams 1996a, 1996b, 2003). Some experience the sights and sounds of their world as being painfully intense (Cordon 1985; Williams 1992, 1996b; Markram, Rinaldi, and Markram 2007). Extreme emotions can cause the individual to become stuck, unable to cease repetition of a movement. Self-confidence and reputation often suffer when others assume a person is repeating an action "on purpose." Sean Barron (Barron and Barron 1992, 181) wrote: "All I wanted was to be like the other kids my age. It felt as if I was weird and strange on the outside, but inside I wasn't like that. The inside person wanted to get out and break free of all the behaviors that I was a slave to and couldn't stop." For many people, as for Sean, simple movements can lead to repetitions or perseveration, even when they want to stop the movement.

Our concern here is not to discard useful information already accumulated via a primarily socially defined approach to autism. Nor are we interested in enhancing a deficit-based approach to understanding autism, or in creating a new disability category. We do not propose to specify a cause of autism or a site of lesion or dysfunction within the central nervous system. Rather, we write to share our emerging awareness that people may struggle with difficulties that are not immediately evident to an outsider. That is, our experience of individuals with autism ought no longer to be assumed the same as their experience. Individuals with the autism label often describe experiences which are not immediately obvious to the rest of us but which may well affect our understanding of their behavior. These experiences frequently fit the definition of sensory and movement differences. Sue Rubin (personal communication, August 4, 2007) described her dilemma with intention and action: "When you said we could stay and asked dad to do the shopping for the Asperger's barbeque, my body relaxed and autism let me eat the melon." And two other autistic adults had the following interaction about sensory and movement differences. Judy Endow (personal communication on Facebook, January 25, 2009) described her experiences in relation to sensory and movement differences:

> I think the fluidity of access to various places in the brain is dependent upon neurological movement between places. I'm no scientist, but have always been able to "see" this inside of me. Sometimes my speaking is hindered, other times my thinking and sometimes my physical movement. The hardest is when thinking is not working smoothly. When that happens I have to line up one thought at a time, like train cars. I like it much better when my thoughts do not have to be methodically lined up, but are more fluid with colors coming in and out and swirling into unique and beautiful patterns. (My thoughts are in pictures and sometimes moving colors.)

Phil Schwarz (personal communication on Facebook, January 25, 2009) commented on Judy's description by using another analogy:

> I think that processing bandwidth—what Judy calls "neurological movement between places"—is a critical factor in autism. I think that those of us who learn to cope develop adaptations that allow more parsimonious use of the bandwidth available to us: love of sameness, or of patterns, or of predictability (so that we can apply the bandwidth we do have to *deviations* from the predicted or from the patterns). There is a coherent autistic aesthetic

sensibility, that is informed by this search for parsimony of bandwidth use, and for titration of excesses.

This paper explores some of the implications of sensory and movement differences in the development and experiences of individuals with the autism label. We note, of course, that some researchers and clinicians completely deny the possibility that individuals with autism might experience any problems with movement. Rimland (1993, 3), a psychologist long a proponent of a biological approach to autism, wrote:

> It has been widely recognized for many decades that the vast majority of autistic persons are quite unimpaired with regard to their finger dexterity and gross motor capabilities. They have in fact often been described as especially dexterous and coordinated. The literature abounds with stories of young autistic children who can take apart and reassemble small mechanical devices, build towers of blocks and dominos higher than a normal adult can, assemble jigsaw puzzles and climb to dangerously high places without falling. The files of the Autism Research Institute contain over 17,000 questionnaires completed by the parents of autistic children. Finger dexterity is one question we've asked about since 1965. Most parents indicate that their children are average or above in the use of their hands. The idea that autism is, or typically involves, a "movement disorder" is simply ludicrous.

Likewise, Mulick, Jacobson, and Kobe (1993), behavioral psychologists, stated unequivocally that clinical experience argues against any motor/movement difficulties, particularly voluntary control of movement in apraxia:

> Scientific evidence for developmental apraxia in autism is lacking. Autistic youngsters are often characterized by *better*-developed [emphasis in original] motor skills than verbal skills, even real non-verbal problem solving talent ... There is no research evidence at all to support

the position that people with autism experience such global problems. The usual clinical finding, familiar to any psychologist who routinely works in this area, is that motor impairment and delay is much less common than communication disorder and delay (Jacobson and Ackerman 1990, 274).

The common approach in autism pays scant attention to possible somatic difficulties resulting from neurological differences. Perhaps, this is a function of the dominance of psychology and psychiatry for the first fifty or more years of the autism story. Yet some psychologists and psychiatrists did report movement differences and even catatonic symptoms in autism long before Rimland or Mulick et al. and others denied the existence of such evidence (e.g., Damasio and Maurer 1978; Wing and Attwood 1987). More recently, many researchers have noted the presence of impairments in basic motor skills: gait, posture, balance, speed, coordination (e.g., Ghaziuddin and Butler 1998; Jansiewicz et al. 2006; Noterdaeme et al. 2002; Rinehart et al. 2006).

Many neuroscientists now are stressing the significance and implications of motor and sensory difficulties in the development of children with autism. For example, Sutera et al. (2007) looked at four-year-olds who had been diagnosed at age two and received early intervention of various amounts and types. Of particular interest were the children who "lost" the diagnosis of autism by age four. Sutera et al. found that the best predictor of this outcome for very young children with autism is motor skill at age two. Mostofsky (2008) noted this finding and addressed concerns about the exclusion of motor problems from the "core" features of autism in the *Diagnostic and Statistical Manual of Mental Disorders* (4th ed., text rev.; *DSM-IV-TR*; American Psychiatric Association [APA] 2000) "... despite [an] abundance of literature suggesting otherwise." A growing number of researchers and clinicians in a broad range of disciplines continue to stress the importance of studying motor function in autism because, as Rogers and Benetto (2002) reported, "... studies show that movement abnormalities are present early in children with autism, and may precede the emergence of the syndrome." Mostofsky noted: "Motor signs can serve as markers for deficits in parallel brain systems important for control of socialization and communication." For example, children with autism are often described as lacking reciprocity. Esther Thelen (1941-2004), an innovative researcher of infant development, upon reviewing the issue of motor development in autism, asked: "How can you talk about 'reciprocity' or lack thereof as a psychological phenomenon if the child has motor problems?" (personal communication 1997). In the course of development, if individuals move and respond in idiosyncratic ways from infancy, they will experience all interactions within a unique frame that most certainly differs from that which is called typical. The cumulative effect of such interactions will be one in which all aspects of relationships, including how to establish and maintain them, may be markedly skewed from the broader cultural consensus and expected rules of how relationships work. (For reviews of the complex and dynamic interrelationship of movement, perception, relationship and cognitive development, see: Stern 2005; Gibson 1979; Thelen and Smith 1995.) Our experience and self-advocate reports have taught us that individuals with autism often are aware of their idiosyncrasies, may not be able to control them but do want communication, participation and relationship. In order to make this possible, we need to acknowledge and accommodate the differences so that communication, relationship and participation can happen.

I. Dynamic interactions of nervous system, body and environment

As we have noted elsewhere (Donnellan, Leary, and Robledo 2006), the writings of many authors interested in movement describe a unity of perception, action, emotion, and thought. Feldenkrais, a physicist, martial artist, and renowned movement innovator noted: "Our self-image consists of four components that are involved in every action: movement, sensation, feeling and thought" (Feldenkrais 1972, 10). Likewise, in his fascinating book, *Awakenings*, Oliver Sacks (1990) wrote of the self-reports of his patients with post-encephalitic Parkinson's disease who temporarily "awoke" through the use of the drug L-Dopa. They all had been sick from the same disease, *encephalitis lethargica*. The area of damage in their brains from the disease was clearly established. Nonetheless, each developed his or her own personalized version of movement disorder and many of their difficulties were unknown to the medical staff until they were able to speak. The variety of manifestations of symptoms encompassed difficulties with many hidden aspects of human experience: perception of the passing of time; interest in normal activities; fatigue; memory; and recurring thoughts.

Thelen incorporated dynamic systems models in her innovative research on movement in child development (Thelen and Smith 1994; Thelen 1995). In this view, perceptions, movement, thoughts, and emotions can be linked together by having coincidentally (and possibly routinely) co-occurred. Experience may selectively reinforce them as a bundle. They can be unbundled or softly assembled as required by the context. The individual is always operating within an environment or context and, as the context changes, systems scan, adjust, and shift as necessary to meet new demands. These contextual shifts play a vital role in movement. Context comes together in such a way as to allow the movement to emerge or not; a movement and, indeed, the person or persons are part of the context (Thelen and Smith 1994). As Bateson (1972) told us years ago, context is far more than what is left when we take out the part we wish to study.

No single component is causal in determining the movement. As these are dynamic systems, the components are the context that determine the product. Thelen and Smith (1994, 73) further explained that "… even behaviors that look wired in or program-driven can be seen as dynamically emergent: behavior is assembled by the nature of the task, and opportunistically recruits the necessary and available organic components (which themselves have dynamic histories) and environmental support." These may be actions, thoughts, words, memories or sense experiences. Recall Proust, where the taste of a cookie released the hundreds of pages of *Remembrance of Things Past*.

Thelen's approach offers new ways to understand the inconsistent abilities and disabilities of individuals with the autism label. Speech is an example of dynamic behavior. Speech is not lost or gained; it emerges when all necessary components recruited and appropriately regulated and organized, allow its production. Stress often makes speech difficult or even impossible. And stress need not be negative; excitement may also cause difficulties. Paradoxically, for some people with sensory and movement differences, stress also may help produce speech. While presenting with the authors at an Autism Society of America conference in July

1996, Arthur Schawlow, Nobel laureate and father of an adult son with autism, reported that his son could say a complete, and original, context-appropriate sentence about once every eight to ten years. He asked the audience how many parents had similar experiences and at least 18 sets of parents raised their hands. They met and compared notes. Most of the labeled children of these individuals were able to speak under extreme, often negative, circumstances. Some had only spoken once or twice in a lifetime.

Reports of this kind are not unusual in the sensory and movement differences literature, among the autism community or our own 100+ years of combined experience with children and adults with the autism label. More common are phenomena such as echolalia, mutism, speech uttered only under unique circumstances, e.g., speaking what they have written. In the dynamic systems model the notion of emergence begins to give us a way to understand and perhaps support people with these differences. Strandt-Conroy (1999) compiled 40 hours of interviews with adults with autism who experienced such symptoms and more. Her interviews had to be adjusted to the specialized needs of the interview-ees. Several could only answer written questions sent in advance; others if they were on the phone and in a warm bath. Likewise, the autistic people in Robledo and Donnellan (2007) each had personalized supports to enable them to participate in the interviews. We refer to these special-ized arrangements as accommodations after Luria (1932) and Sacks (1990). We define accommodations as adjustments or adaptations of an interaction, a task, situation, or the environment that assist a person to temporarily get around difficulties organizing and regulating sensory information or movement (see Donnellan, Leary, and Robledo 2006 for examples).

II. Learning from neurological symptoms in other sensory and movement disorders

In our review of the history of movement differences we found early descriptions of catatonia in the work of Kahlbaum (1874/1973) which seemed startlingly familiar (see Hill and Leary 1993; Donnellan and Leary 1995; Starkstein, Goldar, and Hodgkiss 1995; Leary and Hill 1996). In the nineteenth century there was no clear distinction between neurological and psychiatric symptoms. As the two fields diverged in the early twentieth century, however, some conditions gravitated into one or the other. Catatonia is presently defined as a characteristic of certain kinds of schizophrenia, though many have argued over the years for a more neurological view of the disorder (Rogers 1992; Abrams and Taylor 1976). The discussion of where to place catatonia and catatonic symptoms is once again topical because of the plan to update the *Diagnostic and Statistical Manual* of the APA. Some, in fact, are arguing for the inclusion of catatonia as a separate diagnostic category or under "movement disturbances" (Taylor and Fink 2003; Fink and Taylor 2006; Penland, Weder, and Tampi 2006; Caroff and Ungvari 2007). Irrespective of that discussion, it is useful to look at the symptoms described by Kahlbaum and other early and recent authors as these may illuminate the symptoms seen in individuals with autism and other developmental disabilities.

In Table 3.1, the characteristic features and symptoms on the left side of the table are borrowed from descriptors specific to several kinds of movement disorders (Kalbaum 1874; Fink and Taylor 2006; Caroff and Ungvari 2007; The *Movement* Disorder Society 2012). The list of movement disorders symptoms is not in any particular order or hierarchy; rather, symptoms are listed randomly as taken from the above literature sources. The intent here is to show the scope of symptoms by feature that may account for certain behaviors seen in autism. Examples of behaviors listed on the right side of Table 3.1 appear there because they have been discussed in a previously published review of the autism literature and movement disturbances (Leary and Hill 1996). The majority of these have also been documented and observed throughout many years of clinical practice with a large number of individuals with autism across the life span.

Table 3.1. Characteristic features of substantial movement disturbances and evidence of possible overlap of symptoms in autism.

Movement disturbance feature	Symptoms evidence in autism
Repetitive motor actions.	e.g., Tapping, touching, grimacing.
Rhythmical, cyclical movements.	e.g., Rocking, shrugging, squinting, pouting.
Lack of initiation.	Requires prompts and cues to perform.
Difficulty imitating others' actions.	Both immediate and delayed motor imitation difficulties.
Echophenomena.	Mimesis; elaborate copying of others' actions—verbal and/or motor.
Immobility.	Remains fixed and inert in position and posture for extended time periods.
Withdrawal.	Isolates self away from focal activity and others.
Grimacing.	Facial/oral-motor movements.
Stereotypies.	Repetitive movements of the hands, limbs, extemities, and whole body.
Aversion.	Of eye gaze and attention to others.
Negativism.	Oppositional actions elicited with passive movement and overall behavior.
Automatic obedience; suggestibility.	Extreme compliance in response to verbal suggestion and environmental cues.
Rigidity.	Muscles rigid to passive movement.
Bradykinesia.	Slowness of movements, feebleness.
Tremor.	Essential, intentional, rest, postural, etc.
Forced grasping.	Of another's hands, wrists, etc., or items in the environment.
Akinesia.	Marked absence of action and movements.
Akathisia.	Motor restlessness, moves about but not goal-directed.
Ataxia.	Loss of coordination in motor action execution.

Movement disturbance feature	Symptoms evidence in autism
Perseveration.	Motor or other repeated behavior after being elicited an initial stimulus.
Ambitendency.	Appears "stuck" in indecisive, hesitant movements.
Tics.	Motor and/or verbal.
Obstruction; blocking.	Incomplete movement towards a goal— "gets stuck" en route to goal.
Difficulty with stopping, cessation of movement.	Will continue movements unless redirected or stopped by an external means.
Mannerisms.	Uses intact and entire motor action sequences out of context, e.g., salutes.
Waxy flexibility.	Automatic ease and compliance with assuming unusual postures for extended time.
Ballismus.	Violent, rapid and apparently involuntary actions and movements.
Choreiform movements.	Rapid and apparently involuntary traveling and "dancing" ripples of movement.
Catalepsy (posturing).	Maintains seemingly uncomfortable and imposed postures for extended time.
Atheloid movements.	Slow, writhing movements and actions.
Spasms.	Muscular spasms of varying durations affecting muscle groups.
Dystonias.	Sustained torsion due to muscle contractions in varied muscle groups.
Impulsivity.	Actions and movements triggered suddenly.
Self-injury, mutilation.	Disturbing and persistent attempts to inflict pain on self.
Excitement; frenzy.	Marked episodes of extreme amounts of activity for extended time.
Aggression, destruction.	Unprecipitated violent actions directed to others and the environment.

Movement disturbance feature	Symptoms evidence in autism
Stupor.	Prolonged period of total immobility, lack of responsiveness and mutism.
Rituals.	Object-related actions on objects as part of a routine, repeated event.
Motility changes.	e.g., Toe walking, skipping, hopping.
Changes in speech behavior.	e.g., Mutism; question repetition; echolalia; verbigeration; logorrhoea; foreign accent; changes in prosody; difficulty modulating volume.
Automatic changes.	Changes in typical autonomic functions, e.g., heart rate, perspiration, breathing, core body temperature.

Leary and Hill (1996) analyzed the literature on symptoms associated with established movement disorders and those associated with autism. The greatest difference among these disabilities was the interpretation of the symptoms. In Tourette syndrome, Parkinson's disorder and catatonia, there was a neurological interpretation of symptoms. A social rather than a neurological interpretation was applied if the person had a label of autism. That which is called a "tic" in a person with Tourette syndrome is most often assumed to be a "behavior" (and often a conscious choice) in a person with autism. For symptoms interpreted through a neurological lens, individuals tend to be appropriately supported. In autism, symptoms are viewed frequently as behaviors to be reduced or eliminated often with a negative intervention and results. Table 3.2, below, illustrates descriptions given to similar behaviors dependent on a person's diagnosis.

Movement disturbance feature	Symptoms evidence in autism
Akinesia.	Non-compliance, social indifference.
Festination.	Behavior excess, careless.
Bradykinesia.	Lazy, slow.
Bradyphrenia.	Mental retardation.
Tics.	Aberrant behavior.
Obsessional/adventitious behaviors.	Autistic behavior, "stims."

The sensory and movement differences reported by and observed in individuals with autism may have a significant impact on their and our ability to relate and participate in social interactions. A neurological view of symptoms possibly affecting autistic individuals will help us to understand further the nature of differences experienced by these individuals. While the psychological impact is very real as experienced first-hand by participants in such interactions, it is useful to suspend social interpretations of the symptoms so as not to mistakenly ascribe intent and volition to individuals whose behavior may be contrary to what really is intended and able to be communicated.

Detailed personal descriptions of movement and sensory differences found in other disabilities have given us some additional insight as to what it may be like for a person to deal with various symptoms such as compelling impulses, a loss of conscious control, lack of initiation, akinetic moments and unusual ways of being in the world (e.g., McGoon 1994). Frequently, the person has both the challenge of the movement difference and burden of blame and misunderstanding. In Strandt-Conroy's (1999) research it was often necessary to use vignettes from people with other sensory movement differences to enable the autistic interviewees to recognize their own experience. Most expressed gratitude for the opportunity to learn about movement differences as they often had blamed themselves for their behavior and all thought they were alone in having these difficulties.

III. Implications of sensory and movement differences for understanding people labeled with autism

A different kind of science

> Woe to that science whose methods are developed in advance of its problems, so that the experimenter can see only those phases of a problem for which a method is already at hand. (Murphy 1939, 114)

We have stressed the neurological aspects of what are commonly thought of as autistic characteristics and behavior problems. We do not intend, however, to either suggest a whole new category of disabilities in autism nor to eliminate the psychological aspects. The issues here are similar to the challenges faced by those interested in Tourette syndrome. The syndrome was elucidated before the fields of neurology and psychiatry diverged (Gilles de la Tourette 1885). For many years, psychiatry dominated the discussion and the treatment. In the past few decades, there has been a far greater emphasis on the neurology of the disorder. Yet, it is clear that it is not possible to separate the neurological from the psychological in a living human being. As Sacks suggests (1989), there is need for a different kind of science that views the individual as a whole person, mind and body. This shift has begun in Tourette syndrome. In addition, dynamic systems models of development suggest an emphasis on the unique history and the critical importance of context on the manifestations of the symptoms. Perhaps the present emphasis on discrete "autistic" behaviors tied to specific interventions should be seen in terms of more conscribed value and utility.

Developmental versus acquired symptoms

In addition to the personalized nature of the characteristics and the dynamic nature of the manifestations of a movement difference mentioned above, it is impossible to overemphasize the importance of the developmental aspects of movement differences in autism vs. adult acquired disorders. For example, bradykinesia, or very slow movements, might have a wide range of effects on adults with acquired disorders such as Parkinsonism. In an infant or a toddler, the possible effects of slow responding or delayed initiating would surely have an effect on the entire trajectory of development even if the difference were intermittent or barely perceptible to the parents or professionals. Of course, we are not suggesting that these autistic people have Parkinson's syndrome; rather that they report sensory and movement differences which are not obvious to their caregivers, particularly parents of young children. Yet, the potential changes to the "dance of relationships" (Stern 2000) alone would be worthy of many dissertations in child development. But the complexity of the task ought not deter us from attempting such inquiry because it could have enormous implications for our understanding of human development and diversity.

Interpretation of symptoms as volitional

Many of us have accepted without question the implicit message that unusual movements presented by people with autism are always volitional and often pleasurable. Sensory and movement difference symptoms in autism are consistently interpreted by others as *autistic behaviors*. Neurological symptoms such as sudden, loud vocalizations; being in constant motion; extreme response to minor changes; unusual mannerisms and gait; and "unmotivated" laughter are examples of behaviors commonly thought to be performed "on purpose" and targeted for behavioral intervention. A social interpretation of these symptoms leaves people with the assumption that they occur as a matter of choice, apathy, or learned behavior. Aggression during an episode of catatonic frenzy is viewed differently if the neurological aspects of the person's experience are considered. Typically, reprimands or contingent praise would not be used to change a recognized neurological symptom. As noted, the non-volitional aspects of behavior are rarely considered for people with autism. For example, the authors have all too often heard criticism and disparaging descriptions such as *lazy* or *non-compliant* applied to a person with autism who is in a non-responsive state. Frequently, the difficulty is related to stress, even the stress of excitement. An all too typical example is staff or family reporting that the child or adult *refused* to get out of the car or van to go to a place he or she seems to like. Intervention or support that is based on our social interpretations of symptoms may not always be helpful. Returning the *non-compliant* person to home, school or program usual results in additional trouble. We need a clearer understanding of people's experiences if we are to provide appropriate care and support that boosts self-confidence and is the product of collaboration rather than control. Donnellan, Leary, and Robledo (2006) offer many suggestions for accommodations that may help people with autism deal with these situations.

Interpretation of symptoms as meaningless

Our assumptions about a person's intention or meaning directly influence the way we respond moment to moment, the relationships we form and the support we give to people. When we label aspects of a person's behavior as meaningless, we may miss opportunities to extend learning and develop our relationships. Echolalia serves well as an illustration. In the early years of behavioral intervention for people with autism (e.g., 1960-1980), professionals assessing a child's communication abilities were to assume that echolalia was the "meaningless repetition of a word or word group just spoken by another person" (Fay 1969, 39), a non-functional, undesirable and "sick" behavior of autism (Lovaas 1966; Lovaas, Schreibman, and Koegel 1974), and a communication disorder in itself to be extinguished through behavior modification (Lovaas 1977). The fine and detailed work of researchers such as Baltaxe and Simmons (1977), Prizant and Duchan (1981) and Prizant and Rydell (1984) began to influence our assumptions about the intentions of autistic speakers. Many people now understand that echolalia is neither always meaningless nor always meaningful. Although sometimes not intentional, many who lack other strategies for communicating may use echolalia intentionally to maintain relationships, improve their comprehension of spoken language and to express meaning (see Kanner 1946). Acknowledgment of a person's efforts to accommodate, improvise and create meaning is a cause for celebration and an opportunity to improve communication and boost self-esteem.

Interpretation of symptoms as "not interested" in relating or communicating

People with autism often communicate, behave and participate in unique, very personal, perhaps idiosyncratic ways, that require their partners to be more flexible and open than usual in interpreting meaning and intention. Differences in the way people are able to use their bodies and focus their attention lead many to assume that a person does not care to participate or communicate and does not desire relationship. These assumptions affect our expectations, the way we speak with them and the educational and social opportunities we offer to them. Under the "criterion of the least dangerous assumption" (Donnellan 1984) it is safest to assume that relationships are critical to human beings for learning and development even if, and perhaps especially if, they have difficulties in these areas (Robledo 2006; Fogel 1993).

IV. The critical importance of relationship in learning and development

The past 40 years have witnessed the growth of a body of knowledge, approaches and intervention methodologies designed to address the needs of individuals with autism. Often the kinds of intervention strategies at our disposal are based on ideas and theories that conflict with each other. The content of interventions may be highly prescriptive or more loosely defined. Research can be cited in support of the efficacy of any kind of approach for at least some individuals in some situations. We struggle as well to explain and describe that quality within any intervention that works and leads to growth and development between the partners involved. Perhaps the essential factor underlying any successful intervention has been overlooked or at least not credited in the research. We propose, along with a growing number of investigators, that the undefined element is the presence and nature of the relationship between persons in any interaction.

The role of relationship in learning is the centerpiece of socio-cultural psychology. While most of us believe that learning is enhanced by a facilitative relationship with a *more mature thinker*, western psychology has only recently directed attention to the nature of that relationship. Lev Vygotsky (1896-1934) was a Russian psychologist whose work described and defined the role of relationship in human development. His work emphasized the notion that *cognitive and specific skill development* is the result of *internalizing* interactions with others within a *relationship* (Bodrova and Leong 1996). Ylvisker and Feeney (1998) have translated Vygotskian theory into a support model that focuses on apprenticeship and collaboration between the person and another with more expertise in the areas where support is needed. The "tutor" provides collaborative mediation that is fine-tuned to the learner's changing needs for support to enable participation in meaningful, project-oriented work: "The roots of cognitive, executive and communication functions, as well as behavioral self-regulation, are everyday social interaction routines" (Ylvisker and Feeney 1998, 15-16). In the socio-cultural models of development, relationship with others serves as the springboard for learning. Learning happens within a social context, within a dialogue with others. We acquire cognitive skills, knowledge and *behavior regula-*

tion, not simply through memorization of facts or actions, but through our interactions in the social world where this knowledge has function and meaning.

Inconsistency in abilities

People report sensory and movement inconsistencies such as: fluctuations in speed and clarity of sensory perception; unreliable ability to maintain or release body postures; delays in speed and accuracy of movement and speech; unpredictable changes in muscle tone; unwanted vocal, verbal and physical tics and extraneous non-functional movement (e.g., Mirenda and Donnellan 1986; Williams 1996a; Standt-Conroy 1999; Harp 2008). A sensory and movement difference is characterized by this inconsistency, causing stress for the most common of movements (Baggs 2007). A person struggling with these performance characteristics may not be able to predict, plan for or sustain effective participation. For example, a person with a 14-second delay in her ability to respond to others (e.g., Mirenda and Donnellan 1986) is likely to be misinterpreted and misunderstood and unlikely to be offered time to respond. This is illustrated by Harp (2008) on her blog *Asperger's Square 8* (used with permission).

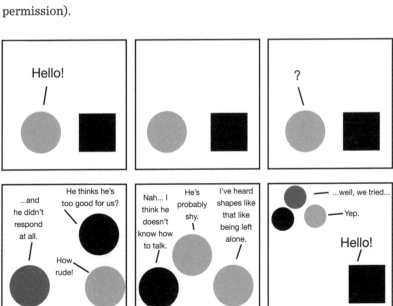

Supporting self-esteem

Humans carry inside themselves an image that includes reasons for and the possibility of change. We need to know that we are OK just as we are, even though there are things we may want to learn or to do better.

A current trend in early intervention for young children with autism is to provide guidance in massive quantities (e.g., 40 hours a week of one-to-one instruction). This guidance is naturally accompanied by frequent corrections and redirection. Given the intensity of this intervention, special care is needed to promote children's self-esteem at any age.

Equally important is the need for positive, optimistic, respectful support for adults with autism. The paucity of quality programs, diminished opportunity for interesting lives, effects of medication and chemical restraint are just a few of the additional burdens on these individuals and their families. Issues of collaboration, personalization and comfort are also essential for children and particularly pressing for the adult population with the autism label. McGinnity and Negri (1995) offer helpful suggestions on how students and staff can learn to be more sensitive to the differences in those on the autism spectrum.

Collaboration, personalization and comfort

The growth of the autism industry over the past two decades has spawned no end of books, interventions, programs and products. Yet, the diagnosis of autism is not prescriptive of the type of supports needed for assisting any particular person to participate, relate and communicate. Supports for people with autism should be personalized, reflect the respect and dignity due to all people and address the challenges with which people struggle to organize and regulate themselves in response to the sensory environment and their movement differences. Appropriate supports require a deep and local knowledge of the individual. This can be gained from those who know and appreciate them but often such information is not available. Then it is even more essential to spend significant time with the person in a variety of activities and settings and with people who respect and admire him or her. We need to learn to listen with all of our senses and compassion (e.g., Savarese 2007; Lovett 1996) and to "presume competence" in all interactions. We do not put people in jeopardy by overestimating their experience. We do look for competence instead of deficits and talk to people in age-appropriate ways. And we model such interactions for all those who are, or may become, willing to know them better.

Moreover, we need to remember that in our journey of change, we all need allies who will collaborate with us to find the most comfortable and effective ways for us to learn to participate in our families, with our friends and as contributing members of our communities (Schwarz 2004; Robledo and Donnellan 2008). This is particularly critical for those persons who are challenged by the movement differences that often make such comfort temporary, personhood elusive and collaboration a mystery. There is much to be learned from self-advocates with autism as well as from individuals who share some of the symptoms of movement differences such as Tourette syndrome, Parkinson's disorder and their supporters (e.g., Williams 1992; McGoon 1994). For example, individuals with Tourette syndrome have taught us that naming a behavior might make it much more difficult for a person to inhibit that behavior. It is roughly analogous to telling a stutterer not to stutter. Anyone familiar with classrooms and programs in autism will recognize the value of that cautionary comment.

V. Conclusion

When I was growing up, speaking was so frustrating. I could see the words in my brain but then I realized that making my mouth move would get those letters to come alive, they died as soon as they were born. What made me feel angry was to know that I knew exactly what I was to say and my brain was retreating in defeat ... (Burke 2005, 250-251)

Jamie Burke is a college student who now is able to speak the words he types with two fingers on his Augmentative and Alternative Communication (AAC) device. We have proposed that many other individuals with the autism label may be challenged by sensory movement differences in starting, stopping, executing, combining and/or switching actions, thoughts, emotions and speech. These symptoms have been described in the literature for many years but generally not integrated into our descriptions or understanding of *autistic behaviors*.

Sensory and movement differences often escape the notice of those of us who do not typically experience them but have been well described by autistic self-advocates and persons interested in individuals with autism and other disability labels. Ignoring these differences (or redefining them as *autistic behaviors* to be controlled) has made life unnecessarily more difficult for individuals with autism and those who care about and for them. Many of the assumptive errors we have made are based on our own social history. In the absence of clarity about the nature of these movement differences, we will continue to be forced into the default position of seeing all unfamiliar behaviors as intentional, deliberate evidence of intellectual impairments and even pleasurable. We have not proposed another list of deficits but a greater understanding of the complexity of what we call *autistic behaviors* and the necessity to re-think our assumptions about them. The task is not going to be easy. Such sensory movement differences are manifest in autism and many other disorders in strikingly unique, personalized and dynamic ways that test present research strategies that rely heavily on a positivist-reductionist philosophy. Yet, some of the brightest scientific lights of the 20th century reminded us that the best way to approach objectivity in science is to view the phenomenon from as many perspectives as possible (Luria 1939; Edelman 1992; Arthur Schawlow, personal communication, 1996). As Einstein shared, "Not everything that counts can be counted and not everything that's counted, counts" (Cunningham and Scott 2004).

There is a long, continual path of misunderstanding to autism. People have been thought of, and referred to, as "non-persons," "behavior problems" and sub-normal in every imaginable way. If they cannot speak, we assume they have little to say and offer only the most limited of communication options. Irrespective of the precision and intensity of our interventions, more often than not they experience isolation, segregation, homogeneous grouping, loneliness, pain and boredom as part of their customary care across the life span. Often their sensory and movement differences contribute to such outcomes as these leave the rest of us unaware of the true nature of their challenges.

Any view of autism at this time needs to reflect the experience of self-advocates with autism and others who describe sensory and movement differences, as well as the latest in the neuroscience and child development literature. We need a research agenda that focuses on understanding and supporting autistic people and others in more respectful, personalized and successful ways. It is the least dangerous assumption (Donnellan 1984) to see all as full human beings who may have formidable and unfamiliar challenges to overcome and who, of course, desire social interaction, communication and participation.

Too often autistic children are raised to believe they are broken and need to be fixed. Adults with autism too often live lives of isolation and poverty. Understanding people's experiences may lead to acceptance, accommodation and appropriate support. To continue down the same paths, well-worn for 65 years, when all these data impel us to *re*think our assumptions and broaden our path is *un*thinkable.

Works Cited

A is for Autism. British Film Institute. 1992. "Fine Take Production" for Channel 4.

Abrams, R., and M. A. Taylor. 1976. Catatonia: a prospective clinical study. *Archives of General Psychiatry* 33 (5): 579-581.

American Psychiatric Association. 2000. *Diagnostic and statistical manual of mental disorders* (4th ed., text rev.). Washington, DC: Author.

Baggs, A. 2007. *I knew moving took effort, but* ... Retrieved January 15, 2009 from Ballastexistenz. http://ballastexistenz.autistics. org/?p=379.

Baltaxe, C., and J. Simmons. 1977. Bedtime soliloquies and linguistic competence in autism. *Journal of Speech and Hearing Disorders* 42:376-393.

Barron, J., and S. Barron. 1992. *There's a Boy in Here*. New York: Simon and Schuster.

Bateson, G. 1972. *Steps to an Ecology of Mind*. New York: Ballantine.

Bedrova, E., and D. Leong. 1996. *Tools of the Mind: The Vygotskian approach to childhood education*. Englewood Cliffs, NJ: Prentice-Hall.

Blackman, L. 1999. *Lucy's Story: Autism and other adventures*. Brisbane, Australia: Book in Hand.

Bluestone, J. 2005. *The Fabric of Autism: Weaving the threads into a cogent theory*. Seattle: Sapphire Enterprises.

Bristol, M. M., D. J. Cohen, E. J. Costello, M. Denckla, T. J. Eckberg, R. Kallen, H. C. Kraemer, C. Lord, R. Maurer, W. J. McIlvane, N. Minshew, M. Sigman, and M. A. Spence. 1996. State of the science in autism: Report to the National Institutes of Health. *Journal of Autism and Developmental Disorders* 26: 121-154.

Burke, J. 2005. The world as I'd like it to be. In *Autism and the Myth of the Person Alone*, ed. D. Biklen. New York: NYU Press.

Caroff, S., and G. Ungari. 2007. Expanding horizons in catatonic research. Guest editorial, *Psychiatric Annals* 37 (1): 7-9.

Condon, W. S. 1985. Sound-film microanalysis: A means for correlating brain and behavior. In *Dyslexia: A neuroscientific approach to clinical evaluation*, eds. F. Duffy and N. Geschwind. Boston: Little, Brown and Co.

Cunningham, H., and D. Scott. 2004. Software architecture for language engineering. *Natural Language Engineering* 10 (3/4): 205-209.

Damasio, A. R., and R. G. Maurer. 1978. A neurological model for childhood autism. *Archives of Neurology* 35 (12): 777-786.

Dhossche, D. M. 2004. Autism as early expression of catatonia. *Medical Science Monitor* 10 (3): RA31-39.

Donnellan, A. M. 1984. The criterion of the least dangerous assumption. *Behavior Disorders* 9: 141-150.

Donnellan, A. M., M. Leary, and J. Robledo. 2006. I can't get started: Stress and the role of movement differences for individuals with the autism label. In *Stress and Coping in Autism*, eds. M.G. Baron, J. Groden, G. Groden, and L. Lipsitt, 205-245. Oxford: Oxford University Press.

Donnellan, A. M., P. Mirenda, R. A. Mesaros, and L. Fassbender. 1984. A strategy for analyzing the communicative functions of behavior. *Journal of the Association for Persons with Severe Handicaps* 2: 201-212.

Edelman, Gerald M. 1992. *Bright Air, Brilliant Fire*. New York: Basic Books.

Endow, Judy. 2006. *Making Lemonade: Hints for autism's helpers*. Cambridge, Wisconsin: CBR Press.

Fay, W. 1969. On the basis of autistic echolalia. *Journal of Communicative Disorders* 2: 38-47.

Feldenkrais, M. 1972. *Awareness through Movement.* New York: Harper-Collins.

Filipek, P., P. Accardo, S. Ashwal, G. Baranek, E. Cook Jr., G. Dawson, D. Gordon, J. Gravel, C. Johnson, R. Kallen, S. Levy, N. Minshew, S. Ozonoff, B. Prizant, I. Rapin, S. Rogers, W. Stone, S. Teplin, R. Tuchman, and F. Volkmar. 2000. Practice parameter: Screening and diagnosis of autism. *Neurology* 55 (4): 468-479.

Fink, M., and M. A. Taylor. 2003. *Catatonia: A clinician's guide to diagnosis and treatment.* Cambridge: Cambridge University Press.

Fink, M., and M. A. Taylor. 2006. Catatonia: Subtype or syndrome in DSM? Editorial. *American Journal of Psychiatry* 163 (11): 1875-1876.

Fogel, A. 1993. *Developing through Relationships.* Chicago: University of Chicago Press.

Gernsbacher, M. A., E. A. Sauer, H. M. Geye, E. K. Schweigert, and H. H. Goldsmith. 2008. Infant and toddler oral- and manual-motor skills predict later speech fluency in autism. *Journal of Child Psychology and Psychiatry and Allied Disciplines* 49 (1): 43-50.

Ghaziuddin, M., and E. Butler. 1998. Clumsiness in autism and asperger syndrome: A further report. *Journal of Intellectual Disability Research* 42: 43-48.

Gibson, J. J. 1979. *The Ecological Approach to Perception.* Boston: Houghton Mifflin.

Gilles de la Tourette, G. 1885. Etude sur nerveus caracteristee par de l'incoordination motrice accompagnee d'echolalie et de copralie. *Archs Neurol* 9: 19-42, 158-200.

Goldman, S., C. Wang, M.W. Salgado, P. E. Greene, M. Kim, I. Rapin. 2009. Motor stereotypies in children with autism and other developmental disorders. *Developmental Medicine & Child Neurology* 51 (1): 30-38.

Grandin, T. 1992. An insider view of autism. In *High Functioning Individuals with Autism*, eds. E. Schopler and G. B. Mesibov, 105-124. New York: Spring.

Hale, M., and C. Hale. 1999. *I Had No Means to Shout!* Bloomington: 1st Books.

Green, D., T. Charman, A. Pickles, S. Chandler, T. Loucas, E. Simonoff, and G. Baird. 2009. Impairment of movement skills of children with autistic spectrum disorders. *Developmental Medicine & Child Neurology* 51: 311-316.

Harp, B. 2008. Asperger Square 8. http://aspergersquare8.blogspot.com/2008/11/square-talk-processing.html.

Hill, D. A., and M. R. Leary. 1993. *Movement Disturbance: A clue to hidden competencies in persons diagnosed with autism and other developmental disabilities.* Madison: DRI Press.

Hill, D. A., and M. R. Leary. 2009. Casting call for a supporting role. *Journal of Intellectual & Developmental Disability* 47 (6): 469-472.

Jacobson, J. W., and L. J. Ackerman. 1990. Differences in adaptive functioning among people with autism or mental retardation. *Journal of Autism and Developmental Disorders* 20: 205-219.

Jansiewicz, E., M. Goldberg, C. Newschaffer, M. Denckla, R. Landa, and S. Mostofsky. 2006. Motor signs distinguish children with high functioning autism and Asperger's syndrome from controls. *Journal of Autism and Developmental Disorders* 36 (5): 613-621.

Kahlbaum, K. [1874] 1973. *Catatonia.* Translated by Y. Levij and T. Pridan. Baltimore: Johns Hopkins University Press.

Kanner, L. 1946. Irrelevant and metaphorical language in early infantile autism. *American Journal of Psychiatry* 103: 242-246.

Leary, M., and D. Hill. 1996. Moving on: Autism and movement disturbance. *Intellectual and Developmental Disability* (formally *Mental Retardation*) 34 (1): 39-53.

Leekam, S. R., C. Nieto, S. J. Libby, L. Wing, and J. Gould. 2007. Describing the sensory abnormalities of children and adults with autism. *Journal of Autism and Developmental Disorders* 37 (5).

Lovaas, O.I. 1966. A program for the establishment of speech in psychotic children. In *Childhood Autism*, ed. J. Wing. London: Pegramon Press.

Lovaas, O. I. 1977. *The Autistic Child: Language development through behavior modification*. New York: Halstead Press.

Lovaas, O. I., L. Schreibman, and R. L. Koegel. 1974. A behavior modification approach to the treatment of autistic children. *Journal of Autism and Childhood Schizophrenia* 4: 111-129.

Lovett, H. 1996. *Learning to Listen: Positive approaches and people with difficult behavior*. Baltimore: Paul H. Brookes.

Luria, A. R. [1932] 1976. *The Nature of Human Conflicts: Or emotion, conflict and will*. New York: Liveright.

Magg, J. W., S. A. Wolchik, R. Rutherford Jr., and B. T. Parks. 1986. Response covariation on self-stimulatory behaviors during sensory extinction procedures. *Journal of Autism and Developmental Disorders* 16: 119-132.

Maurer, R. G. 1993. What autism and facilitated communication have to teach us about the neurology of relationship. Audiotape from lecture. Toronto: MacKenzie Group International.

McGinnity, K., and N. Negri. 2005. *Walk Awhile in My Autism*. Cambridge, WI: CBR Press.

McGoon, D. C. 1994. *The Parkinson's Handbook*. New York: W.W. Norton.

Markham, H., T. Rinaldi, and K. Markham. 2007. The intense world syndrome—An alternative hypothesis for autism. *Frontiers in Neuroscience* 1 (1): 77-96.

Mirenda, P., and A. Donnellan. 1986. Effects of adult interaction style on conversational behavior in students with severe communication problems. *Language, Speech, and Hearing Services in Schools* 17: 126-141.

Mostofsky, S. H. 2008. Anomalous motor circuit activity and connectivity in autism. Paper presented at the meeting of the Child Neurology Society, Santa Clara, CA.

Mostofsky, S., P. Dubey, V. Jerath, E. Jansiewicz, M. Goldberg, and M. Denckla. 2006. Developmental dyspraxia is not limited to imitation in children with autism spectrum disorders. *Journal of the International Neuropsychological Society* 12 (03): 314-326.

Mostofsky, S. H., S. K. Powell, D. J. Simmonds, M. C. Goldberg, B. Caffo, and J. J. Pekar. 2009. Decreased connectivity and cerebellar activity in autism during motor task performance. *Brain* 132 (pt. 9): 2412-25.

Mulick, J. A., J. W. Jacobson, and F. H. Kobe. 1993. Anguished silence and helping hands: Autism and facilitated communication. *Skeptical Inquirer* 17: 270-280.

Nayate, A., J. Bradshaw, and N. Rinehart. 2005. Autism and Asperger's disorder: Are they movement disorders involving the cerebellum and/or basal ganglia? *Brain Research Bulletin* 67: 327-334.

Noterdaeme, M., K. Mildenberger, F. Minow, and H. Amorosa. 2002. Evaluation of neuromotor deficits in children with autism and children with a specific speech and language disorder. *European Child & Adolescent Psychiatry* 11 (5): 219-225.

Penland, H. R., N. Weder, and R. R. Tampi. 2006. The catatonic dilemma expanded. *Annals of General Psychiatry* 5 (14): 1-9.

Prizant, B., and J. Duchan. 1981. The functions of immediate echolalia in autistic children. *Journal of Speech and Hearing Disorders* 46: 241-249.

Prizant, B., and P. Rydell. 1984. Analysis of functions of delayed echolalia in autistic children. *Journal of Speech and Hearing Research* 27: 183-192.

Rimland, B. 1993. Editor's notebook. *Autism Research Review International* 7 (3): 3.

Rincover, A. 1978. Sensory extinction: A procedure for eliminating self-stimulatory behavior in developmentally disabled children. *Journal of Abnormal Child Psychology* 6 (3): 299-310.

Rinehart, N., B. Tonge, R. Iansek, J. McGinley, A. Brereton, P. Enticott, and J. Bradshaw. 2006. Gait function in newly diagnosed children with autism: Cerebellar and basal ganglia related motor disorder. *Developmental Medicine and Child Neurology* 48 (10): 819-824.

Robledo, J., and A. Donnellan. 2008. Properties of supportive relationships from the perspective of academically successful individuals with autism. *Intellectual and Developmental Disabilities* 46 (4): 299-310.

Rogers, D. 1992. *Motor Disorder in Psychiatry: Towards a neurological psychiatry*. Chichester: John Wiley and Sons.

Rogers, S., and L. Benetto. 2002. Le fonctionnement moteur dans le cas d'autisme. *Enfance* 54 (1): 63-73.

Rubin, S., D. Biklen, C. Kasa-Hendrickson, P. Kluth, D. Cardinal, and A. Broderick. 2001. Independence, participation, and the meaning of intellectual ability. *Disability & Society* 16 (3): 415-429.

Sacks, O. W. 1989. Neuropsychiatry and tourette's. In *Neurology and Psychiatry: A meeting of minds*, ed. J. Mueller. Basel: Karger.

Sacks, O. 1990. *Awakenings*. New York: Harper Perennial.

Savarese, R. 2007. *Reasonable People: Autism and adoption*. New York: Other Press.

Schwarz, P. 2004. Building alliances: Community identity and the role of allies in autistic self-advocacy. In *Ask and Tell: Self-advocacy and disclosure for people on the autism spectrum*, ed. Stephen Shore. Shawnee Mission, KS: Autism Asperger Publishing Co.

Sigman, M., and M. A. Spence. 1996. State of the science in autism: Report to the National Institutes of Health. *Journal of Autism and Developmental Disorders* 26 (2): 121-154.

Starkstein, S. E., J. C. Goldar, and A. Hodgkiss. 1995. Karl Ludwig Kahlbaum's concept of catatonia. *History of Psychiatry* 6 (22 pt. 2): 201-207.

Strandt-Conroy, K. 1999. Exploring movement differences in autism through firsthand accounts. Ph.D. diss., University of Wisconsin, Madison.

Stern, D. N. 2000. *The Interpersonal world of the infant*. New York: Basic Books.

Sullivan, A. 2002. Inertia: From theory to praxis. Retrieved from http://archive.autistics.org/library/inertia.html.

Sutera, S., J. Pandey, E. Esser, M. Rosenthal, L. Wilson, M. Barton, J. Green, S. Hodgson, D. Robins, T. Dumont-Mathieu, and D. Fein. 2007. Predictors of optimal outcome in toddlers diagnosed with autism spectrum disorders. *Journal of Autism and Developmental Disorders* 37 (1): 98-107.

Taylor, M., and M. Fink. 2003. Catatonia in psychiatric classification: A home of its own. *American Journal of Psychiatry* 160: 1233-1241.

Taylor, B. A., H. Hoch, M. Weissman. 2005. The analysis and treatment of vocal stereotypy in a child with autism. *Behavioral Interventions* 20 (4): 239-253.

Thelen, E. 1995. Motor development: A new synthesis. *American Psychologist* 50 (2): 79-95.

Thelen, E., and L. B. Smith. 1994. *A Dynamic Systems Approach to the Development of Cognition and Action.* Cambridge, MA: MIT Press.

Tomchek, S. D., and W. Dunn. 2007. Sensory processing in children with and without autism: A comparative study using the short sensory profile. *American Journal of Occupational Therapy* 61 (2): 190-200.

Williams, D. 1992. *Nobody Nowhere.* New York: Avon.

Williams, D. 1994. *Somebody Somewhere.* New York: Times Books.

Williams, D. 1996a. *Like Color to the Blind.* New York: Times Books.

Williams, D. 1996b. *Autism: An inside-out approach.* London: Jessica Kingsley.

Williams, D. 2003. *Exposure Anxiety—The invisible cage: An exploration of self-protection responses in the autism spectrum disorders.* London: Jessica Kingsley.

Wing, L. 1981. Language, social and cognitive impairments in autism and severe mental retardation. *Journal of Autism and Developmental Disorders* 11: 31-44.

Wing, L., and A. Attwood. 1987. Syndromes of autism and atypical development. In *Handbook of Autism and Pervasive Developmental Disorders*, eds. D. Cohen and A. Donnellan, 3-19. New York: Wiley.

Ylvisker, M., and T. J. Feeney. 1998. *Collaborative Brain Injury Intervention: Positive everyday routines.* San Diego: Singular Publishing Group, Inc.

CHAPTER FOUR

I Can't Get Started:
Stress and the Role of Movement Differences in People with Autism

Anne M. Donnellan
Martha R. Leary
Jodi Patterson Robledo

*Someone who has much better inherent communication
ability than I do but who has not even taken a close look
at my perspective to notice the enormity of the chasm between us tells me that my failure to understand is because
I lack empathy.*—Jim, as quoted by L. Cesaroni and
M. Garber

In the public perception, the word autism conjures up an image of a
person rocking back and forth, hands flapping in front of eyes that seem
to focus in an unknown space—a person remote from and disinterested
in the social milieu (Crowley 2000, 2003; Nash 2002). For many years,
professional descriptions, definitions, and common assumptions about
people with autism have reinforced that image and named the unusual
ways of moving and acting as "behaviors." Within the professional world
that arranges and provides support for people with autism, the word
"behavior" often became shorthand for bizarre, bad, repetitive, self-
stimulatory, or useless ways of spending time. Much of the literature is
concerned with manipulating, managing, or eliminating behaviors with
little or no reference to how these might reflect the experience of the
labeled individual. Moreover, the professional models for addressing autism are usually couched in social definitions (e.g., avoiding eye contact,
disinterest in social interaction, no imaginative play) that reflect our

experience as much as, or more than, that of the labeled person. Because of the communication difficulties pathognomonic to the disorder, these individuals often have difficulty explaining their behavior. Thus, we end up assuming our experience of them matches their own experience, an inadequate substitute for their perspective at best.

Despite this obvious breech, many professionals believe that we already understand what autism is, if not the exact cause of the disorder (Donnellan 1999). In fact, the description of autism is too often a teleological exercise with the same symptoms used to both describe and explain it. When one asks why the person displays "autistic symptoms," one is told that he does it because he "has autism," or because he does not have a "theory of mind module," which is why he is autistic, and his autism is why he does what he does.

If parents and professionals are to begin to understand the phenomenon called autism, and through this understanding provide personalized support, it seems evident that the expressed experience of those who are categorized as autistic must be included (Lovett 1996). Therefore, in this chapter, the words of those with autism will be used to explore the stress with which these individuals live. We will use the literature on "movement differences/disturbances" (Donnellan and Leary 1995; Leary and Hill 1996) to help guide that exploration and identify accommodations that might help to minimize stress.

Research that explores the relationship between autism and movement differences has been accumulating slowly since Kanner (1943, 1944) first described repetitive movements, insistence on sameness, differences in the use of facial expression, and limited use of gesture as characteristics of autism. Our reviews of the literature have uncovered historical references to movement differences for people with symptoms associated with autism (Earl 1934; Kahlbaum 1874/1973; Rutter 1996; Rutter, Greenfield, and Lockyear 1967), as well as more recent research (Donnellan and Leary 1995; Leary and Hill 1996). Young and Donnellan (1997) found that the movement differences most commonly cited in the literature include gross and fine motor difficulties (Gittelman and Birch 1967); initiation failure or difficulties (Damasio and Maurer 1978; Maurer and Damasio 1982; Rutter et al. 1967; Schopler, Reichler, and Renner 1986; Wetherby and Prutting 1984); awkwardness and clumsiness in arms and legs; facial-grimacing or teeth-grinding (Bender 1947; Kanner

1943); and hyperkinesis or hypokinesis (Gittelman and Birch 1967; Menolascino 1965; Rutter 1966; Rutter et al. 1967; Wortis 1958). Although movement differences are frequently mentioned in the literature on autism, few papers exist that focus on the implications these symptoms might have for the people labeled with autism. Early works by Damasio and Maurer (1978) and Maurer and Damasio (1982) are particularly noteworthy exceptions.

Our work over the past 12 years has focused on understanding symptoms of movement differences in people labeled with autism and in people with other labels, such as Parkinson's disease, postencephalitic Parkinson's disease, Tourette's disorder, and catatonia (Donnellan and Leary 1995; Leary and Hill 1996; Leary, Hill, and Donnellan 1999; Patterson 2002a, 2002b; Strandt-Conroy 1999; Strandt-Conroy and Donnellan, in preparation). Our emphasis has been on understanding the symptoms commonly associated with movement differences, rather than on the syndromes, diagnostic categories, or etiologies. Our interest has centered on the possible effects that differences in movement may have on a person's ability to organize and regulate movement in order to communicate, relate to others, and participate in his or her family and community. Conversely, we have an interest in how moving differently affects the image a person projects to others, leading others to make assumptions about a person's interests, potential for forming relationships, intellectual functioning, and emotions.

Through most of this chapter, we use the term "movement difference," rather than "movement disorder" or "movement disturbance," to acknowledge that not all of the differences that people experience need be viewed as pathological. Rather, moving and behaving differently is merely part of their day-to-day experience. For example, the person who twirls in a small circle after standing or before sitting may be described as moving differently. The act of twirling does not impact negatively on life and, for most people, is not necessarily a problem. It may, in fact, be an accommodation or a way that a person may temporarily get around difficulties in making the transition from standing and sitting. It may thus be seen as no more odd than straightening one's tie before beginning a speech. When movement differences cause harm or truly disrupt a person's ability to participate, the term "disturbance" may be applied. Difficulties with self-injurious or aggressive behaviors or difficulties of overall activity, such as stupor or frenzy, would fall into the category of movement disturbance. The term "disorder" and "disturbance" are commonly used in the literature for other diagnostic categories as well. For these reasons, we will generally use the term "movement difference" except where movement disturbance would obviously apply.

This chapter offers information on the symptoms of movement differences reported and observed for some people with autism. We will present the range and intensity of expression of symptoms with first-person accounts of how the symptoms have affected people's lives. We will consider stress both as a trigger for unusual, atypical, or uncontrolled movements, as well as an outcome for people who have significant differences in their ways of moving and behaving. Finally, we address some of the implications for supporting people challenged with these differences.

I. What is a movement difference?

Leary, Hill, and Donnellan (1999) defined a movement difference as a difference, interference, or shift in the efficient, effective use of movement. It is a disruption in the organization and regulation of perception, action, posture, language, speech, thought, emotion, and/or memory. Typically, the word "movement" refers to observable actions, such as posture, muscle tone, head and eye movements, facial expression, vocalizations, speech, whole body movements, reaching, gesturing, running, and walking. Our use of the word movement is consistent with research that considers internal mental processes of sensory perceptions (e.g., touch, taste, smell, vision, hearing, proprioception), language, thoughts, and emotions as aspects of human movement.

There is a unity of perception, action, emotion, and thought reflected in the writings of many authors interested in movement. The physicist, martial artist, and movement innovator Moshe Feldenkrais (1972) wrote: "Our self-image consists of four components that are involved in every action: movement, sensation, feeling and thought" (10). In his fascinating book, *Awakenings*, Oliver Sacks (1990) wrote of the experience of his patients with postencephalitic Parkinson's disease. The diagnosis for these patients was movement disorder. The variety of manifestations of symptoms encompassed many hidden aspects of human experience, including difficulty with perception of the passing of time, interest in normal activities, fatigue, memory, and recurring thoughts.

Esther Thelen (1995), a developmental psychologist, has researched and described movement in relation to child development. In her view, perceptions, movement, thoughts, and emotions can be linked by having coincidentally (and possibly routinely) co-occurred. Experience may selectively reinforce them as a bundle. They can be unbundled or softly assembled as required by the context. The individual is always operating within an environment or context and, as the context changes, systems scan, adjust, and shift as necessary to meet new demands. These contextual shifts play a vital role in movement. Context changes come together in such a way as to allow the movement to emerge; the movement and, indeed, the person are part of the context.

No one component is causal in determining the movement. As these are dynamic systems, all components and context determine the product (Thelen 1995; Thelen and Smith 1994). Thelen and Smith further explained, "even behaviors that look wired in or program-driven can be seen as dynamically emergent: behavior is assembled by the nature of the task, and opportunistically recruits the necessary and available organic components (which themselves have dynamic histories) and environmental support" (73).

An example of this is seen in the dynamic nature of speech. Speech is not lost or gained; rather it emerges when all components and context, appropriately regulated and organized, allow its production. For many persons, autistic or not, stress makes speech difficult and even impossible at times. Paradoxically, for some people with movement differences, stress can help produce speech. The late Arthur Schawlow, Nobel laureate and father of an adult son with autism, reported that his son could say a complete, and original, context-appropriate sentence about once every 8-10 years. He asked an audience at the Autism Society of America conference how many parents had similar experiences and about 15 sets of parents raised their hands. They met briefly and compared notes. Most of the labeled children of these individuals were able to speak under extreme, often negative, circumstances. Some had only spoken once or twice in a lifetime (A. Schawlow, personal communication, July 1996).

II. Interpreting symptoms of movement differences in people with autism

Parents, teachers, and people who themselves experience these movement differences have consistently reported disturbances of sensation and movement associated with autism (e.g., Rubin et al. 2001). Researchers have studied autism in relation to a number of disturbances of sensation and movement. These findings are summarized in Table 4.1.

Table 4.1. Symptoms of movement differences found in autism.

Symptoms	Research
Apraxia/dyspraxia or difficulties in motor planning and sequencing of movements.	Ayres 1979; Biklen 1990; Brasic, Barnett, Will, Nadrich, Sheitman et al. 2000; DeMyer, Alpern, Barton, DeMyer, Churchill, et al. 1972; Jones and Prior 1985.
Abnormalities of gait and posture.	Bond 1986; Ornitz 1974; Vilensky, Damasio, and Maurer 1981.
Parkinsonian symptoms such as akinesia/dyskinesia or difficulties initiating or switching movements, freezing, or stopping movements.	Damasio and Maurer 1978. Maurer and Damasio 1982.
Tourette's disorder, including stereotyped movements, vocal, verbal and physical tics, and obsessive-compulsive traits.	Comings and Comings 1991; Realmuto and Main 1982; Sverd 1991; Wing and Attwood 1987.
Catatonia or catatonic-like phenomena including mutism, echolalia, repetitive movements, automatic obedience, odd hand postures, interruption and freezing of movements, increased slowness affecting passivity, and apparent lack of motivation and frenzy, excitement, or agitation.	Ahuja 2000; Chaplin 2000; Hare and Malone 2004; Kahlbaum 1973; Realmuto and August 1991; Wing and Attwood 1987; Wing and Shah 2000.

Autism, apraxia, Parkinson's disease, Tourette's disorder, and catatonia comprise clusters of symptoms diagnosed through behavioral observation. The coincidence of symptoms does not necessarily denote one particular etiology. However, examination of the similarities of symptoms among these various syndromes may assist us in understanding aspects of autism that present challenges to people in communicating, relating to others, and participating in typical activities. We are interested in understanding the possible neurological basis for many symptoms of autism that are currently considered to be "behaviors." In contrast, a social interpretation of these symptoms may leave people with the assumption that the symptoms with which people struggle are matters of choice, apathy, or learned behavior. For example, aggression during an episode of catatonic frenzy is viewed differently if the neurological aspects of the person's experience are considered. Would punishment be used to change the behavior of a person with a recognized neurological symptom? Would criticism and discouraging descriptions such as "laziness" be applied to a person in a catatonic stupor? Would a person with Parkinson's disease be scolded for reacting slowly when instructed to do something? Assumptions based on our social interpretations of symptoms may not always be helpful. We need a clearer understanding of people's experiences if we are to provide appropriate care and support that boosts self-confidence and is the product of collaboration rather than control.

Social interpretation of these symptoms is not unique to autism. Symptoms of sensory and movement differences in people labeled with developmental disorders may also be interpreted as a part of mental retardation or a learning difficulty without acknowledgment of the possible neurological basis for the symptoms. Rogers (1992) and his colleagues believe that unusual and abnormal movements of people labeled as mentally retarded or as having an intellectual handicap are often viewed as a side effect, a part of retardation, or as a kind of self-stimulation. When people with movement disorders such Parkinson's disease or Tourette's disorder show the same unusual movements, the behaviors are acknowledged for their neurological base and described in neurological terms; thus for one group, there is a social interpretation of behavior and for another group, there is a neurological description. Many of us have accepted without question the implicit message that unusual movements presented by people with autism are volitional and pleasurable. Table 4.2 illustrates the different labels given to behavior dependent on a person's diagnosis.

Table 4.2. Differences in labeling.

People with movement disorders	People labeled with autism
Akinesia.	Noncompliance.
Festination.	Behavior excess.
Bradykinesia.	Laziness.
Bradyphrenia	Mental retardation.
Tics.	Aberrant behavior.
Obsessions.	Autistic behavior.

During the early 1990s, a small group of people, working both independently and as a team, were committed to increasing the understanding of symptoms in autism. One of the products of this synergy was an exploratory analysis using the symptoms of autism in a sample of published research accounts and the *Diagnostic and Statistical Manual of Mental Disorders*, third revised edition (*DSM-III-R*; American Psychiatric Association 1987) to compare with symptoms of movement disturbance as categorized in the Modified Rogers Scale (Leary and Hill 1996). Rogers (1992) and his colleagues have carefully examined movement differences as an integral part of some psychiatric and developmental disorders. They viewed the symptoms of catatonia, for example, as neurologically based movement disorders. The Modified Rogers Scale (Lund, Mortimer, Rogers, and McKenna 1991) has been used to detail the motor disorders associated with catatonia, schizophrenia, and developmental disabilities.

The exploratory analysis presented by Leary and Hill (1996) helped us understand the wide range and complexity of symptoms of movement disturbance (see Table 4.3). It was clear that at least some individuals labeled with autism have symptoms fitting most of the categories of the

Modified Rogers Scale, suggesting the possibility that the core characteristics of autism may be based, in part, on the presence of neurological symptoms that affect sensation and movement. As documented in several disorders affecting sensation and movement, such as Parkinson's disease, catatonia, and Tourette's disorder, these symptoms frequently interfere with, and may even supplant, a person's intentional movement. Because people with autism have grown up with these differences, their behaviors have been affected by the experience of sensory and movement challenges. As practitioners, we had relied upon the possible communicative intentions of a person's behavior as guideposts for providing them with support. In considering the possibility that some behaviors may not be intentional, even though they might be "communicating" vital information about an individual, we were faced with a new challenge. Movement and sensory differences may affect a person's ability to perceive, act, and respond accurately—that is, in a way that reflects his/her intention. Thus, our understanding of people's behaviors needed fine-tuning. We now had to consider that our intuitive ivnterpretations of behavior needed to include the possibility that the observed behavior was the result of difficulties organizing and regulating sensation and movement. In other words, "Behaviors may not be what they seem" (Leary and Hill 1996, 44).

Table 4.3. Autism research and diagnostic criteria compared with features of movement disturbance.

Features of movement disturbance[a]	Autism research	DSM-III-R criteria for autism
Posture:		
Simple abnormal posture.	Flexion dystonia: Maurer and Damasio 1982; odd hand postures: Wing and Attwood 1987; Walker and Coleman 1976.	Failure to cuddle; odd hand postures.
Complex abnormal posture.	Posturing: Realmuto and August 1991; freezing: Wing and Attwood 1987.	Odd body postures.
Persistence of imposed postures.	Catalepsy: Realmuto and August 1991.	Catatonic posturing.
Tone:		
Abnormal tone.	Abnormalities in muscle tone: Gillberg, Rosenthal, and Johansson 1983; Maurer and Damasio 1982.	Failure to cuddle.
Gegenhalten (springy resistance to passive movement).		
Mitgehen (anglepoise lamp-raising of arm in response to light touch).		
Abnormal movements; face and head:		
Simple brief/ dyskinesialike; repetitive, rhythmical ticlike.	Myoclonic jerk of head: Walker, Coleman, and Ornitz 1976; bruxism: Bebko and Lennox 1988, Ornitz and Ritvo 1976; mouthing: Walker and Coleman 1976.	

Features of movement disturbance[a]	Autism research	DSM-III-R criteria for autism
Simple sustained/ grimacelike; spasmodic, not completely fixed.	Disturbance in facial expression: Maurer and Damasio 1982; grimace or rigidity for no apparent reason: Schopler et al. 1986, Walker and Coleman 1976; decreased use of facial expression: Schopler et al. 1986.	Lack of facial responsiveness.
Complex mannerism/ stereotypylike; turning away, side to side, searching movements.	Looks out of corners of eyes; avoids looking adult in the eye: Schopler et al. 1986; eye-gaze/ocular abnormalities: Churchill and Bryson 1972, Hutt and Ounsted 1966, Mirenda et al. 1983.	Facial expression and gesture is absent or minimal or socially inappropriate in form; lack of eye contact.
Abnormal movements; trunk and limbs:		
Simple brief/ dyskinesialike; random/repetitive, rhythmical ticlike.	Involuntary motor tics: Wing and Attwood 1987, Comings and Comings 1991, Realmuto and Main 1982; choreiform and athetoid movements: Maurer and Damasio 1982, Walker and Coleman 1976; dyskinesia: Maurer and Damasio 1982.	Arm flapping; abnormalities of motor behavior; gesture is absent or minimal or socially inappropriate in form.
Simple sustained/ dystonialike; abnormal muscle stretch and flex.	Flexion dystonia: Maurer and Damasio 1982.	
Complex mannerism/ stereotypylike.	Motor stereotypies: DeMyers et al. 1972, Hutt et al. 1965, Kern et al. 1984, Maurer and Damasio 1982, Meiselas et al. 1989, Ornitz and Ritvo 1976, Ornitz 1974, Ornitz and Ritvo 1968, Ritvo et al. 1971, Sorosky et al. 1968, Walker and Coleman 1976.	Motor stereotypies include peculiar hand movements, rocking, spinning, dipping and swaying movements of the whole body.

Features of movement disturbance[a]	Autism research	DSM-III-R criteria for autism
Abnormal ocular movements:		
Increased blinking.		
Decreased blinking.		
Eye movements; to and fro, roving, conjugate.		
Purpose movement:		
Abruptness/rapidity of spontaneous movements; suddenness quality.		
Slowness/feebleness of spontaneous movement; weak, languid, labored.	Bradykinesia: Maurer and Damasio 1982; dyspraxia: DeMyer 1975, DeMyer et al. 1972, DeMyer et al. 1981, Jones and Prior 1985.	
Iterations of spontaneous movements; gesture, mannerism repeated.	Spatial/logic symmetrizing and ordering: Frith 1971, Kanner 1943, prior and Hoffman 1990, Prior and MacMillan 1973; obsessive-compulsive behaviors: Baron-Cohen 1989, Frith 1971, Kanner 1943, Maurer and Damasio 1982; object exploration through proximal senses: Frith and Hermelin 1969, Goldfarb 1956, Masterton and Biederman 1983, Maurer and Damasio 1982, Ornitz 1974, Sorosky et al. 1968; self-injurious behavior: Favell et al. 1978, Gabony 1991, Gedye 1989, Guess and Carr 1991, Rolider and VanHouten 1985, Walker and Coleman 1976, Winchel and Stanley 1991; persistent strange or peculiar body	Abnormalities of motor behavior; self-injurious behavior.

Features of movement disturbance[a]	Autism research	DSM-III-R criteria for autism
	movements despite attempts to discourage them: Schopler et al. 1986; perseveration: Chess 1972, Frith 1970, 1971, Hoffman and Prior 1982, Kanner 1943, Maurer and Damasio 1982.	
Other: echopraxia/ blocking/ambitendence; copying action/ freezing/ an opposing action interruption.	Echopraxia: Carr 1979, Konstantareas 1985; hypermimesis: Bartak, Rutter, and Cox 1975, Curcio and Piserchia 1978, DeMyer 1975, 1976, Rutter 1974.	Repetitively mimics actions.
Gait:		
Exaggerated associated movements.		
Reduced associated movement.	Loss of associated movements: Bartak et al. 1975, DeMyer et al. 1972, Maurer and Damasio 1982, Vilensky et al. 1981.	
Slow/shuffling.	Brandykinesia: Maurer and Damasio 1982.	
Manneristic, bizarre.	Gait disturbance: Bond 1986, Hutt et al. 1964, Maurer and Damasio 1982, Sorosky et al. 1968, Vilensky et al. 1981; toe walking: Schopler et al. 1986.	Walking tiptoe; jumping.
Speech:		
Aprosodic; abnormal rate, volume, intonation.	Dysprosody: Baltaxe 1981, Ornitz and Ritvo 1968; poor speech volume modulation: Baltaxe 1981, Ornitz and Ritvo 1968; abnormal tone, rhythm, volume: Schopler et al. 1986.	Abnormal speech melody.

Features of movement disturbance[a]	Autism research	DSM-III-R criteria for autism
Mutism.	Mutism: Curcio 1978, Konstantareas 1985, LaVigna 1977, Maurer and Damasio 1982, Ornitz and Ritvo 1968, Ritvo et al. 1971; lack of communicative initiations: Curcio 1978, Loveland and Landry 1986, Maurer and Damasio 1982, Mundy et al. 1990, Ornitz and Ritvo 1968, Prizant and Wetherby 1985, Rapin 1987, Ritvo et al. 1971.	Language may be totally absent.
Indistinct/unintelligible speech; mumbling, poor articulation, nonsocial speech.	Use of jargon: Schopler et al. 1986; vocal, verbal tics: Comings and Comings 1991, Realmuto and Main 1982, Wing and Attwood 1987.	
Other: echolalia/palilalia/ speech mannerisms.	Echolalia: Baltaxe and Simmons 1977, Kanner 1943, Ornitz and Ritvo 1968, Paccio and Curcio 1982, Prizant and Duchan 1981, Prizant and Rydell 1984, Rapin 1987, Simon 1975; topic perseveration: Kanner 1943; unconventional expression of intent: Prizant and Wetherby 1985.	Delayed or immediate echolalia; verbal stereotypies including repetition of words, phrases.
Overall behavior:		
Marked overactivity.	Catatonic excitement: Wing and Attwood 1987; extreme response to minor environmental changes: Campbell et al. 1972, Geller et al. 1981, Kanner 1943, Ornitz and Ritvo 1968, Prior and MacMillan 1973; hyperkinesis: Sorosky et al. 1968; explosive/violent movement episodes: Campbell et al. 1972.	Catatonic phenomena, particularly excitement or posturing; aggressive behavior.

Features of movement disturbance[a]	Autism research	DSM-III-R criteria for autism
Marked underactivity.	Hypomimesis: Bartak et al. 1975, Curcio 1978, Curcio and Piserchia 1978, Dawson and Adams 1984, DeMyer 1975, DeMyer et al. 1972, 1981, Schopler et al. 1968; almost never initiates: Schopler et al. 1986; almost never responds to the adult: Schopler et al. 1986; catatonic stupor: Realmuto and August 1991; decreased responsiveness: Lovaas et al. 1971, Ornitz and Ritvo 1968, Prizant and Wetherby 1985, Rapin 1987.	Indifference to affection or physical contact; no or impaired imitation.
Excessive compliance/ automatic obedience.		
Poor/feeble compliance.		
Other: negativism.	Command negativism/ blocking/ substitution: Clark and Rutter 1977, Morrison et al. 1971, Volkmar 1986, Volkmar et al. 1985, Wallace 1975.	Oppositional behavior; aversion to physical contact.
Other: engages in rituals.	Ritualistic behavior: Frith 1971, Kanner 1943, Maurer and Damasio 1982, Prior and MacMillan 1973.	Ritualistic, repetitive actions: following routines in a repetitive way.

Reprinted with permission from Leary and Hill 1996.

[a]Movement features represent items adapted from the Modified Rogers Scale (Lund, Mortimer, Rogers, and McKenna 1991).

III. First-hand experiences of individuals with autism

Within the last two decades, numerous individuals with autism have shared their unique experiences of living with autism resulting in a plethora of published first-hand accounts. Many professionals are seeking out and listening to these individuals to better understand this complex disorder (Cesaroni and Garber 1991; Patterson 2002a; Strandt-Conroy 1999; Young 2000). Individuals have been able to share their experiences through interviews, personal communication, and published accounts. These accounts come from individuals who can speak or type independently. In almost every first-hand account, individuals with autism report the experience of the stress of living in bodies that often do not work and move the way they want them to, resulting in extreme anxiety in their day-to-day lives.

A common theme that has emerged in the first-hand accounts fits in well with the dynamic systems model described earlier. That is, stress and difficulties with sensation and movement are described by labeled people as not necessarily having a cause and effect relationship. They suggest that the relationship would be better described as a causal loop, instead of linear as "*A* causes *B*" or "*B* causes *A*." Instead, stress and difficulties with sensation and movement interact dynamically.

Stress can play a significant role in a person's ability to organize and regulate actions and postures. It can also affect speech and language, as well as emotions, perceptions, and memories. Often stress can cause unusual sensations and movements to escalate (Brenner, Friedman, and Merrit 1947). Some individuals report that they may feel physically unaware of their body and movements (e.g., Blackman 1999; Hale and Hale 1999; Williams 1996a, 1996b, 2003). Williams (1996b), for example, reported how stress affected her movement, causing her to feel pushed beyond her limits. She described three involuntary situations that might occur during an episode of stress. She might become dissociated, thus causing her to lose all conscious connection with her movements. Or she might shut down completely, causing her movement to become involuntarily "frozen." She likened this to the feeling of "test anxiety." Finally, overload from stress might cause her painful sensory hypersensitivity.

She also described the feeling of stress spiraling out of control, taking her to a point where she was completely unaware of her body in space. Stress can be immense when sensations and movements are unreliable and unpredictable. Imagine having to cross the street. You know that you only have a certain amount of time to get to the other side. Knowing in the back of your mind that you might become stuck and unable to move when you are in the middle of the street would cause a great deal of anxiety and stress. If this stress causes you to avoid such situations, it will have a direct impact on your daily activities.

In the following section, first-hand accounts are used to explore the complexity of the dynamics of autism, stress, sensation, and movement differences.

Experiences of stress and anxiety

Donna Williams has written numerous insightful books describing her experience of autism. Recently, she published *Exposure Anxiety—The Invisible Cage* (2003). Similar to conditions such as agoraphobia and reward deficiency syndrome, Williams defined exposure anxiety as a "self-parenting survival mechanism, an intense often tic-like involuntary self-protection mechanism that jumps in to defend against sensed 'invasions.' " (10). Williams went on to describe it as "feeling your own existence too close up, too in your face" (10-11), like a "vulture" that was watching and waiting, affecting every moment, especially when the situation was stressful: "The more I wanted to say or show something, the more my own Exposure Anxiety was tuned in, hanging on my every expression. My body, my facial expression, my voice and my words were pulled about by some wild horse inside of me. I'd want to say I was sad, my face would be beaming. I'd want to sit calm and still and enjoy a sense of company, my body would be propelled into wild diversion responses demonstrating discomfort and hypersensitivity. I'd try to tell someone I liked them and swear at them, try to show caring and be compelled to do something to repel them" (103).

Struggling against the will of her body was something that Williams had to deal with on a daily basis. Williams also described the complex self-protective responses often necessary to cope. She raised interesting questions about how exposure anxiety affects movement and how these differences can appear so odd:

Why can someone with Exposure Anxiety be expressively and naturally laughing out loud in the back garden but somehow "stuck," compliant, or performing when in front of others? Why they can't get together to make breakfast once you are up, or run the bath, or get dressed, but seem to do a whole range of things which might prove they were capable of these? Why might someone with Exposure Anxiety be able to initiate communication with their own reflection and yet unable to respond as themselves when shown affection? Or be able to initiate an activity, but when you try to initiate exactly the same activity with them, appear uninterested, distracted or disowning? Why, although they have an ability, do they appear to freeze and become incapable in front of others or when asked to perform a task on command? (Williams 2003, 21-22)

Having all these questions and few answers lead to a number of emotions, including stress and anxiety. Many individuals with autism report that fear, anxiety, and stress are the dominant emotions of their everyday life.

Challenges in organizing and regulating actions

Sensory and movement differences can have a direct impact on the individual's action. This can involve difficulties initiating and executing movements. It can also affect difficulties with stopping, combining, and switching movements. Organizing and regulating sensory information and movement to perform tasks may be frustrating for people with these differences. Extreme emotions can cause the individual to become stuck, unable to stop a movement. Sean Barron (Barron and Barron 1992) recalled, "All I wanted was to be like the other kids my age. It felt as if I was weird and strange on the outside, but inside I wasn't like that. The inside person wanted to get out and break free of all the behaviors that I was a slave to and couldn't stop" (181). For many of these individuals, as for Sean, simple movements can lead to repetitions or perseveration, even if the individual wants to stop the movement.

Some individuals report that they get stuck and unable to initiate movement. Williams (1996b) described this experience as a "suffocating and frightening experience of helplessness" (171). Williams (1996a) recalled, "I found myself physically stuck and physically disconnected. I struggled to 'remember' how to cross the room or open a drawer, but I was now trying to remember with my body and my body had little memory of moving as me. Inside of me I was thinking, Come on, leg, you know what to do. But it was like my body couldn't hear me, like I had no body-memory" (99).

It is little wonder that the fear of being stuck like this in public would cause these individuals to live in a nearly constant state of stress and panic. When asked if he feels stress when he is stuck, Charles Martel Hale, Jr. (Hale and Hale 1999) replied, "Yes. It feels like I am doing a marathon just to move" (35).

Feeling disconnected from your body has been likened to being a puppet on strings with someone else in control. Williams (1996a) stated, "If not for a sense of humor I might have killed my body outright in retaliation" (89). Often, Williams would want to go in one direction, but her body would take her in another. Her body seemed to be off on a track of its own. This complete loss of control of the body may cause frustration, anxiety, and stress within these individuals. Charles recalled that his movement disorder is most apparent when he is unable to respond to someone or something in an appropriate manner (Hale and Hale 1999). Although his intelligence told him how to respond, his body would not always follow along: "For instance, when I should be smiling, sometimes I know that I am not smiling but may be even frowning. This causes me a great deal of pain and makes me look as though I am not comprehending when, in fact, I am crying to respond in an appropriate manner" (32).

Sean Barron (Barron and Barron 1992) recalled the intense frustration and stress when he was unable to perform fine motor tasks, such as buttoning or tying his shoes: "Many times I ripped the buttons off my shirts and broke my laces because I was so furious with the damn things when they refused to work" (200). Temple Grandin recalled feelings of stress when being asked to perform two motor tasks at the same time: "Getting all the parts to work together is a monumental task" (Grandin and Scariano 1986, 26). Transferring the knowledge of the movement to actual performance of the task left these individuals completely exhausted. Jim, a participant in a study by Cesaroni (1990), reported that combining and synchronizing movements was as difficult as trying to make your eyes blink at opposing times.

Individuals with autism say that knowing that others judge them by their actions causes them pain, stress, and frustration. Charles is constantly stressed by the fact that how he moves within his environment affects the way he is perceived: "I hope people will begin to understand that appearances do not always indicate how a person thinks and responses do not show our abilities ... I know that it is difficult for anyone to understand unless he has the problem himself. If people could give us a chance in life to prove ourselves, many people would be happier and feel a part of society and not just misfits" (Hale and Hale 1999, 32-33).

Experience of perceptual differences

Perception can also be greatly affected through this loop of stress and movement differences. Williams (1996a) recalled that escalators provoked dizziness and loss of awareness of where her body was in space. For Grandin (1995), various stimuli such as a telephone ringing or the arrival of the mail, could cause a full blown stress attack. Tito Rajarshi Mukhopadhyay (2000) found that open space was a stressor for him. Open space made him feel as though his body was being scattered. Tito's reaction to this stressor would be to tantrum. This fear of open spaces caused him stress for many years.

These individuals tell of experiencing differences in sensory integration where information from one sense may blend with another sense. For some individuals, labeled people as well as those who are not, this may be pleasant. For others it is a stressor. This blending of senses is known as synesthesia, which may result in hearing colors, seeing music, and tasting objects (Ramachandran and Hubbard 2003). Jim, a participant in Cesaroni's study (1990), described his experience with synesthesia: "Sometimes the channels get confused, as when sounds come through as color. Sometimes I know that something is coming in somewhere, but I can't tell right away what sense it's coming through" (74).

Other individuals describe an inability to process two or more sensations that are occurring at the same time. Rand (as cited in Strandt-Conroy 1999) described this difficulty combining different kinds of sensory input as, "sometimes only one thing can go in at one time. So the sight could go in first, then fade out because the sound is coming in. When the sight fades only the sound is left, it is the only information the person is getting, which makes it sound louder because it is all he can focus on" (79).

Some individuals with autism report that difficulty with organizing and regulating sensory information causes them to have unusual responses to sensations of hearing, vision, touch, taste, and smell. Judy Barron (Barron and Barron 1992) described many of the sensory experiences that brought stress into her son Sean's life: "The one thing that did hurt him was having his scalp touched; when I washed his hair he squirmed and cried out, trying to push my hands away. Though I was as gentle as possible, it was obviously painful to him. It was even worse when I brushed his hair—he screamed 'OW!' over and over, wrenching away from me" (34).

Sean noticed that these sensory experiences made him different from others, causing him anxiety every day (Barron and Barron 1992). He described sitting in a bathtub as painful. He was extremely sensitive to the squishy feeling around him: "When they insisted I 'sit right,' it only compounded the problem. I had no choice—I had to sit in an unnatural way, so baths were a trying experience. Also it made me feel that there was something wrong with me because I had to sit that way" (96). Even a bath, a very relaxing sensation to many people, caused Sean extreme discomfort and distress.

Temple Grandin (Grandin and Scariano 1986) was very clear about the effect of sensory overreactions in her daily living: "The clamor of many voices, the different smells, perfume, cigars, damp wool caps and gloves—people moving about at different speeds, going in different directions, the constant noise and confusion, the constant touching, were overwhelming" (21). Grandin also described how these overwhelming reactions would often cause her to act out: "I would invariably react by hitting another child or by picking up an ashtray or anything else that was handy and flinging it across the room" (20).

From time to time, we all experience difficulties with a repetitive thought, but people with sensory and movement differences report unmanageable repetitive thoughts. Kathy, another participant in the Strandt-Conroy (1999) study described how intrusive thoughts could lead her to distraction and stress:

I think in some situations it's just harder for me not to have intrusive thoughts. Some autistic people, they say, block things out or they shut things down or whatever. My mind doesn't think—I'm not able to stop an intrusive thought or block something out unless it's something really, really, really mild—but if it's severe, it all comes in and there's no way I can stop it. I'm not able to tune out anything. Intrusive thoughts would be nonsense syllables or something. I don't understand why this is—but if I was trying to study a foreign language or if I tried to study anything with odd-sounding words, I'd get nonsense syllables and stuff would pop in my mind and anxiety. It doesn't make a bit of sense. I don't know why it happens. (125-126)

Other individuals described their defenses against an environment that caused them so much stress. Lucy Blackman (1999) described how she had to accommodate to perceptual inconstancy: "On the good days, my world was one of time and 'feeling' and light and movement all in one, but fear or other unpleasant sensations fragmented my surround, so I relied on activities such as swaying, humming and running in circles, which defended me against uninterrupted exposure to my sound-environment" (34-35).

Blackman (1999) went on to describe the behaviors she used to accommodate her sensitivity to overwhelming auditory stimulation: "Because other people's sound processing was alien to me, I had no idea that sound should not be like a pressure-cooker lid. I put my hands to my ears for loud sudden noises, but the continuous clamor of everyday life was only relieved by movement. Even in the classroom there was visual stimulation and noise, which combined with my own breathing and a buzzing effect that I think was my own inner ear. I rocked, swayed and scampered, even though I knew how to sit in one place and that it was expected of me" (51).

Donna Williams (1996b) told how constant adaptations and accommodations to unusual sensory experiences can be emotionally and mentally stressful, especially after years of these experiences: "After 10, 20, or 30 years, people with systems integration problems, due to whatever reason, have pretty much developed adaptations to their difficulties which might be mentally and emotionally difficult to change. Also, in correcting an underlying problem someone has taken many years adapting to, the impact of these changes upon one's identity and personality may sometimes be more than the mind or emotions can handle in too big a dose" (67).

Challenges of speaking

Sensory and movement difference can also have a profound effect on speech, language, and all aspects of communication. Within a conversation there is a labyrinth of complexity. For people with sensory and movement differences, even typical daily interactions can be extremely anxiety-provoking. Lindsay (one respondent quoted in Strandt-Conroy 1999), expressed the intense stress caused by conversations:

> 1. Paying attention to the other person in the first place is difficult enough, and causes enough anxiety, add 2. The stress of me dealing with this onslaught of noise from this strange person ... 3. The knowledge that they expect me to be able to understand what they are saying, and 4. The effort of trying to do this ... 5. That they figure I'm supposed to have thoughts on this ... whatever it is, and of course, they are (or were) supposed to give THEIR thoughts on the subject, I now have one more thing to add to my list of things I've got to do ... figure out what their thoughts are on the subject, and then see if I can in any way make that acceptable to me in any way, even though I don't understand it (understanding is way too impossible and difficult a concept that I don't even bother with it ...) and more often than not I cannot. And 6. I am now supposed to EXPRESS my opinions (or pseudo opinions), fluently, coherently, and rapidly!! 7. The fact that this is impossible, **PLUS** 8. The expectation/demand that all of this WILL be met, and anything else is unacceptable, and unacceptability is not allowed!!!!! And 9. The entire interaction (which is repeated endlessly throughout the

entire encounter) is supposed to take place in a matter of
a few seconds!!!!! (114-115)

Coordinating the sensations and movements involved in speech is
a lot to handle in a matter of seconds. It is no wonder that many individuals appear to withdraw or limit their participation in situations
that require these kinds of interactions. Yet, trying to avoid them would
certainly have a negative impact on your social life and cause additional
stress and anxiety.

Although stress typically increases difficulties with speech, these
individuals can sometimes perform better under stress (Sacks 1990). As
noted earlier, many parents of individuals with autism report that during extremely stressful situations their children, whom they say never
speak, are able to get words out very clearly, such as, "Fire, everyone get
out of here," or "I'm very hungry." Temple Grandin (Grandin and Scariano 1986) recalled a similar experience:

> It also was sort of a miracle that I had been able to get the
> word "ice" out clearly and succinctly. As an autistic child,
> difficulty in speaking was one of my greatest problems.
> Although I could understand everything people said,
> my responses were limited. I'd try, but most of the time
> no spoken words came. It was similar to stuttering: the
> words just wouldn't come out. Yet, there were times when
> I said words like "ice" quite clearly. This often occurred
> during a stressful period such as the car accident when
> stress overcame the barrier which usually prevented me
> from speaking. (14)

On the other hand, many individuals report that they want to speak,
but combining all the actions appropriately is often an impossible task.
Lucy Blackman (1999) experienced this in many daily interactions: "My
speech really just bulges out of my mouth like a balloon, and the real
thoughts in my head just keep on a direct line. The direct line and the
balloon are related, but they do not correspond, and the more the balloon bulges, the less sense it makes, until it bursts, leaving nearly all my
thoughts scattered, and me wild with anger and shame" (135).

Thomas KcKean (1994) described his experience with speech: "There are, on occasion, still times when I want to talk, but I can't. I can try and try and try, but I can't talk. There is a fear holding me back. I do not know what it is I am afraid of, I only know that it is a feeling of fear unlike any other feeling of fear I have known. It is not that I do not want to talk, it is that I am unable to at that moment" (39).

Donna Williams (1992) reported a similar experience of fear regarding communication: "The anxiety of my inner battle was becoming unbearable. I could say words but I wanted to communicate. I wanted to express something. I wanted to let something out. The anxiety would have been so easy to give in to; whereby I would again lose all awareness of self and surroundings" (19).

Williams (1992) described increased difficulties finding words and initiating speech as her emotional intensity increased: "At worst, the stress of direct, emotionally loaded communication either blocks the brain's ability to retrieve all or any of the words needed to speak a fluent sentence or won't allow the process of articulation to begin, leaving the words echoing within the speaker's head. The frustration of this can lead, as I described, to the deafening scream of frustration that may or may not get out of the speaker's mouth" (208).

And, Lindsay, as reported in Strandt-Conroy (1999), stated how he accommodates himself to the stress of retrieving and initiating speech: "What I do is think in ideographs or thought-pictures and then translate them into speech as I go, which normally gives my speech a slight hesitancy, and the degree of this hesitancy is a very good stress-gauge. When I am under a good deal of stress my speech becomes markedly hesitant, but when I am comfortable in a situation then the hesitancy is something that only I can notice" (116).

Routines, rituals, and perceptual motor habits

Perceptual motor habits are those skills that a person has acquired through extensive experience. Perceptual motor habits allow us the freedom to move, think, and talk without conscious attention to performing a skill. Sensory and movement differences can also have an effect on a person's ability to establish and sustain perceptual motor skills. For some people with sensory and movement differences, it is difficult to establish perceptual motor habits or, once established, the perceptual motor habit must be performed in the same way each time. A lack of flexibility in this skill base may mean that combining the skill with other events or in different settings forces the person to use conscious thought to perform the skill. People report that enormous effort is needed to think about moving in the most mundane ways. Geneva, a participant in a study by Strandt-Conroy (1999), pointed out how using conscious thought for movement and perception brought increased stress to her everyday life:

> People don't realize the major problem that nobody ever sees or realizes is how much conscious thinking we have to do just to function. Walking takes thinking. So if I am walking and you ask me a question I could trip or I could mess up the sentence and put the wrong word in. Or have to stop and say what did you say? I can walk with my girl friend down the street and carry on a conversation as long as she is right there but I have to look down at the side-walk. I have to keep track of where the sidewalk is and where any obstacles are and all that stuff and sometimes if I have to keep walking and I feel like I am going to blow any second I make sure the path is clear ahead of me and close my eyes and continue walking. (124)

Often people establish routines as an accommodation to difficulties with perceptual motor habits. When fewer aspects of a task vary, they report that less effort is needed to perform the task. Rand reported in Strandt-Conroy (1999) that routine and sameness assist him in finding meaning in his environment:

> Some people who are different like routines. They like to know what is going to happen next, and they like it to be the same thing that happened last time. When in-formation, which is sights, sounds, tastes, smells, and touches, goes into their head, if it is information they're used to because they've had this information before, it can go into their head on the same pathways to the same

places and get processed the same way as before. ⸮ someone learns that a picture hanging on a wall ⸮ hangs straight, if they see a picture hanging stra⸍ information is easy to process because it is the same as before. It goes along the same pathways to the same places, maybe those places are checkpoints that decide what the information means. Like it is flat, it is colorful, it is scenery, it is hanging straight on the wall. So it gets to the same result. It is a picture. But if a picture is hanging crookedly, it might start being processed along the same pathways to the same checkpoint, but then it might suddenly stop at some checkpoint because something is not the same as before so some checkpoint made a different decision about the information. Then the information might go off that pathway along different pathways, and whenever different pathways have to be used they could turn out to be bad ones, which means the information could just stop completely or get backed up or go off on wrong pathways. So it might never get to the same result, that it is a picture, or it might finally get there, except that it took longer and was a lot more work. (126-127)

IV. Experiences with emotional regulation and expression

Sensory and movement differences can also affect an individual's emotional expression. When a person uses his or her voice, gesture, and facial expressions in unusual ways, we may find it puzzling. When, in addition, we cannot see and hear the conventional expressions of emotion, we may assume the person does not feel emotion. Kathy, a participant in Strandt-Conroy (1999), reported feeling as though she was on an emotional roller coaster. Barbara, a participant in the same study, reported that there was never a time when she felt completely free of concern about emotions. Others report similar challenges in controlling emotions, expressing emotions, identifying emotions, and changing emotions. Barbara explained: "I think I've had times where I wasn't able to express how I was feeling and sometimes it was hard to experience my feelings directly. And one of the biggest problems was that I tried to ex-ss how I felt and people just didn't understand, my feelings were just o much different than another person that they just simply disregarded it" (Strand-Conroy 1999, 105).

Not having her feelings understood or recognized could trigger intense anxiety for Barbara. This kind of stress is reported by the participant in Jolliffe, Lansdown, and Robinson (1992) who stated, "It occurs at any time, but always when I know I have to go somewhere stressful. Sometimes the pain is so bad that my whole body becomes stiff and then I am unable to move" (14).

There is also an assumption that people with autism do not want to interact with others. People's reactions to behaviors they do not understand can lead to isolation for many people with autism. Barbara described this in the Strandt-Conroy (1999) study as,

> I had no meaningful relationship with anybody. An autistic person has to jump through hoops in order to be accepted by others. I wasn't good enough for anybody. They didn't like my behavior and I couldn't make friends very good—there was nobody around I could be myself with because the only people were involved with me were those who were paid to make me behave. There was nobody I knew then that would let me be myself. There was nobody who would like me as I was. I felt unwanted. I would be told "people won't accept you if you do this—people won't accept you if you do that." There's no way I could've made myself quiet enough and calm enough and attractive enough to make people accept me. It just wasn't in there. (109-110)

Although many individuals report that they have challenges when it comes to emotions, it is not an absence of interest in emotional interaction. They continue to try to relate to others. Jim, in the Cesaroni (1990) study, shared his perspective regarding the common assumption that people with autism lack empathy: "Someone who has much better inherent communication ability than I do but who has not even taken a close look at my perspective to notice the enormity of chasm between us tells me that my failure to understand is because I lack empathy" (94-95).

Cesaroni (1990) pointed out that "Jim raised an interesting question which merits consideration: if a large amount of effort and energy is devoted in trying to understand others' perspectives, does Jim have less empathy than those people who not only do not understand him, but who do not even notice they do not understand him?" (95).

Concluding remarks on first-hand accounts

The first-hand reports from people with autism provide us with powerful insights into how stress affects their symptoms and how the appearance of their symptoms is affected by stress. People need support that acknowledges their differences, accepts them the way they are, and provides them with the tools they need to learn and to cope with a world that may often be overwhelming. Donna Williams (2003) comments on treatment instruction and education that emphasizes "normality" while ignoring a person's true nature: "If you gain expression or skills that are not connected to self, they represent feels like a façade [sic], a cardboard reality, a parody. It can work for survival if you are really pushed, but it is not really the kind of stuff you can use as a basis for an enjoyable existence because it's disconnected from any internal emotional intrinsic reward. Such apparent 'success' may feel intensely alienating and isolating" (290).

Understanding how sensory and movement differences affect everyday existence is an important step. Finding ways to assist a person to accommodate and to promote body movement control and awareness are also key. Throughout this discovery process, we need to rethink commonly held assumptions about these individuals in order to listen to them and provide them with the appropriate support, presuming competence and seeing them as complete human beings, not as individuals with something missing. The voice of the labeled individual must be included in our new understanding of autism and sensory and movement differences. On this basis, we can begin to address them as people who need unique accommodations and support.

Stress, sensation, and movement have a direct impact on daily living. Speaking, facial expression, action, and emotion are all organized and regulated by sensation and movement. A person's emotional state and the level of intensity of emotions, whether these are positive or negative in nature, may make the balance between inhibition and activation more difficult to achieve (Brenner et al. 1947; Leary and Hill 1996; Maurer 1992, 1993). For many, unusual sensations and movements are less pronounced and less problematic when a person is distracted (Brenner et al. 1947). Distraction may be an effective support strategy for some people and in some situations. The following section provides more accommodations for individuals experiencing sensory and movement differences.

V. Accommodations

We draw on the historic works of Aleksander Romanovich Luria, a Russian psychologist and neurologist, in using the term "accommodations" to describe those supports that temporarily assist a person with difficulties in sensation and movement control, in participation, and behavior regulation. Luria (1932/1976) details many accommodations devised by or for individual people in his book, *The Nature of Human Conflicts*. After years of research working directly with people challenged by differences in their abilities to organize and regulate sensation and movement, he wrote of the need for people to develop accommodations or substitutions for the usual methods of motivation that may or may not be available to people during an episode of movement disturbance. Years later, Oliver Sacks (1990) credited Luria for his understanding of the importance of accommodating rather than battling such problems by force of will. Sacks used a metaphor to describe the process of accommodating to the challenges of organizing and regulating sensation and movement: "Neither defiance nor denial is of the least use here: one takes arms by learning how to negotiate or navigate a sea of troubles, by becoming mariner in the seas of one's self. 'Accommodation' is concerned with weathering the storm" (265).

Accommodations are personalized strategies that assist in temporarily overcoming differences in learning style, sensory integration, and/or movement. We all use accommodations to temporarily compensate for difficulties we may have in starting, executing, and stopping movements. We may also need accommodations for combining and switching behavior, thoughts, perceptions, speech, language, memories and emotions. Some common accommodations include the use of gesture, touch, and rhythm. Also, behavior rituals, sequences, and changing the aspects of tasks have proven effective, as well as visualization, music, and other strategies. These accommodations will be different for each person and the person's need for accommodations may vary from day-to-day or hour-to-hour. Accommodations may be effective for a time and then lose their effectiveness for a person. It is always a good idea to have a "menu" of possible accommodations for a particular person, considering alternative accommodations when needed.

Accommodations cannot be explained in a developmental framework. That is, for most accommodations there are no prerequisite skills, no linear progressions. Although some factors may seem to play a more central role in assisting a person to accommodate, it is often an array of accommodations that allow skills to emerge. Given appropriate supports from past experience, other people, and the environment, a person may be able to demonstrate competencies that have not been evident before. Broderick and Kasa-Hendrickson (2001) provide a thoughtful qualitative analysis of one teen labeled with autism and his acquisition of reliable speech at age 13. The authors viewed this young man's progress as reflecting a dynamic systems model for development, as described by Thelen and Smith (1994), rather than the more traditional linear model for development. Broderick and Kasa-Hendrickson note that no single component of the array of supports for speaking appeared more important than another and his development did not follow the usual expected sequence of learning to "listen, speak, read, write" (23). Instead, his emerging speech "was a complex, dynamic, and fluid expansion of [his] expressive communication system, a system in which he continues to integrate both speech and typing in complex and novel ways" (22). They emphasized that the whole experience of communicating and receiving support to speak was greater than the sum of the individual supports provided.

Labeled people often devise their own accommodations, without the assistance of others. For example, people who have difficulty passing through a doorway or making other transitions, such as from wood flooring to carpet, report that taking a step backward during the transition may ease their ability to move and avoid their getting "stuck" in a doorway. Others may wave or flap to help propel themselves through. Some of the accommodations that people have devised for themselves may appear unusual or bizarre to others. Family and professionals may recommend that a person change a particular accommodation for a specific reason (e.g., because the accommodation causes damage to or hurts self or others or limits a person's access to many environments). It is, therefore, critical to recognize the possible function that an unusual behavior may serve and to provide alternative accommodations to fulfill that function.

Accommodations are strategies that people use to find the balance they need to regulate sensation and movement when the natural, unconscious mechanisms are not enough (Donnellan and Leary 1995). Accommodations do not necessarily replace instructional strategies but may be used to personalize more conventional programs. The following accommodations have been developed by individuals who exhibit movement differences and by the professionals and family members who support them (Donnellan et al. 2003; Williams 1992, 1994, 1996a, 1996b, 2003). The descriptions of accommodations we provide here are not exhaustive, as this is meant only to be a brief introduction. Nonetheless, because accommodations are so personalized, there is no limit to the style and number of accommodations that can be created. There are as many accommodations as there are people and situations to use them (Donnellan and Leary 1995). Although these accommodations are in no way a cookbook or how-to guide, we hope they will spark interest and creativity when it comes to providing and creating accommodations.

Accommodations for organizing and regulating actions

People often experience difficulties initiating, executing, stopping, combining, continuing, and switching actions and postures, including movements of the whole body, facial expression, gestures, and head movements. They and their families or caregivers often work out ways of supporting movement that is functional, timely, and done with less effort. These accommodating strategies can boost a person's confidence and may reduce stress that results from unreliable movement.

Use of touch. Some individuals with autism have reported the use of touch as a very useful accommodation. For some, a gentle touch to their arm, shoulder, or back can help initiate an action. The film *Awakenings*, based on the book by Sacks (1990), illustrates how one patient is able to stand and move only when the nurse is touching his back. Touch is the preferred way to gain some people's attention, such as touching an arm or hand, and waiting for attention before speaking.

Use of rhythm. Rhythm is a well-known facilitator for most people. In fact, many couples credit their ability to dance well together for the onset of their relationship. Using a rhythm, tempo, or any rhythmic sound can be especially helpful during transition times. Moving with another person in rhythm can be used to help initiate action for people with movement differences. Sacks (1990) reported that one of his patients was able to initiate action when he walked with her. She explained that she felt the power of his walking, which assisted her in her own movements. Some individuals report that performing a task to a certain tune or rhythm can often help as well. Music is often a preferred activity for people labeled with autism. Children who show little imitative ability or emotional expression can be seen to jump, dance, and smile with a favorite television character dancing to music. The use of music as an accommodation must be personalized. Sacks (1990) relates that one patient only moved to music that "moved" her. Some people hum or sing softly to themselves while working or playing. Rhythm can be found in many activities, including reading aloud from a storybook or reciting poetry. Some individuals comment that slight sounds in the environment, such as the sound of a clock ticking, can provide the necessary tempo. Ralph Maurer (1993), a psychiatrist specializing in understanding people labeled with autism, has noted that people who rock their bodies, walk with skating-type movements, or otherwise move rhythmically may be trying to compensate for difficulties in establishing a rhythm for movement. He recommended that supporters pay close attention to the rhythm that people use when rocking. Matching this rhythm may provide a way for a supporter to enhance a relationship with a person.

Use of imagery. Many people in sports, business, and health have used imagery-based programs successfully. June Groden and her colleagues, in collaboration with Joseph Cautela, successfully adapted covert conditioning procedures for people with special needs that are based on visualization and imagery (Groden, Cautela, LeVasseur, Groden, and Bausman 1991). Imagery and visualization may help some individuals to get started or stay with an activity, as well as to cope with possible disruptions in specific situations. Grandin (1995) reported how she easily thought in pictures; her thoughts were similar to that of a film. Actual visual representations, such as photographs or drawings, are often used to establish an image. For other people, imagining a detailed scene may be enough. Luria (1932/1976) reported that his patient, Ivan, had great difficulty getting out of his bed in the morning. Ivan used a combination of visual representation and imagery to accommodate to this difficulty. He painted a tree next to his bed so that he could arise in the morning by imagining himself climbing a tree.

In addition to imagery-based accommodations, many people use things that they are able to see or read to help accommodate. Some move well when they see sequences or steps that are written in words or represented in drawings. Others have told us that looking toward a destination or watching someone else move can provide the support they need. The placement of objects can be a useful accommodation, for example, providing the motivation to do a task when the tools are assembled and visible. Objects can be used to cue an established skill or perceptual-motor habit, such as seeing the dishtowel as a cue to dry and put away the dishes. Even a simple gesture or facial expression may provide the needed trigger for an individual. Remembering the last time the sequence was performed may help some individuals perform it again. Specifically going through the steps of the action in one's mind prior to an event may also be helpful.

Use of words. There are many ways to use spoken or written words as accommodations. In this chapter, we cover a few verbal accommodations related to organizing and regulating actions and behavior that may be useful for some individuals.

The ritualized use of key words, or "catch phrases," may be a helpful accommodation for some people. People report that hearing the words said in a specific tone of voice or from a specific person may help them initiate an action or maintain self-control. Saying these words softly or silently to oneself or listening to a recording of a specific voice may be used as an accommodation. One person mentioned that carrying a short note in her pocket helped her to get through difficult times.

Use of preparation. Preparation for change and transition may present a special challenge for people with unusual sensory and movement abilities. Transitions are often reported to be times of uncertainty; many people are aware that minor changes will stretch their flexibility and tap their energy. Some people report that they have a less stressful experience if a situation is explained from their own point of view in advance. Perhaps because some people need more than the usual amount of time for organizing and regulating their actions and emotions, they appreciate getting information on events well before the event is to occur.

Many people have experience with stories told to them during a quiet and calm time and which relate to future events. Carol Gray (1994, 2000) has assembled many good examples of social stories that provide guidelines for using stories more effectively. It is helpful to know details such as who, what, when, where, and how long. These stories may be in written form or spoken. When a story is repeated, some people appreciate the sameness and want to hear the same words, while others like the story to contain other words and new details. People frequently report that the best situation for listening to these kinds of details is one that does not require looking directly at the speaker or repeating the information provided. For some, tests of comprehension, such as answering questions about the information, are not helpful or necessary. Other people like the opportunity to repeat back the information in order to use it for themselves whenever needed. Preparation for change may reduce the stress of anticipation by supporting a person's confidence and assisting in planning.

Use of prompts. The use of verbal prompts to support a person to initiate or complete a task may be an appropriate accommodation for some people, in some situations. Experience and reports from others, however, indicate that many people become unable to perform a task without those spoken prompts. When a person is learning a task that should be done independently (e.g., getting dressed, showering), cues and prompts used as accommodations need to be carefully considered. In this case, support should focus on providing cues in such a way that the person may be able to do the task independently in the future. When spoken instructions are used to assist a person, the immediate results are often positive as the person does what is said. However, the spoken words may inadvertently become part of the task and a person may continue to need a supporter to say, "Put on your sock," long after the sequence is learned. Speaking involves relationship. If the task is not one of relationship, speaking during the task about how to do it should be kept to a minimum. (For more information on the effective use of cues and prompts, see Donnellan, LaVigna, Negri-Shoultz, and Fassbender 1988.)

Use of scent. Accommodations using smell can also be very effective for some individuals. The scent of coffee can get many of us moving in the morning. Certain scents can relax some individuals and help them regulate their actions. Other scents, such as food cooking, can bring a person to the kitchen. Some people have reported success in using a form of classical conditioning, where a scent becomes associated with relaxation and self-control and is used to elicit those feelings during times of stress. As many people have negative reactions and profound sensitivity to scents, caution should be exercised in exploring scent as an accommodation.

Defining the task. When an individual has difficulty maintaining an action or attending to a task, it often helps to choose tasks with clear beginnings and endings, such as stacking chairs, making popcorn, emptying waste baskets, and washing very dirty dishes. Even if the task does not have a clear beginning or end, you can create them by using time markers, such as a bell ring. It is also helpful to make the transformation or result of an activity more salient or obvious. Using color is an excellent way to achieve this. You can use opaque foams and colored cleansers for scrubbing. Colored paper to end a stack can work as well. Teaching a motor pattern "rule" can help some individuals with both initiating and maintaining an action. Examples of this would be cleaning from one corner to another, washing each plate in a specific motion, and taking everything from the counter top and putting it on the table.

Accommodations for perceptual differences

Each person has a unique and individual sensory system. An accommodation for one person may be a trigger for another. It is important to have knowledge of the individual and understand how their perceptual differences may challenge them. It may be helpful to work with sensory integration specialists, occupational therapists, physical therapists, or other professionals for specific guidance.

Environmental accommodations may help some people by fine-tuning the aspects of an environment that promote a person's optimum participation and reduce stress. The accommodations below are a sampling, useful for some people in some situations.

Materials. Many materials may assist in sensory integration and body comfort, thereby reducing stress levels for some individuals. The following materials have been successfully used as accommodations: tumble foam chairs, bean bag chairs, chewy and crunchy things, tube necklaces, "feel good box," black light, weighted vest, foot or hand vibrators, light box, tinted glasses, earplugs or earphones, and heavy, padded clothing.

Reduce sound. Some individuals are sensitive to a variety of sounds. Pay special attention to background noise and sudden noises. Notice how competing noise, white noise, and loud noises affect a person's ability to pay attention. Remember that sometimes the senses mix. For example, for some people a loud noise may affect their ability to see things clearly or to remain standing. A way to reduce auditory reverberation might be to use carpet, cork flooring, ceiling tiles, and/or large padded furniture. It is vitally important to have quiet spaces to get away from the stimulation of daily activity.

Reduce clutter and distractions. Visual perception can also be challenging for many individuals. Reduce visual clutter while keeping materials visible and accessible. Reduce glare and visual refraction by turning off unnecessary lighting, especially fluorescent lighting; using matte finishes on surfaces and walls; using lamps instead of overhead lights; choosing low wattage light bulbs; and using soft colored light that cuts down contrast and color contrast in a room. Choice of colors for walls, floors, and furniture are important. Solid colors for the walls sometimes helps people with depth perception differences to judge distances. One plain wall in a room can provide a visually "quiet" space. Floors and walls should not be the same color. Some people report being able to move better when the floor pattern is compelling, such as floor tiles in a black and white pattern. An example of this is presented in the film *Awakenings*, where a patient is able to cross the room once the black and white pattern has been continued (Sacks 1990). In the bathroom, a floor that contrasts in color to the toilet and other fixtures is helpful to some. Too much sameness among colors of walls, floors, furniture, and fixtures may make it difficult to see them as separate. The furniture might be positioned around the periphery of the room in order to move around the room more freely or "navigate" without barriers or obstacles.

Understanding touch. Individuals have reported many accommodations concerning touch. Some people have difficulty with being touched and have learned to accommodate by avoiding the touch of others. Touch may be easier for some to tolerate if it is firm touch rather than light touch and is predictable or rhythmical. Grandin (Grandin 1995; Grandin and Scariano 1986) created a "squeeze machine" that provided firm pressure to her body that helped relieve intense anxiety and stress. Some individuals report that hugs and massage help provide comfort and kinesthetic feedback, while for others, such intense touch can be very uncomfortable or cause agitation.

Experimenting with different modalities. Combining input from different sensory channels may be difficult for some people. Try stressing one modality at a time. For example, use fewer gestures when speaking, use touch sparingly, and signal your intention to touch before doing so. It is also important to not expect eye contact while a person listens. Consider that movement of others in the area may compete for attention. Experiment to find the right combination for accommodating to a person's perceptual differences.

Accommodations for speaking and interactions

When interactions and speaking are difficult for a person, interpersonal accommodations that explore ways to develop and sustain a relationship are important. Interpersonal accommodations are aspects of support that focus on accommodating a person's differences within the relationship. When people do not use words to communicate and have difficulty using their bodies to express meaning, others sometimes assume the person does not understand what is being said. People who do not have a full range of facial expressions or cannot use their bodies or voices to express emotions are sometimes thought to not have feelings. People have told us that this is one of the most devastating aspects of learning, sensory, and movement differences. Speak to people directly. Although a person's disability may affect various aspects of interaction, it is most helpful to speak to people in a way that acknowledges their competencies. If comprehension appears to be a problem, use augmentation to add meaning to your words; explain yourself in several different ways or illustrate your meaning in some other way, through pictures with words modeling the activity. People must feel that they are part of the communication world in order to find the motivation needed to participate. Provide people with information, friendship, humor, and intellectual stimulation. Do not be afraid to ask an individual about the best way to support him or her.

A partner in an interaction with a person who senses and moves differently may consider accommodating or adapting communication in ways that may not be obvious to most people. Small changes may have a large impact on a person's ability to participate. During an interaction, remember that the melody of your voice may add or distract from your meaning. Try speaking with more or less intonation in your voice, using a soft melody to your voice, whispering, or speaking in a rhythm. A slower pace is often helpful for anyone when the person, place, or activities are unfamiliar. Pause after speaking (sometimes up to 20 seconds) and allow extra time for a person to respond (Mirenda and Donnellan 1986). Creating or maintaining a rhythm during the conversation may be helpful for some. If the individual is swaying or moving in a certain way, it may be helpful to match that movement or rhythm.

An interpersonal accommodation with great significance for many people is a partner who does not demand eye contact in order to continue an interaction. The lack of direct eye-to-eye gaze simplifies listening for some and produces a comfort that allows an easier flow of speech and other forms of expression. Some individuals need more personal space or distance between them and their partner, while others need to be in physical contact with a partner in order to stay with an interaction. For some individuals, physical contact can allow the emergence of speech.

Many people and their families report a benefit from an accommodation that combines touch, rhythm, communication, and emotional support to type or point to produce written language. This is sometimes called facilitated communication. Support to the person's hand, wrist, arm, shoulder, or back helps some individuals communicate. This accommodation has been the center of research and media attention, much of it negative. Nonetheless, since the mid-1990s when the controversy was at its peak, some people who type to talk have worked hard to establish the validity and reliability of their words (Biklen and Cardinal 1997). Some who began typing with physical support are now able to type without touch, but may need the presence of a trusted facilitator who provides other supports important for communicating (Broderick and Kasa-Hendrickson 2001; Mukhopadhyay 2000; Rubin et al. 2001). There are many resources available for those interested in knowing more about facilitated communicating (Biklen 1993; Biklen and Cardinal 1997; Brandl 1999; Crossley 1997; Donnellan, Sabin, and Majure 1992).

Accommodating for emotional regulation and expression

Each of us has specific ways to modulate our emotions and to reduce emotional overload, although we often use these accommodations unconsciously. We use emotional accommodations to regulate both positive and negative emotions as may be seen on television game shows where winning and losing contestants struggle to "keep it together" with loud screaming, attempts to fight back tears, jumping up and down, wringing of hands, and repetitive speech, such as, "Oh my gosh, oh my gosh, oh my gosh!"

Some people with autism report that they work very hard to control emotions, both the initiation of the right emotion and the regulation of the intensity of the emotion. Many report "unfiltered emotions," or difficulty identifying which emotion one is feeling. They report that others often misunderstand their behaviors and their attempts to control emotions, partly because the context or source of an emotional stressor may not be evident or problematic to those around them. Imagine those game show contestants emoting strongly while standing in line at the grocery. Within the store context, the contestants would appear totally inappropriate.

The challenges with which people with autism struggle are often extreme. The most obvious emotional accommodation is to support and promote the confidence and self-esteem of people. Assuming and expressing confidence in a person can be a powerful support and should not be underestimated. Some individuals report that they can sense when a supporter is annoyed or frustrated. Humor can be used to distract a person from an anxious mood and make a situation seem less serious. The attitudes of supporters, whether or not these are specifically expressed, may affect an autistic person's performance, just as they affect the rest of us.

Some people report difficulty with knowing which emotion they are expressing. It may be helpful to let a person know when you see a fleeting sign of a positive emotion. Although a person may appear to be focused on other things and not show conventional signs and signals of relationship, they may be interested in and want relationships with other people. Let them (and others) know that you can see they are acting friendly, even if the signs and signals are unusual or fleeting.

It may be best to discuss difficulties of past behavior during calm and quiet times rather than bringing them up before or during an activity when there may be a problem. While briefing a person just before entering a challenging situation may serve as a reminder for some, for others, it may highlight the problems that they may encounter. In contrast, people report that when others express confidence in their abilities and highlight their competencies, they enter a situation with less anxiety. Some people report that when they are focused on self-control and a supporter brings up the topic of behavior to avoid, the person is more likely to have a problem. As with stuttering or other movement difficulties, naming a behavior to avoid sometimes causes that behavior to happen. Many people report that distraction from thinking about the behavior is more effective than direct reference to it. If one must talk about behavior in a situation, the focus should be on the positive behavior rather than the negative.

During difficult times, when a person needs assistance to maintain self-control, reduce the need to interpret the meaning of your words and use clear language with clear references. Keep conversational "banter" to a minimum, indicate topic switches clearly, and be clear in your intentions and message. Provide the person with more space, both physical space and spaces in the interaction. Having a space to self-regulate helps some individuals with emotional regulation and expression. Consider teaching a person to leave or avoid sources of provocation.

When a person is vulnerable or is having difficulty with emotional expression or regulation, try to monitor and limit the emotional load of the interaction. Individuals report a loss of sense of control at transition times or shifts from the expected. Some report feelings of performance anxiety with exposure of self and the experience of being the center of attention as too scary. Some report hyperexperienced sensations and emotions that can build when triggered by intense situations. The experience is too much feeling and may lead to destruction of one's own work, objects in the environment, attacking one's own body, or shutting down.

Emotions can build up, get mixed up, or become "stuck." "A little bit scared" can turn into terror, yet may be expressed by laughing. "A little bit upset" can turn into furious. "A little bit amused" can turn into manic, hysterical laughing. Direct confrontations may be raw, exposing, and emotionally provoking. When a person is vulnerable or losing control, a direct reference to the situation may be very unhelpful. Often, distraction and indirect references to the situation work better. Make a nonverbal offer, for example. Hold out your hand as an offer of support or gently push an object in the person's direction rather than ask if the person wants it. Try using the third person when describing what needs to be done: "When a person feels confused, it sometimes helps to ... ," and then suggest a course of action. Direct your comments to "another" person or speak to the materials in front of you. Use objects to illustrate or explain interactions.

VI. Conclusion

In this chapter, we suggest that the first-hand accounts of individuals with the problems associated with autism provide a rich source of evidence for the presence of sensory and movement differences and disturbances in the lives of these individuals. We have an emerging awareness that behaviors may not be what they seem. We need to rethink many of our previous assumptions regarding people's behavior, paying attention to the insights of people labeled with autism, as well as published literature on sensory and movement differences. Some of the implications informing our thinking include (1) self-stimulatory behaviors may not be volitional or pleasurable; (2) automatic, habitual, impulsive, or over-learned responses may be difficult for a person to inhibit; (3) random bursts of activity, rapid fatigue, lethargy, or disturbances of a person's overall behavior may signal acute difficulties organizing and regulating sensation and movement; and (4) overreacting or not responding may be related to sensory integration and movement difficulties. These difficulties often are not evident to us because we are constrained by our neuro-typical experience and social judgments and by the communication difficulties inherent in autism. Additionally, we suggest that the difficulties these labeled people have regulating and organizing thought, sensory, perceptual, motor, and emotional experience may cause, and even be exacerbated by, stress. It is not our intention to develop yet another set of characteristics to add to the plethora of diagnostic checklists available in our field. Rather, we hope to connect the experience of individuals with autism to the wide range of information about sensory and movement differences found in the literature beyond the field of autism.

We offer the notion of accommodations which was introduced and brilliantly presented by Luria (1932/1976) and by Sacks (1990) as a model of support. Personalized accommodations can be added to the other positive supports recommended for individuals with the labels of autism and other developmental differences. Personalized accommodations are also consistent with the principles of Person-Centered Planning, as discussed and practiced by many of our colleagues (e.g., Cattermole and Blunden 2002; Falvey, Forest, Pearpoint, and Rosenberg 1997; O'Brien and O'Brien 1998; Snow 1994). Our experience and that of our many colleagues who espouse such a personal and practical approach has the added benefit of expanding our own sense of empathy for those who have an often stressful experience navigating the ordinary events of life. To borrow from the words of the great physician and philosopher, Maimonides, once we can begin to understand their experience, we can never again see in these people anything but ourselves.

Acknowledgment

Extracts from the unpublished dissertation, *Exploring Movement Differences in Autism through First-hand Accounts*, are reprinted with the permission of Karen Strandt-Conroy.

Works Cited

Ahuja, N. 2000. Organic catatonia: A review. *Indian Journal of Psychiatry* 42 (4): 327-346.

American Psychiatric Association. 1987. *Diagnostic and Statistical Manual of Mental Disorders: Revision,* 3rd ed. Washington, DC: Author.

Baltaxe, C. 1981. Acoustic characteristics of prosody in autism. In *Frontiers of Knowledge in Mental Retardation, Vol. 1: Social, educational, and behavioral aspects,* P. Mittler, ed., 223-233. New York: Pro Ed.

Baltaxe, C., and J. Simmons. 1977. Bedtime soliloquies and linguiatic competence in autism. *Journal of Speech and Hearing Disorders* 42: 376-393.

Baron-Cohen, S. 1989. Do autistic children have obsessions and compulsions? *British Journal of Clinical Psychology* 28: 193-200.

Barron, J. and S. Barron. 1992. *There's a Boy in Here.* New York: Simon and Schuster.

Bartak, L., M. Rutter, and A. Cox. 1975. A comparative study of infantile autism and specific developmental receptive language disorder: I. The children. *British Journal of Psychiatry* 126: 127-145.

Bebko, J., and C. Lennox. 1988. Teaching the control of diurnal bruxism to two children with autism, using a simple cueing procedure. *Behavior Therapy* 19: 249-255.

Bender, L. 1947. Childhood schizophrenia: Clinical study of one hundred schizophrenic children. *American Journal of Orthopsychiatry* 17: 40-56.

Biklen, D. 1990. Communication unbound: Autism and praxis. *Harvard Educational Review* 60: 291-314.

Biklen, D. 1993. *Communication Unbound: How facilitated communication is challenging traditional views of autism and ability/disability.* New York: Teachers College Press.

Biklen, D., and D. Cardinal, eds. 1997. *Contested Words, Contested Science: Unraveling the facilitated communication controversy.* New York: Teachers College Press.

Blackman, L. 1999. *Lucy's Story: Autism and other adventures.* Brisbane, Australia: Book in Hand.

Bond, S. L. 1986. *The gait of adolescent males with autistic behaviors: A pilot study.* Unpublished Master's thesis, MacMaster University School of Graduate Studies (Hamilton, Ontario).

Brandl, C. 1999. *Facilitated Communication Case Studies: See us smart!* Ann Arbor, MI: Robbie Dean Press.

Brasic, J., J. Barnett, M. Will, R. Nadrich, B. Sheitman, R. Ahmad, M. Mendonca, D. Kaplan, and C. Brathwaite. 2000. Dyskinesias differentiate autistic disorder from catatonia. *CNS Spectrums* 5 (12): 19-22.

Brenner, S., A. Friedman, and H. Merrit. 1947. Psychiatric syndromes in patients with organic brain disease. 1. Diseases of the basal ganglia. *American Journal of Psychiatry* 135: 1242-1243.

Broderick, A., and C. Kasa-Hendrickson. 2001. "Say just one word at first": The emergence of reliable speech in a student labeled with autism. *Journal of the Association for Persons with Severe Handicaps* 26 (1): 13-24.

Campbell, M., et al. 1972. Lithium and chlorpromazine: A controlled crossover study of hyperactive severely disturbed young children. *Journal of Autism and Childhood Schizophrenia* 2: 234-263.

Carr, E. 1979. Teaching autistic children to use sign language: Some research issues. *Journal of Autism and Developmental Disorders* 9: 345-359.

Cattermole, M., and R. Blunden. 2002. *My Life: A person-centered approach to checking outcomes for people with learning difficulties.* Worchester, England: BILD Publications.

Cesaroni, L. 1990. *Exploring the autistic experience through first-hand accounts from high-functioning individuals with autism.* Unpublished doctoral dissertation, University of Toronto, Ontario.

Cesaroni, L., and M. Garber. 1991. Exploring the autistic experience of autism through first hand account. *Journal of Autism and Developmental Disorders* 21: 303-313.

Chaplin, R. 2000. Possible causes of catatonia in autistic spectrum disorders. *British Journal of Psychiatry* 177: 180.

Chess, S. 1972. Neurological dysfunction and childhood behavioral pathology. *Journal of Autism and Childhood Schizophrenia* 2: 299-311.

Churchill, D., and C. Bryson. 1972. Looking and approach behavior of psychotic and normal children as a function of adult attention or preoccupation. *Comprehensive Psychiatry* 13: 171-177.

Clark, P., and M. Rutter. 1977. Compliance and resistance in autistic children. *Journal of Autism and Childhood Schizophrenia* 7: 33-34.

Comings, D., and B. Comings. 1991. Clinical and genetic relationships between autistic-pervasive developmental disorder and Tourette syndrome: A study of 19 cases. *American Journal of Medical Genetics* 39: 180-191.

Cowley, G. 2000, July 31. Understanding autism. *Newsweek*: 46-54.

Cowley, G. 2003, September 8. Boys, girls and autism. *Newsweek*: 42-50.

Crossley, R. 1997. *Speechless: Facilitating communication for people without voices.* New York: Penguin.

Curcio, F., and E. Piserchia. 1978. Sensorimotor functioning and communication in mute autistic children. *Journal of Autism and Childhood Schizophrenia* 8: 181-189.

Damasio, A., and R. Maurer. 1978. A neurological model for childhood autism. *Archives of Neurology* 35: 777-786.

Dawson, G., and A. Adams. 1984. Imitation and social responsiveness in autistic children. *Journal of Abnormal Child Psychology* 12: 209-226.

DeMyer, M. 1975. Research in infantile autism: A strategy and its results. *Biological Psychiatry* 10: 433-450.

DeMyer, M. 1976. Motor, perceptual-motor and intellectual disabilities of autistic children. In *Early Childhood Autism*, 2nd ed., L. Wing, ed., 169-196. Oxford: Pergamon Press.

DeMyer, M., G. Alpern, S. Barton, W. DeMyer, D. Churchill, J. Hingtgen, C. Bryson, et al. 1972. Imitation in autistic, early schizophrenic, and non-psychotic subnormal children. *Journal of Autism and Childhood Schizophrenia* 2: 263-287.

DeMyer, M., J. Hingtgen, and R. Jackson. 1981. Infantile autism reviewed: A decade of research. *Schizophrenia Bulletin* 7: 388-451.

Donnellan, A. 1999. Invented knowledge and autism: Highlighting our strengths and expanding the conversation. *The Journal of the Association for Persons with Severe Handicaps* 24 (3): 230-236.

Donnellan, A., G. LaVigna, N. Negri-Shoultz, and L. Fassbender. 1988. *Progress Without Punishment: Effective approaches for learners with behavior problems.* New York: Teachers College Press.

Donnellan, A., and M. Leary. 1995. *Movement Differences and Diversity in Autism/Mental Retardation.* Madison, WI: DRI Press.

Donnellan, A., M. Leary, J. Miller, M. Lapos, C. Doran, and J. Marquette. 2003. *Exploring Accommodations: Some things to consider when supporting people with learning, sensory, and movement differences.* Madison, WI: DRI Press.

Donnellan, A., L. Sabin, and L. Majure. 1992. Facilitated communication: Beyond the quandary to the questions. *Topics in Language Disorders* 12 (4): 69-82.

Earl, C. 1994. The primitive catatonic psychosis of idiocy. *British Journal of Medical Psychology* 14: 230-253.

Falvey, M., M. Forest, J. Pearpoint, and R. Rosenberg. 1997. *All My Life's a Circle: Circles, maps and paths.* Toronto: Inclusion Press.

Favell, J., J. McGimsey, and M. Jones. 1978. The use of physical restraint in the treatment of self-injury and as a positive reinforcement. *Journal of Applied Behavior Analysis* 11: 225-241.

Feldenkrais, M. 1972. *Awareness Through Movement.* New York: HarperCollins.

Frith, U. 1970. Studies in pattern detection in normal and autistic children. *Journal of Abnormal Psychology* 76: 413-420.

Frith, U. 1971. Spontaneous patterns produced by autistic, normal, and subnormal children. In *Infantile Autism: Concepts, characteristics, and treatment*, M. Rutter, ed., 113-131. London: Churchill-Livingstone.

Frith, U., and B. Hermelin. 1969. The role of visual and motor cues for normal, subnormal and autistic children. *Journal of Clinical Psychology and Psychiatry* 10: 153-163.

Gabony, P. 1991. Research supplement: Self-injurious behavior: A unitary phenomenon or a set of diverse behaviors? *British Journal of Special Education* 18 (Research Suppl.): 59-63.

Gedye, A. 1989. Extreme self-injury attributed to frontal lobe seizures. *American Journal on Mental Retardation* 94: 20-26.

Geller, B., L. Guttmacher, and M. Bleeg. 1981. Coexistence of childhood onset pervasive development disorder and attention deficit disorder with hyperactivity. *American Journal of Psychiatry* 138: 388-389.

Gillberg, C., U. Rosenhall, and E. Johansson. 1983. Auditory brainstem responses in childhood psychosis. *Journal of Autism and Developmental Disorders* 13: 19-32.

Gittelman, M, and H. Birch. 1967. Childhood schizophrenia: Intellect, neurologic status, perinatal risk, prognosis, and family pathology. *Archives of General Psychiatry* 11: 620-634.

Goldfarb, W. 1956. Receptor preferences in schizophrenic children. *Archives of Neurology and Psychiatry* 76: 643-653.

Guess, D., and E. Carr. 1991. Emergence and maintenance of stereotypy and self-injury. *American Journal on Mental Retardation* 96: 299-319.

Grandin, T. 1995. *Thinking in Pictures: And other reports from my life with autism*. New York: Doubleday.

Grandin, T., and M. Scariano. 1986. *Emergence: Labeled autistic*. Novato, CA: Arena.

Gray, C. 1994. *Comic Strip Conversations*. Arlington, TX: Future Horizons.

Gray, C. 2000. *The New Social Story Book: Illustrated edition*. Arlington, TX: Future Horizons.

Groden, J., J. Cautela, P. LeVasseur, G. Groden, and M. Bausman. 1991. *Imagery Procedures for People with Special Needs: Breaking the barriers II*. Champaign, IL: Research Press.

Hale, M., and C. Hale. 1999. *I Had No Means to Shout!* Bloomington, IN: First Books.

Hare, D., and C. Malone. 2004. Catatonia and autistic spectrum disorders. *Autism* 8 (2): 183-195.

Hoffman, W., and M. Prior. 1982. Neuropsychological dimensions of autism in children: A test of the hemispheric dysfunction hypothesis. *Journal of Clinical Neuropsychology* 4: 27-41.

Hutt, C., S. J. Hutt, D. Lee, and C. Ounsted. 1964. Arousal and childhood autism. *Nature* 204: 909-919.

Hutt, C., and C. Ounsted. 1966. The biological significance of gaze aversion with particular reference to the syndrome of infantile autism. *Behavioral Science* 11: 346-356.

Hutt, S. J., C. Hutt, D. Lee, and C. Ounsted. 1965. A behavioral and electroencephalographic study of autistic children. *Journal of Psychiatric Research* 3: 181-197.

Jollife, T., R. Lansdown, and C. Robinson. 1992. Autism: A personal account. *Communication* 26: 12-19.

Jones, V., and M. Prior. 1985. Motor imitation abilities and neurological signs in autistic children. *Journal of Autism and Developmental Disorders* 15: 37-46.

Kahlbaum, K. [1874] 1973. *Catatonia*. Translated by Y. Levij and T. Pridan. Baltimore: Johns Hopkins University Press.

Kanner, L. 1943. Autistic disturbances of affective contact. *Nervous Child* 2: 217-250.

Kanner, L. 1944. Early infantile autism. *Journal of Pediatrics* 25: 211-217.

Kern, L., R. Koegel, and G. Dunlap. 1984. The influence of vigorous versus mild exercise on autistic stereotyped behaviors. *Journal of Autism and Developmental Disorders* 14: 57-67.

Konstantareas, M. 1985. Review of the evidence on the relevance of sign language in the early communication of autistic children.

LaVigna, G. 1977. Communication training in mute, autistic adolescents using the written word. *Journal of Autism and Childhood Schizophrenia* 7: 135-149.

Leary, M., and D. Hill. 1996. Moving on: Autism and movement disturbance. *Mental Retardation* 34 (1): 39-53.

Leary, M., D. Hill, and A. Donnellan. 1999, November. *Autism: Myths and misunderstandings.* Presented to the School of Psychology, University of Michigan, Ann Arbor.

Lovaas, O., et al. 1971. Selective responding by autistic children to multiple sensory input. *Journal of Abnormal Psychology* 77: 211-222.

Lovett, H. 1996. *Learning to Listen: Positive approaches and people with difficult behavior.* Baltimore: Paul H. Brookes.

Loveland, K., and S. Landry. 1986. Joint attention and language in autism and developmental language delays. *Journal of Autism and Developmental Disorders* 16: 335-349.

Lund, C., A. Mortimer, D. Rogers, and P. McKenna. 1991. Motor, volitional and behavioral disorders in schizophrenia 1: Assessment using the modified Rogers scale. *British Journal of Psychiatry* 158: 323-336.

Luria, A. R. [1932] 1976. *The Nature of Human Conflicts: Or emotion, conflict and will.* New York: Liveright.

Masterson, B., and G. Biederman. 1983. Proprioceptive versus visual control in autistic children. *Journal of Autism and Developmental Disorders* 13: 141-152.

Maurer, R. G. 1992. *The neurology of facilitated communication* (Audiotape from proceedings, Autism Society of America). Albuquerque, NM: Audio Archives.

Maurer, R. G. 1993. *What autism and facilitated communication have to teach us about the neurology of relationship* (Audiotape from lecture). Toronto: MacKenzie Group International.

Maurer, R. G., and A. R. Damasio. 1982. Childhood autism from the point of view of behavioral neurology. *Journal of Autism and Developmental Disorders* 12: 195-205.

McKean, T. 1994. *Soon Will Come the Light*. Arlington, TX: Future Horizons.

Meiselas, K., et al. 1989. Differentiation of stereotypies from neuroleptic-related dyskinesias in autistic children. *Journal of Clinical Psychopharmacology* 9: 207-209.

Menolascino, F. 1965. Psychoses of childhood: Experiences of a mental retardation pilot project. *American Journal of Mental Deficiency* 70: 83-92.

Mirenda, P., and A. Donnellan. 1986. Effects of adult interaction style on conversational behavior in students with severe communication problems. *Language, Speech, and Hearing Services in Schools* 17: 126-141.

Mirenda, P., A. Donnellan, and D. Yoder. 1983. Gaze behavior: A new look at an old problem. *Journal of Autism and Developmental Disorders* 13: 197-409.

Morrison, D., D. Miller, and B. Meija. 1971. Effects of adult verbal requests on the behavior of autistic children. *American Journal of Mental Deficiency* 75: 510-518.

Mukhopadhyay, T. R. 2000. *Beyond the Silence*. London: National Autistic Society.

Mundy, P., M. Sigman, and C. Kasari. 1990. A longitudinal study of joint attention and language development in autistic children. *Journal of Autism and Developmental Disorders* 20: 115-128.

Nash, J. 2002, May 6. The secrets of autism. *Time* 159 (18): 46-56.

O'Brien, J., and C. L. O'Brien. 1998. *A Little Book About Person-Centered Planning*. Toronto: Inclusion Press.

Ornitz, E. 1974. The modulation of sensory input and motor output in autistic children. *Journal of Autism and Childhood Schizophrenia* 4: 197-215.

Ornitz, E., and E. Ritvo. 1968. Perceptual inconstancy in early infantile autism. *Archives of General Psychiatry* 18: 78-98.

Ornitz, E., and E. Ritvo. 1976. The syndrome of autism: A critical review. *American Journal of Psychiatry* 113: 609-621.

Paccia, J., and F. Curcio. 1982. Language processing and forms of immediate echolalia in autistic children. *Journal of Speech and Hearing Research* 25: 42-47.

Patterson, J. 2002a. *Social behavior of individuals with autism found in first-hand accounts.* Unpublished master's thesis, University of San Diego, San Diego.

Patterson, J. 2002b. *Movement differences: Data collected from first-hand accounts of autism.* Unpublished manuscript.

Prior, M., and W. Hoffman. 1990. Brief report: Neuropsychological testing of autistic children through an exploration with frontal lobe tests. *Journal of Autism and Developmental Disorders* 20 (4): 581-590.

Prior, M., and M. Macmillan. 1973. Maintenance of sameness in children with Kanner's syndrome. *Journal of Autism and Developmental Disorders* 20: 581-590.

Prizant, B., and J. Duchan. 1981. The functions of immediate echolalia in autistic children. *Journal of Speech and Hearing Disorders* 46: 241-249.

Prizant, B., and J. Duchan. 1981. The functions of immediate echolalia in autistic children. *Journal of Speech and Hearing Disorders* 46: 241-249.

Prizant, B., and P. Rydell. 1984. Analysis of functions of delayed echolalia in autistic children. *Journal of Speech and Hearing Disorders* 27: 183-192.

Prizant, B., and A. Wetherby. 1985. Intentional communicative behavior of children with autism: Theoretical and practical issues. *Australian Journal of Human Communication Disorders* 13: 21-59.

Ramachandran, V., and E. Hubbard. 2003. Hearing colors, tasting shapes. *Scientific American,* May: 53-59.

Rapin, I. 1987. Searching for the cause of autism: A neurologic perspective: In *Handbook of Autism and Pervasive Developmental Disorders,* D. Cohen and A. Donnellan, eds., 710-717. New York: Wiley.

Realmuto, G., and G. August. 1991. Catatonia in autistic disorder: A sign of comorbidity or variable expression? *Journal of Autism and Developmental Disorders* 21: 517-528.

Realmuto, G., and B. Main. 1982. Coincidence of Tourette's disorder and infantile autism. *Journal of Autism and Developmental Disorders* 12: 367-372.

Richer, J., and R. Coss. 1976. Gaze aversion in autistic and normal children. *Acta Psychiatrica Scandinavica* 53: 193-210.

Ritvo, E., et al. 1971. Effects of L-dopa in autism. *Journal of Autism and Childhood Schizophrenia* 1: 190-205.

Rogers, D. 1992. *Motor Disorder in Psychiatry: Towards a neurological psychiatry.* Chichester, England: Wiley and Sons.

Rolider, A., and R. Van Houten. 1985. Movement suppression time-out for undesirable behavior in psychotic and severely developmentally delayed children. *Journal of Applied Behavior Analysis* 18: 275-288.

Rubin, S., D. Biklen, C. Kasa-Hendrickson, P. Kluth, D. Cardinal, and A. Broderick. 2001. Independence, participation, and the meaning of intellectual ability. *Disability & Society* 16 (3): 415-429.

Rutter, M. 1966. Prognosis: Psychotic children in adolescence and early adult life. In *Early Childhood Autism*, J. K. Wing, ed., 83-98. Oxford: Pergamon Press.

Rutter, M. 1974. The development of infantile autism. *Psychological Medicine* 4: 147-163.

Rutter, M., D. Greenfield, and L. Lockyer. 1967. A five to fifteen year follow-up study of infantile psychosis. II. Social and behavioral outcome. *British Journal of Psychiatry* 113: 1183-1199.

Sacks, O. 1990. *Awakenings.* New York: Harper Perennial.

Schopler, E., R. Reichler, and B. Renner. 1986. *The Childhood Autism Rating Scale (CARS).* Los Angeles: Western Psychological Services.

Simon, N. 1975. Echolalic speech in childhood autism. *Archives of General Psychiatry* 32: 1439-1446.

Snow, J. 1994. *What's Really Worth Doing and How to Do It.* Toronto: Inclusion Press.

Sorosky, A., et al. 1968. Systematic observations of autistic behavior. *Archives of General Psychiatry* 18: 439-449.

Strandt-Conroy, K. 1999. *Exploring movement differences in autism through first-hand accounts.* Unpublished doctoral dissertation, University of Wisconsin-Madison.

Strandt-Conroy, K., and A. Donnellan (in preparation). *Autism and movement differences: Evidence from self-reports.* Unpublished manuscript.

Sverd, J. 1991. Tourette syndrome and autistic disorder: A significant relationship. *American Journal of Medical Genetics* 39: 173-179.

Thelen, E. 1995. Motor development: A new synthesis. *American Psychologist* 50 (2): 79-95.

Thelen, E., and L. B. Smith. 1994. *A Dynamic Systems Approach to Development and Cognition.* Cambridge, MA: MIT Press.

Vilensky, J., A. Damasio, and R. Maurer. 1981. Gait disturbance in patients with autistic behavior. *Archives of Neurology* 38: 646-649.

Volkmar, F. 1986. Compliance, noncompliance, and negativism. In *Social Behavior in Autism*, E. Schopler and G. Mesibov, eds., 171-188. New York: Plenum Press.

Volkmar, F., E. Hoder, and D. Cohen. 1985. Compliance, "negativism," and the effects of treatment structure in autism: A naturalistic, behavioral study. *Journal of Child Psychology and Psychiatry* 26: 865-877.

Walker, H., and M. Coleman. 1976. Characteristics of adventitious movements in autistic children. In *The Autistic Syndrome*, M. Coleman, ed., 135-144. Amsterdam: North Holland.

Wallace, B. 1975. Negativism in verbal and nonverbal responses of autistic children. *Journal of Abnormal Psychology* 84: 138-143.

Wetherby, A., and C. Prutting. 1984. Profiles of communicative and cognitive-social abilities in autistic children. *Journal of Speech and Hearing Research* 27: 364-377.

Williams, D. 1992. Nobody Nowhere. New York: Avon.

Williams, D. 1994. Somebody Somewhere. New York: Times Books.

Williams, D. 1996a. *Like Color to the Blind*. New York: Times Books.

Williams, D. 2003. *Exposure Anxiety—The Invisible Cage: An exploration of self-protection responses in the autism spectrum disorders*. London: Jessica Kingsley.

Winchel, R., and M. Stanley. 1991. Self-injurious behavior: A review of the behavior and biology of self-mutilation. *American Journal of Psychiatry* 148: 306-317.

Wing, L., and A. Attwood. 1987. Syndromes of autism and atypical development. In *Handbook of Autism and Pervasive Developmental Disorders*, D. Cohen and A. Donnellan, eds., 3-19. New York: Wiley and Sons.

Wortis, J. 1958. Schizophrenia symptomatology in mentally retarded children. *American Journal of Psychiatry* 115: 429-431.

Young, S. 2000. *Tears fall you can't see: Autism, personhood and expression of self*. Unpublished doctoral dissertation, University of Wisconsin-Madison.

Young, S., and A. Donnellan. 1997. *Rethinking autism and mental retardation: A review of what we think we know*. Unpublished manuscript.

CHAPTER FIVE

Casting Call for a Supporting Role

David A. Hill

Martha R. Leary

We all need support to participate in our complex lives. Supports that the majority of people need (e.g., friends, schools, car repair mechanics, tax preparation) are often invisible (Snow 1998). The invisibility comes from how common and frequent the need is among people. Because most of us need a school to learn and a mechanic to fix the car, we do not view these services as support. When people need supports that are not so ordinary (e.g., support to learn how to play, support to eat, support to communicate), they are viewed as different or exceptional. The difference presents an opportunity to explore the nature of support relationships. The basis for any personalized support is the relationship. Yet, in practice, the support relationship remains poorly defined and a relatively unexamined concept.

We focus in this article on defining the role of the supporter in providing personalized assistance to a person with unique support needs. Personalized assistance needs to be responsive to a range of needs, including recognizing and making use of a person's skills, compensating for areas where skills may not develop, and offering the opportunity for entering new realms and learning new skills. Relationships are the basis for providing support. Figure 5.1 shows a dynamic description of aspects of relationships.

Relationships develop: They have a life story and exhibit creative spurts of growth.

Relationships are dialogical: They evolve through discourse.

Relationships are meaningful: They involve emotions, attachments, responsibilities and insights.

Relationships are dynamically stable: They resist change but are locally variable.

Relationships are cultural: They are embedded in histories of practice, traditions, and guidance.

(Fogel 1993)

Figure 5.1. Relationships as the basis for providing support: a dynamic representation of the aspects of relationships.

Assumptions guiding support

We believe that there are necessary principles and assumptions that must guide supportive relationships. Essentially, these principles and assumptions compose the value statements that we have distilled from our own and others' experiences of mutually successful relationships:

- All people communicate. Communication occurs in the context of relationships. Typically, we use intuition and history of interactions to assign meaning to behavior. For some people, communication may be unconventional and hard to interpret. To negotiate meaning within a relationship, it may be necessary to suspend trust in our intuitions and assumptions about meaning (Leary and Hill 1996).
- Progress in development occurs in relationship and through mutual responding based on genuine appreciation and valuing of the other person.
- We all have different abilities at different times and in different contexts. True support emerges out of collaboration in finding solutions to challenges and working toward agreed on goals.
- The relationship is a covenant. Both partners are committed in kind to the development of the relationship.
- The relationship is neither affirmed nor nullified by a partner's performance. The overriding aim is unconditional support of another to grow and participate in an ever-increasing number of richer relationships with others.

- The support relationship is not about power or control. Rather, it is a shared enterprise that is complex, fluid, and negotiated, with the goal of promoting participation, sometimes through difficult transitions and change, with appropriate safeguards.

Supporting roles

We find it useful to consider support needs within two broad categories: *Times of Stability* and *Times of Growth, Transition, and Change*. These two support-need categories fall under the umbrella of our third category, *Safety*, both within and outside of the support relationship. We have explored ways to describe supportive relationships by suggesting possible role metaphors to amplify and underscore some of the less tangible and other, more apparent, dimensions of support. The tables below illustrate the dimensions of support and the support roles. Table 5.1 (Times of Stability) highlights support functions that relate to the day to day, routine activities for which a person may need support. Table 5.2 (Times of Growth, Transition, and Change) highlights support functions that are necessary because of changes in circumstances, new opportunities, and/or turmoil or crises. Table 5.3 (Safety) highlights support functions that recognize the possible threats from within or outside of the relationship. The support needs, opportunities, and dangers for these categories become our themes for describing the work of the supporter in terms of role metaphors. Given these support needs, what kind of supporting roles are useful or necessary? Figure 5.2 provides a list of properties of successful, supportive relationships we have found in our research.

The reader is encouraged to consider, experiment, and, ultimately, exercise supporting roles. This process may help identify a person's support needs, critically assess gaps in support or missed opportunities, consider areas for enrichment, and alert concern for potential dangers and barriers. Not all of the supporting roles will be relevant for a specific person. These support needs and roles are intended for reflection and contemplation rather than being prescriptive. The role of a supporter is created each moment.

Trust.

Intimacy.

Presumption of competence.

Understanding.

Shared vision of independence.

Good communication.

(Robledo and Donnellan 2008)

Figure 5.2. Six properties of successful supportive relationships.

Support for stability

The need for supportive relationships is a common, shared need for all persons, regardless of ability. The kind of support that is needed varies, given different situations and circumstances, for any individual. We cover five support needs that are necessary to support stability. These are provided in Table 5.1, with descriptors of the supporting roles that one may fill.

Table 5.1. Times of Stability.

Support needs	Supporting roles
Accept person "as is." No blame. Personalized assistance. Enable fullest participation.	Steward, valet, aide-de-camp, dresser, shadow, companion, devotee, friend, assistant, helpmate, first-mate.
Match a person's rhythm, rate, and pace.	Associate, collaborator, confidant, hinge, joint, dance partner, reflector, mirror, transposer, modulator, resonator, transmitter, metronome, invited guest, coupling.
Observe, listen for, clarify, and confirm intentions.	Agent, attaché, copilot, decipher, detective, filter, moderator, checker, fact-finder.
Repair mismatched agendas.	Mediator, contractor, tailor, fence builder.
Promote interactions, social conventions, and hospitality.	Navigator, orchestrator, framer, architect, choreographer, convener, assembler, cabinetmaker, concierge, arranger, scribe.

Support for growth, transition, and change

In addition, there are times when individuals, or the community and the settings that they participate in, change. During these times of growth, transition, transformatiov n, or crises, the nature and functions of support need to change as well. Supports at these episodic intervals must have qualities such as being observant, deliberate, mindful, and creative. In Table 5.2, we have identified five support needs within this category of support and have provided a related list of supporting roles to illustrate this.

Table 5.2. Times of Growth, Transition, and Change.

Support needs	Supporting roles
Promote person's performance and competence.	Helmsman, mentor, guide, advisor, walking stick, editor, buffer, coach.
Inform about differences. Introduce strategies.	Counselor, invited speaker, assessor, diagnostician, academic, beacon, researcher, archivist, glossary educator.
Highlight the physical and social environment. Uncover hidden information.	Cartographer, photographer, scout, surveyor, sonographer, meteorologist, trend watcher, reporter, explorer, political pundit, foreign correspondent, archaeologist, travel agent.
Detect details related to change.	Paraphraser, translator, articulator, narrator, auditor, detective.
Identify and support new relationships. Promote relationships that develop capacity.	Ambassador, publicist, protocol officer, consul, diplomat, engineer, developer, negotiator, representative, mediator, designer, advocate, manager, bridge builder, organizer, provisional leader, governess, emperor.

Support for safety

A relationship between two people opens up both parties to certain vulnerabilities. These are inherent risks involved within and outside the support relationship. Vigilance is required to protect the integrity, health, safety, and comfort of the individuals. In Table 5.3, we have identified three support needs that serve this purpose. We provide descriptors to illustrate these supporting roles.

Table 5.3. Safety.

Support needs	Suporting roles
Reflect on progress toward goals. Alert person to pitfalls. Revisit established values.	Visionary, strategic planner, mentor, mother superior, philosopher, confessor, contemplative thinker.
Describes health and safety concerns and possible consequences.	Medic, practical nurse, emergency worker, crossing guard, prevention officer, risk manager, actuary.
Monitor and report on situational realities.	Critic, evaluator, auditor, quality inspector, appraiser, data manager.

Dangerous roles

Several dangerous roles to be avoided are also presented in Table 5.4 below. These dangerous roles can be insidious and may ultimately sabotage or harm the support relationship beyond repair.

Table 5.4. Dangerous Roles.

Handler, warden, keeper-of-the-keys, regulator, boss, slave, censor, gatekeeper, imperialist, guard, dictator, SWAT-team officer, spy, double agent, control freak.

Summary

We believe that relationships are the basis for personalizing unique supports for people. We have identified a number of support needs and supporting roles. The supporting-role metaphors we have offered are examples to consider when one needs to fulfill a particular support function. The dangerous roles presented represent those actions or approaches that may sabotage the support relationship. The challenge is to consider, through an open dialogue, which support functions are a best fit for a person's life circumstances.

Acknowledgments

We thank everyone who helped us to think critically about what it means to be supportive. Specifically, thank you to Beth Gallagher, Ryan Matthews, Judith McGill, Miriam Miller, Anne O'Bryan, Larry O'Bryan, Jodi Robledo, and Judith Snow, who have constructively shaped and challenged our thinking.

References

Fogel, A. 1993. *Developing Through Relationships.* Chicago: University of Chicago Press.

Leary, M. R., and D. A. Hill. 1996. Moving on: Autism and movement disturbance. *Mental Retardation* 34: 39-53.

Robledo, J. A., and A. M. Donnellan. 2008. Properties of supportive relationships from the perspective of academically successful individuals with autism. *Intellectual and Developmental Disabilities* 46: 299-310. doi: 1934-9491-46-4-299.

Snow, J. 1998. *What's Really Worth Doing and How to Do It: A book for people who love someone labeled disabled.* Toronto: Inclusion Press.

CHAPTER SIX

Moving On: Autism and Movement Disturbance

Martha R. Leary
David A. Hill

[It is inconceivable how] someone who has much better inherent communication abilities than I do but who has not even taken a close look at my perspective to notice the enormity of chasm between us tells me that my failure to understand is because I lack empathy. —Jim, in Cesaroni and Garber 1991

A cluster of socially determined behaviors defines the syndrome of autism. Typically, individuals manifesting certain behaviors that meet accepted criteria are said to "have" autism. However, autism is not a disease (Rapin 1987). Autism "is the 'way people are' rather than a 'thing people have' " (McKinlay 1989, 202). A label of autism does not predict the particular symptoms that an individual will display. McKinlay also cautioned that the diagnosis of autism should prompt further investigation and in itself is not an explanation for the complex of symptoms seen. We acknowledge the apparent social utility of "autism" as a diagnostic label for a heterogeneous group of individuals but concur with McKinlay that investigation of specific symptoms is necessary.

An appreciation of the neurological symptoms that are common in some people labeled with autism may help to explain some of the differences seen in communicating, relating, and engaging in activity and to understand the nature of the differences of his or her experiences. This understanding could lead to changes in the timing, presentation, and expectations for interactions. Understanding the nature of the differences may also assist in planning for appropriate skill development. We are not interested in exploring neurological symptoms for the purpose of identifying new areas of deficit or new symptoms to "fix" or eliminate. Rather, the exploration may yield an increased understanding of individual differences.

In the present paper we have chosen a specific area of neurological functioning in which to explore particular symptoms seen in some individuals with autism. Our focus on movement disturbance symptoms seemed appropriate given current discussions, clinical interest, and the need to reconsider earlier investigations published on the topic in light of information from people who live with these symptoms. In this article we have outlined an exploratory and speculative look at the presence of symptoms of movement disturbance in individuals with autism. Our focus was on the potential value in viewing behaviors seen in autism from a movement disturbance perspective.

Does a diagnosis contribute to an understanding of people?

Professionals who assist parents and people with disabilities at the time of diagnosis to understand the nature of disability are guided by diagnostic manuals as a source of information concerning the presence of clinical features and as the basis for diagnoses (e.g., *Diagnostic and Statistical Manual of Mental Disorders—DSM-IV*, American Psychiatric Association 1994). As noted by the American Psychiatric Association (1987a):

> These diagnostic criteria reflect a consensus of current formulations of evolving knowledge in our field but do not encompass all the conditions that may be legitimate objects of treatment or research efforts. The purpose is to provide clear descriptions of diagnostic categories in order to enable clinicians and investigators to diagnose, communicate about, study and treat the various mental disorders. (vii)

Although there is now general consensus that symptoms of autism are caused by disorders of the central nervous system (Ritvo and Ritvo 1992), the psychological/psychiatric language continues to predominate characterizations of people with autism. At one time the presence of neurological dysfunction was a reason to rule out autism as a diagnosis (Darby and Clark 1992). Yet, definitions of autism continue to list behaviors without referring to neurological symptoms. This practice has continued in part because the diagnostic criteria commonly used (e.g., *DSM-IV*, American Psychiatric Association 1994) often do not describe symptoms (e.g., abnormal posture, abnormal tone) but, rather, particular behaviors in a socially interpreted context (e.g., failure to cuddle). For the purpose of diagnosis, behaviors are often described with phrases such as "prefers to," "failure to," or "unusual interest in" without specifying what particular symptoms may lead to that impression.

For example, the *DSM-IV* describes one characteristic behavior as "lack of spontaneous seeking to share enjoyment ... interest or achievements." If the person's symptoms include a lack of ability to initiate or an extreme delay in responding to others (i.e., akinesia/dyskinesia or bradykinesia), it may be extremely difficult to be spontaneous. If it takes the person 3 minutes, rather than the socially expected 3 seconds, to organize perceptions, attention, motivation, and body movements, the opportunity for spontaneous interactions may often pass with the partners switching to new topics and/or becoming involved in new activities. The person with these challenges may appear to be unmotivated and nonresponsive. Applying a social context to the behavior observed distracts from an appreciation of the possible neurological explanations for behavior. Hence, the person's behavior is interpreted based on judgments about the individual's preferences and motivations.

What is a movement disturbance?

The term *movement disturbance* is used here because it is *not* indicative of a syndrome. Instead, it is a term that describes symptoms involving both the loss of typical movement and excessive atypical movements (Marsden 1984a). Movement disturbances are found in a large number of syndromes and may be caused by many different pathologies (Marsden 1984b).

A movement disturbance may cause difficulties with the dynamics of movement as in starting, executing (e.g., speed, control, target, rate, rhythm, coordination), continuing, stopping, combining, or switching movements. The complexity of movements disturbed may range from simple movements (e.g., nodding the head, using facial expression, gesturing to add meaning) to those affecting overall levels of activity and behavior (e.g., combining movements to complete a task, adding new information to a conversation, monitoring the speed of movements). Many individuals who experience movement disturbance report differences in internal mental processes, such as perception, changes in attention, consciousness, motivation, and emotion (e.g., Bliss 1980; Kahlbaum 1874/1973; Rogers 1992; Sacks 1990). The individual affected may report that most aspects of daily life are disrupted or distorted. The pervasiveness of the impact on the individual's self-expression (e.g., through postures, movements, speech, language, thoughts, attention, emotion, perception) has prompted Rogers (1990) to consider applying the terms *psychomotility disorders* rather than *motor disorders* to the disturbance. Our working definition of *movement disturbance* in the present paper is an interference in the efficient, effective use of movement that cannot solely be accounted for by paralysis or weakness. Movement disturbance is synonymous with a disruption in the regulation of movement.

The severity of a movement disturbance may be judged by the effect on the individual or partner in an interaction. The degree of interference on interactions may be latent, distracting, derailing, or pervasive. The frequency, duration, intensity, and composition of each episode may vary given different contexts, emotions, and physical states. The constraints and forces on movement depend on balancing inhibition and activation in order to meet the demands of a situation. Emotional state and level of intensity, whether positive or negative in nature, may make this balance even more difficult to achieve (Maurer 1992, 1993). In a study of 17 patients with various movement disturbances, Brenner, Friedman, and Merrit (1947) found that the only consistent feature was the effect of their psychic state on their abnormal movements. The atypical movements of these individuals were more prominent when they experienced emotional excitement and less prominent when they were distracted.

The phenomenon of *kinesia paradoxa* (Sacks 1990) complicates an understanding of movement disturbance. In extreme cases involving akinesia (e.g., lack of movement, difficulty initiating and/or switching movements), it is not uncommon for an individual to experience "sudden and total (though transient) disappearance or deflation [of symptoms] ... This mixture of akinesia and a sort of motor genius is very characteristic" (10). With *kinesia paradoxa* the individual who typically experiences severe difficulties with the most simple of movements may suddenly perform complex, skilled movements and then return to prior inactivity.

Table 6.1. Studies of individuals with autism in which movement disturbance phenomena were discussed.

Study	Movement disturbance
Ayres 1979; Biklen 1990; DeMyer et al. 1972; Jones and Prior 1985.	Apraxia/dyspraxia (e.g., difficulty with motor planning and sequencing of movements).
Bram, Meier, and Sutherland 1977; Gillberg 1991; Wing and Attwood 1987.	Lack of gross motor control or clumsiness.
Bond 1986; Ornitz 1974; Vilensky, Damasio, and Maurer 1981.	Abnormalities of gait and posture.
Damasio and Maurer 1978; Maurer and Damasio 1982.	Akinesia/dyskinesia (e.g., difficulty initiating or switching movements, freezing or stopping movement); bradykinesia (e.g., slowness of movement).
Comings and Comings 1991; Realmuto and Main 1982; Sverd 1991; Wing and Attwood 1987.	Tourette syndrome (e.g., stereotyped movements; vocal, verbal, and physical tics; obsessive-compulsive traits).
Realmuto and August 1991; Wing and Attwood 1987.	Catatonic-like phenomena (e.g, mutism, echolalia, repetitive movements, automatic obedience, odd hand postures, interruption and freezing of movements, stupor, and frenzy or excitement).

Table 6.2. Exploratory analysis of symptoms of movement disturbance in individuals with autism

Features of movement disturbance[a]	Autism research	DSM-III-R criteria for autism
Posture:		
Simple abnormal posture.	Flexion dystonia: Maurer and Damasio 1982; odd hand postures: Wing and Attwood 1987; Walker and Coleman 1976.	Failure to cuddle; odd hand postures.
Complex abnormal posture.	Posturing: Realmuto and August 1991; freezing: Wing and Attwood 1987.	Odd body postures.
Persistence of imposed postures.	Catalepsy: Realmuto and August 1991.	Catatonic posturing.
Tone:		
Abnormal tone.	Abnormalities in muscle tone: Gillberg, Rosenthal, and Johansson 1983; Maurer and Damasio 1982.	Failure to cuddle.
Gegenhalten (springy resistance to passive movement).		
Mitgehen (anglepoise lamp-raising of arm in response to light touch).		
Abnormal movements; face and head:		
Simple brief/ dyskinesialike; repetitive, rhythmical ticlike.	Myoclonic jerk of head: Walker, Coleman, and Ornitz 1976; bruxism: Bebko and Lennox 1988, Ornitz and Ritvo 1976; mouthing: Walker and Coleman 1976.	

Features of movement disturbance[a]	Autism research	DSM-III-R criteria for autism
Simple sustained/grimacelike; spasmodic, not completely fixed.	Disturbance in facial expression: Maurer and Damasio 1982; grimace or rigidity for no apparent reason: Schopler et al. 1986, Walker and Coleman 1976; decreased use of facial expression: Schopler et al. 1986.	Lack of facial responsiveness.
Complex mannerism/stereotypylike; turning away, side to side, searching movements.	Looks out of corners of eyes; avoids looking adult in the eye: Schopler et al. 1986; eye-gaze/ocular abnormalities: Churchill and Bryson 1972, Hutt and Ounsted 1966, Mirenda et al. 1983.	Facial expression and gesture is absent or minimal or socially inappropriate in form; lack of eye contact.
Abnormal movements; trunk and limbs:		
Simple brief/dyskinesialike; random/repetitive, rhythmical ticlike.	Involuntary motor tics: Wing and Attwood 1987, Comings and Comings 1991, Realmuto and Main 1982; choreiform and athetoid movements: Maurer and Damasio 1982, Walker and Coleman 1976; dyskinesia: Maurer and Damasio 1982.	Arm flapping; abnormalities of motor behavior; gesture is absent or minimal or socially inappropriate in form.
Simple sustained/dystonialike; abnormal muscle stretch and flex.	Flexion dystonia: Maurer and Damasio 1982.	
Complex mannerism/stereotypylike.	Motor stereotypies: DeMyers et al. 1972, Hutt et al. 1965, Kern et al. 1984, Maurer and Damasio 1982, Meiselas et al. 1989, Ornitz and Ritvo 1976, Ornitz 1974, Ornitz and Ritvo 1968, Ritvo et al. 1971, Sorosky et al. 1968, Walker and Coleman 1976.	Motor stereotypies include peculiar hand movements, rocking, spinning, dipping and swaying movements of the whole body.

Features of movement disturbance[a]	Autism research	DSM-III-R criteria for autism
Abnormal ocular movements:		
Increased blinking.		
Decreased blinking.		
Eye movements; to and fro, roving, conjugate.		
Purpose movement:		
Abruptness/rapidity of spontaneous movements; suddenness quality.		
Slowness/feebleness of spontaneous movement; weak, languid, labored.	Bradykinesia: Maurer and Damasio 1982; dyspraxia: DeMyer 1975, DeMyer et al. 1972, DeMyer et al. 1981, Jones and Prior 1985.	
Iterations of spontaneous movements; gesture, mannerism repeated.	Spatial/logic symmetrizing and ordering: Frith 1971, Kanner 1943, prior and Hoffman 1990, Prior and MacMillan 1973; obsessive-compulsive behaviors: Baron-Cohen 1989, Frith 1971, Kanner 1943, Maurer and Damasio 1982; object exploration through proximal senses: Frith and Hermelin 1969, Goldfarb 1956, Masterton and Biederman 1983, Maurer and Damasio 1982, Ornitz 1974, Sorosky et al. 1968; self-injurious behavior: Favell et al. 1978, Gabony 1991, Gedye 1989, Guess and Carr 1991, Rolider and VanHouten 1985, Walker and Coleman 1976, Winchel and Stanley 1991; persistent strange or peculiar body	Abnormalities of motor behavior; self-injurious behavior.

Features of movement disturbance[a]	Autism research	DSM-III-R criteria for autism
	movements despite attempts to discourage them: Schopler et al. 1986; perseveration: Chess 1972, Frith 1970, 1971, Hoffman and Prior 1982, Kanner 1943, Maurer and Damasio 1982.	
Other: echopraxia/ blocking/ambitendence; copying action/ freezing/ an opposing action interruption.	Echopraxia: Carr 1979, Konstantareas 1985; hypermimesis: Bartak, Rutter, and Cox 1975, Curcio and Piserchia 1978, DeMyer 1975, 1976, Rutter 1974.	Repetitively mimics actions.

Gait:

Exaggerated associated movements.		
Reduced associated movement.	Loss of associated movements: Bartak et al. 1975, DeMyer et al. 1972, Maurer and Damasio 1982, Vilensky et al. 1981.	
Slow/shuffling.	Brandykinesia: Maurer and Damasio 1982.	
Manneristic, bizarre.	Gait disturbance: Bond 1986, Hutt et al. 1964, Maurer and Damasio 1982, Sorosky et al. 1968, Vilensky et al. 1981; toe walking: Schopler et al. 1986.	Walking tiptoe; jumping.

Speech:

Aprosodic; abnormal rate, volume, intonation.	Dysprosody: Baltaxe 1981, Ornitz and Ritvo 1968; poor speech volume modulation: Baltaxe 1981, Ornitz and Ritvo 1968; abnormal tone, rhythm, volume: Schopler et al. 1986.	Abnormal speech melody.

Features of movement disturbance[a]	Autism research	DSM-III-R criteria for autism
Mutism.	Mutism: Curcio 1978, Konstantareas 1985, LaVigna 1977, Maurer and Damasio 1982, Ornitz and Ritvo 1968, Ritvo et al. 1971; lack of communicative initiations: Curcio 1978, Loveland and Landry 1986, Maurer and Damasio 1982, Mundy et al. 1990, Ornitz and Ritvo 1968, Prizant and Wetherby 1985, Rapin 1987, Ritvo et al. 1971.	Language may be totally absent.
Indistinct/unintelligible speech; mumbling, poor articulation, nonsocial speech.	Use of jargon: Schopler et al. 1986; vocal, verbal tics: Comings and Comings 1991, Realmuto and Main 1982, Wing and Attwood 1987.	
Other: echolalia/palilalia/ speech mannerisms.	Echolalia: Baltaxe and Simmons 1977, Kanner 1943, Ornitz and Ritvo 1968, Paccio and Curcio 1982, Prizant and Duchan 1981, Prizant and Rydell 1984, Rapin 1987, Simon 1975; topic perseveration: Kanner 1943; unconventional expression of intent: Prizant and Wetherby 1985.	Delayed or immediate echolalia; verbal stereotypies including repetition of words, phrases.
Overall behavior:		
Marked overactivity.	Catatonic excitement: Wing and Attwood 1987; extreme response to minor environmental changes: Campbell et al. 1972, Geller et al. 1981, Kanner 1943, Ornitz and Ritvo 1968, Prior and MacMillan 1973; hyperkinesis: Sorosky et al. 1968; explosive/violent movement episodes: Campbell et al. 1972.	Catatonic phenomena, particularly excitement or posturing; aggressive behavior.

Features of movement disturbance[a]	Autism research	DSM-III-R criteria for autism
Marked underactivity.	Hypomimesis: Bartak et al. 1975, Curcio 1978, Curcio and Piserchia 1978, Dawson and Adams 1984, DeMyer 1975, DeMyer et al. 1972, 1981, Schopler et al. 1968; almost never initiates: Schopler et al. 1986; almost never responds to the adult: Schopler et al. 1986; catatonic stupor: Realmuto and August 1991; decreased responsiveness: Lovaas et al. 1971, Ornitz and Ritvo 1968, Prizant and Wetherby 1985, Rapin 1987.	Indifference to affection or physical contact; no or impaired imitation.
Excessive compliance/ automatic obedience.		
Poor/feeble compliance.		
Other: negativism.	Command negativism/ blocking/ substitution: Clark and Rutter 1977, Morrison et al. 1971, Volkmar 1986, Volkmar et al. 1985, Wallace 1975.	Oppositional behavior; aversion to physical contact.
Other: engages in rituals.	Ritualistic behavior: Frith 1971, Kanner 1943, Maurer and Damasio 1982, Prior and MacMillan 1973.	Ritualistic, repetitive actions: following routines in a repetitive way.

[a]Movement features represent items adapted from the Modified Rogers Scale (Lund, Mortimer, Rogers, and McKenna 1991).

Autism and movement

Descriptions of children and adults with specific handicaps involving communication, social relationships, productive activity and movement disturbance have been reported in the medical literature for more than a century (e.g., Earl 1934; Kahlbaum 1874/1973). More specifically, some individuals with autism have been described as having varied disturbances of movement. Table 6.1 lists several of the authors who have described the presence of movement disturbance phenomena in individuals with autism.

Despite a substantial number of studies in which investigators described movement disturbance in some individuals with autism (e.g., 155 reported in Table 6.2), little interest was generated. The research on the variable of movement disorder was difficult to fit into the existing understanding of autism. Were movement disturbance symptoms simply additions to the list of possible symptoms seen in autism, or did symptoms of movement disturbance provide new information for understanding many of the core characteristics of autism? Golden (1987), in his review of the work of Maurer and Damasio (1982), noted that the core characteristics of autism (i.e., impairments in social interaction, verbal and nonverbal communication, imaginative activity, and repertoire of activities and interests) could not be adequately accounted for by akinesia/dyskinesia and bradykinesia.

However, it *is* possible to consider the impact of these movement disturbances on the core characteristics of autism. For example, akinesia/dyskinesia and bradykinesia may affect a person's ability to initiate, switch, efficiently perform, or continue any action, including those involved in communicating, interacting socially, or performing useful activities. Difficulties with initiation of speech (Prizant and Wetherby 1985), slowness in responding to another person (Mirenda and Donnellan 1986), or stopping or freezing during an activity (Vilensky, Damasio, and Maurer 1981) are examples of how movement disturbance phenomena might influence interactions with individuals labeled with autism. Other movement disturbance phenomena presented in Table 6.1 may also be viewed in relation to the core characteristics of autism. Stereotypic movements that seem to be unrelated to an interaction (e.g., handflapping) might influence a partner to assume that a person is not interested in the interaction, preferring to engage in repetitive behaviors. Disturbances of catatonic-like phenomena may affect posture, muscle tone, walking, speaking, and repetitions of movements as well as the rate and intensity of activity or behavior. Behavioral states vary in catatonia. Individuals may shift from stupor, mutism, and a lack of response to frenzy, aggression, and explosive or violent outbursts. Movement disturbance can clearly have a profound effect on a person's ability to regulate movement in order to effectively communicate, relate, and participate with others. Once this possibility is acknowledged, it becomes necessary to suspend absolute trust in one's intuitive interpretation of actions and intent. Behaviors may not be what they seem.

As early as 1991, we were influenced by the work of Rogers and his colleagues, who have focused on defining the symptoms of movement disturbance in persons with severe psychiatric illness and those with developmental disabilities (Lund, Mortimer, Rogers, and McKenna 1991; McKenna, Lund, Mortimer, and Biggins 1991; Rogers 1985, 1992; Rogers, Karki, Bartlett, and Pocock 1991). Rogers (1985) developed an observational checklist that he and his colleagues subsequently adapted and named the Modified Rogers Scale (Lund et al. 1991; McKenna et al. 1991). The development, administration, reliability, and validity of the Modified Rogers Scale are described in Lund et al. (1991). The Modified Rogers Scale was found to be robust regardless of the population or setting observed.

In March 1992, we conducted an exploratory analysis of movement disturbance symptoms in individuals labeled with autism (presented in Table 6.2). Rogers (personal communication, June 18, 1992) reviewed and agreed with our adapted format of the Modified Rogers Scale. We used this scale to categorize symptoms of movement disturbance in autism by sampling the literature on autism in which other authors described or remarked on possible movement disturbance phenomena. Similarly, symptoms of autism taken from the *DSM-III-R* criteria (American Psychiatric Association 1987b) were categorized using the Modified Rogers Scale. Specifically, we were interested in discovering whether any of the socially referenced characteristics of autism could be based on neurological symptoms of movement disturbance.

Caution is necessary when interpreting the exploratory analysis presented in Table 6.2 despite our complete agreement as to classification of a symptom on the scale. We did not systematically attempt to find contradictory examples in the literature, though none were encountered in the sampling. It was not our intent that other investigators replicate this kind of analysis using the Modified Rogers Scale. Table 6.2 is included to provide references for the autism literature explored in support of the view that symptoms of movement disturbance are present for some individuals labeled with autism.

Our exploratory analysis underscored the wide range and complexity of movement disturbance symptoms. There was evidence that at least some individuals labeled with autism have symptoms fitting most of the categories on the Modified Rogers Scale. This prompted a fundamental shift in our interpretation of behavior. The socially referenced core characteristics of autism (e.g., *DSM-IV*) may be based in part on the presence of neurological symptoms affecting movement. Our analysis calls into question many previously held assumptions about why people labeled with autism behave in certain ways.

Could an understanding of movement disturbance contribute to an understanding of behavior in autism?

Based on and following the exploratory analysis, we considered in more practical terms the relation between symptoms of movement disturbance and symptoms of autism. It was possible to group symptoms into three levels of disturbance: those affecting (a) motor function, (b) volitional movements, and (c) overall behavior and activity. For clarity, at each level of movement disturbance, we have listed some examples using common terms and phrases describing behaviors of individuals labeled with autism or movement disturbance. The following list contains symptoms of disturbances of motor function affecting posture, muscle tone, associated movements (i.e., natural movements of the body accompanying other actions, such as swinging of the arms while walking), and extraneous movements (i.e., additional non-purposeful movements such as tics):

Flexion dystonia (e.g., transient stretch and flex of the limbs and trunk of the body).

Odd hand and body postures.

Abnormalities in muscle tone.

Grimace or rigidity for no apparent reason.

Facial expression and gesture absent or minimal or socially inappropriate in form.

Lack of eye contact (e.g., looks out of corners of eyes, avoids looking adult in the eye).

Involuntary motor tics (e.g., arm-flapping).

Choreiform and athetoid movements (e.g., involuntary writhing or dance-like movements).

Dyskinesia (e.g., decrease in voluntary, spontaneous, and associated movements).

Motor stereotypies (e.g., peculiar hand movements, rocking, spinning, dipping, and swaying movements of the whole body).

Vocal and verbal tics (e.g., unusual vocalizations or combinations of sounds).

Loss of associated movements (e.g., lack of or unusual swinging of arms while walking).

Rogers (1992) observed that "motor disorders in mental handicap were dealt with very simply. Atypical movements in the mentally handicapped were often lumped together as 'self-stimulation'" (62). For example, many specific interventions have been designed to deal with self-stimulatory behaviors in the belief that individuals with autism engage in these behaviors for pleasure or because they choose not to participate in social interaction (e.g., Favell and Green 1981; Foxx 1982; Rincover 1981; Volkmar 1986). Recently published first-hand accounts of individuals with autism do not corroborate many of these assumptions (Barron and Barron 1992; Cesaroni and Garber 1991; Grandin and Scariano 1986; Jolliffe, Lansdown, and Robinson 1992). For example, Jim reported that "stereotyped movements aren't things I decide to do for a reason; they're things that happen by themselves when I'm not paying attention to my body" (Cesaroni and Garber 1991, 309). Symptoms of disturbances of motor function outlined earlier highlight the benefit of describing specific symptoms without making social judgments.

Symptoms of disturbance of volitional movements that are performed for a purpose are as follows:

Slowness/feebleness of spontaneous movements.

Motor planning difficulties.

Repetitious spontaneous movements (e.g., ordering; lining-up; separating items into discrete numerical or spatial piles; obsessive-compulsive behaviors; exploring objects through smell, taste, and/or touch; persistent patterns of body movements; self-injurious behaviors; motor perseveration; repetitive mimicry of another's actions and/or behavior).

Gait disturbances (e.g., reduced associated movements such as arm swing; slow, shuffling walk; manneristic or bizarre walking pattern, such as lunging, jumping, or toe walking.

Speech/language disturbances (e.g., atypical speech melody, poor speech volume control, atypical speech rate and rhythm, mutism, lack of communicative initiations, use of jargon, repetition of words and phrases, and perseverative speech, e.g., topics, questions, words).

Disturbances at this level affect the motivation or will to move.

Symptoms of disturbances of volitional movements presented above underscore why others may perceive an individual with autism to have peculiar preferences and to lack motivation. Common descriptions of characteristics of people labeled with autism have included noncompliance, perseveration, inflexibility, rigidity, and restricted range of interests. These descriptions fail to recognize the neurological requirements for performing spontaneous and purposeful behavior. As speech-language pathologists, we find it compelling that the most characteristic features of "autistic" speech (e.g., mutism, atypical speech melody, jargon, echolalia, and perseverative speech) are defined as disturbances of movement according to the Modified Rogers Scale. If symptoms involve disturbances of volitional movements, caution must be taken in ascribing interpretations concerning preference and motivation. Luria (1932/1960) elaborated on "the problem of will" (397) and voluntary control of behavior, which he defined as "the ability to create stimuli and to subordinate them" (401). Organization of behavior is the net result of this process. If stimuli are absent, misinterpreted, or unable to be subordinated through established hierarchies of control, then the individual will exhibit a breakdown in the organization and control of volitional behavior. Damasio (1994) proposed that body states or feelings are an integral part of the decision-making process. Without reliable information from one's body, the most trivial of decisions may be overwhelming.

The following are symptoms associated with disturbances of overall behavior or activity:

Catatonic excitement (e.g., frenzy or marked overactivity).

Extreme response to minor environmental changes.

Aggressive behavior.

Hyperkinesis (e.g., constant movement).

Explosive or violent movement episodes (e.g., tantrums).

Aversion to affection or physical contact.

Catalepsy (e.g., persistent, strange postures freezing during movement).

Bradykinesia (e.g., excessively slow execution of movement).

Mutism (e.g., no use of speech or use of speech only rarely while under stress).

No or impaired imitation.

Lack of response (e.g., when name is called or to a sudden sound).

Lack of initiation (e.g., waits for instructions before moving).

Catatonic stupor (e.g., stationary states accompanied by an intensification of attention as in a trance).

Negativism (e.g., does the opposite of actions requested).

Indifference to physical contact.

Ritualistic, repetitive actions and talk.

Follows routines in a repetitive way.

Movement phenomena described here are marked by extremes of rate or intensity.

Symptoms described above involve disturbances of overall behavior and activity that are among the most challenging of behaviors seen in people with autism. Individuals displaying symptoms along this continuum of behavior may be thought of as unreachable, in another world, apathetic, lazy, nonresponsive, agitated, aggressive, violent, destructive, or out of control. Symptoms of this kind of disturbance place the individual at risk for intrusive procedures and/or removal to restrictive environments that exclude typical experiences. When planning intervention, it is important to analyze the precipitating and maintaining factors for behaviors and the possible communicative functions these serve. It may also be constructive to investigate how individuals with symptoms of movement disturbance have managed to accommodate extreme fluctuations in overall behavior and level of activity (see Sacks 1990, for "accommodations"). A shift in focus to a movement perspective may prompt new "sense-making" (Duchan 1986) of behavior, with a goal of assisting the individual to regulate and modulate behavioral states rather than to eliminate behavior.

In addition to the observable movement disturbances described previously, a number of associated phenomena, frequently reported to be present with movement disturbance, are also reported in autism. Table 6.3 lists these phenomena.

Associated phenomena often reported to coexist with the physical symptoms of movement disturbance and autism are presented in Table 6.3. Beyond the observable symptoms (see Table 6.2), changes in internal mental processes including attention, perception, emotional state, and thought, may accompany symptoms of movement disturbance. When symptoms of movement disturbance are present, it is probable that internal mental processes are also affected (Lohr and Wisniewski 1987; Rogers 1990).

Table 6.3. Phenomena Associated with Autism

Associated phenomena	Study
Perceptual disturbances[a]	Ayres 1979; Ayres and Heskett 1972; Cesaroni and Garber 1991; Condon 1975; Hermelin 1972; Lovaas et al. 1971; Masterton and Biederman 1983; Ornitz and Ritvo 1974; Ornitz and Ritvo 1968; Ornitz and Ritvo 1976; Ritvo et al. 1971.
Arousal/attention difficulties[a]	Ciesielski et al. 1990; Dawson and Lewy 1989; Garretson et al. 1990; Geller et al. 1981; Gold and Gold 1975; C. Hutt et al. 1964; Lovaas et al. 1971; Ornitz and Ritvo 1968; Ornitz and Ritvo 1976; Schreibman and Lovaas 1973; Wilhelm and Lovaas 1976.
Emotional lability[a]	Realmuto and August 1991.
Arithmomania.	Hill 1975; Rimland 1978; Rosen 1981; Sacks 1987; Steel et al. 1984; Treffert 1988; Treffert 1989.
Seizure disorders[a]	Golden 1987; Olsson et al. 1988; Ritvo and Freeman 1984.
Abnormal EEGs, ABR, CT scans, MRI findings.	Balottin et al. 1989; Courchesne et al. 1987; DeMyer et al. 1981; Fein et al. 1981; Gedye 1991; Gillberg et al. 1983; Gillberg and Svendsen 1983; Golden 1987; Grey-Walter et al. 1971; Hashimoto et al. 1989; Nowell et al. 1990; Olsson et al. 1988; Ritvo and Freeman 1984.
"Soft" neurological signs.	Jones and Prior 1985; Maurer and Damasio 1982; Sorosky et al. 1968.
Manifestation of "organic" dysfunction.	Ashimoto et al. 1989; Fein et al. 1981; Gillberg and Svendsen 1983; Hauser et al. 1975; Hetzler and Griffin 1981; Hoffman and Prior 1982; Maurer and Damasio 1982; Olsson et al. 1988; Prior and Hoffman 1990; Ritvo and Freeman 1984; Wetherby et al. 1981.

Note: These associated phenomena were identified in the literature on movement disorder.
[a]Phenomenon listed in *DSM-IV* criteria for autism.

What are some implications for individuals?

The discussion so far has centered on the presence of symptoms of movement disturbance in individuals labeled with autism. Much of the information about movement disturbances has come from the experience of people who acquire symptoms after a period of typical development. For autism, onset of symptoms is frequently observed within the first year of life and usually before 30 months of age. It is likely that the symptom complex of autism reflects a unique course of development (Rapin 1987) brought about by atypical epigenetic factors (i.e., the individually determined constraints on development) and subsequent structural and functional neurological differences (Bauman 1992; Edelman 1992). The impact of these developmental differences on the individual is powerful and may account for many of the unique expressions of symptoms among individuals labeled with autism. These differences in development may account for some of the variations observed between the syndromes of autism and acquired movement disturbances.

Often people with autism are informally grouped according to their perceived functioning level (e.g., high or low functioning). However, the presence of movement disturbance symptoms may not be limited to individuals within any particular group. Given the wide ranging expression of symptoms of movement disturbance (see Tables 6.2 and 6.3), it is possible that the symptoms cross any such group boundaries. The symptoms may be present in individuals irrespective of perceived functioning level. For any individual, symptoms may cluster around one particular level of disturbance or may be expressed at all three levels.

In contrast to a typical view that the symptoms of autism are fairly static and constant, symptoms of movement disturbance would appear to be more dynamic (e.g., the extreme of *kinesia paradoxa*). Such a dynamic view of symptoms may be useful in understanding some of the apparent fluctuations and inconsistencies in performance often reported for individuals with autism. In our clinical work we have talked to parents who report that their nonspeaking child has voiced a complex utterance, only once. Other parents have reported children with difficulty climbing stairs who suddenly scaled towers or balanced skillfully on a ledge. These temporary displays of skill remain unexplained.

There may also be a need for closer examination of neurological symptoms both at initial diagnosis of autism and over time. The diagnostic criteria for autism reflect symptoms of the syndrome in early childhood, when the majority of individuals are diagnosed (Cohen, Paul, and Volkmar 1987). Longitudinal follow-up of individuals has been sporadic. Only recently has the literature addressed the development of additional symptoms at or about the time of adolescence that are outside the currently accepted criteria for autism (Realmuto and August 1991; Wing and Attwood 1987). Often an individual is given an additional diagnostic label and is considered to have a comorbid condition. It may be helpful to have more longitudinal documentation of changes in the intensity and complexity of symptoms experienced by individuals labeled with autism (Windsor, Doyle, and Siegel 1994).

In this article we have presented information from a novel perspective. In the process of our work, we came to question professionals' descriptions of people, our own beliefs about disability, and the possible lack of facts supporting those beliefs. Things are not always what they seem. Ideas must be sought from those who consider the multiple and complex interactive variables that constitute human experience. There is a need for exploration of the experiences of others: people with disabilities, colleagues who share a common discipline, and those in fields that may not seem relevant to the study of autism.

> Scientific observation is not merely pure description of separate facts. Its main goal is to view an event from as many perspectives as possible. (Luria 1979, 77)

Authors' note: The authors gratefully acknowledge the support and assistance of the individuals with disabilities and our colleagues who have helped us to learn, stimulated discussion, and encouraged us to keep pushing the limits. The authors thank the boards and staff of The Geneva Centre in Toronto, Ontario, and Kerry's Place in Aurora, Ontario, for making their resources available to us.

Works Cited

Barron, J., and S. Barron. 1992. *There's a Boy in Here.* New York: Simon and Schuster.

Bartak, L., M. Rutter, and A. Cox. 1975. A comparative study of infantile autism and specific developmental receptive language disorder: 1. The children. *British Journal of Psychiatry* 126: 127-145.

Bauman, M. 1992. An interview with Dr. Margaret Bauman, advocate. *Autism Society of America* 24 (4): 1, 13-15.

Bebko, J. M., and C. Lennox. 1988. Teaching the control of diurnal bruxism to two children with autism using a simple cueing procedure. *Behavior Therapy* 19: 249-255.

Biklen, D. 1990. Communication unbound: Autism and praxis. *Harvard Educational Review* 60: 291-314.

Bliss, J. 1980. Sensory experiences of Gilles de la Tourette syndrome. *Archives of General Psychiatry* 37: 1343-1347.

Bond, S. L. 1986. *The gait of adolescent males with autistic behaviors: A pilot study.* Unpublished Master's thesis, MacMaster University School of Graduate Studies (Hamilton, Ontario).

Bram, S., M. Meier, and P. J. Sutherland. 1977. A relationship between motor control and language development in an autistic child. *Journal of Autism and Childhood Schizophrenia* 7: 57-67.

Brenner, C., A. P. Friedman, and H. H. Merrit. 1947. Psychiatric syndromes in patients with organic brain disease. 1. Diseases of the basal ganglia. *American Journal of Psychiatry* 135: 1242-1243.

Campbell, M., B. Fish, J. Korein, T. Shapiro, P. Collins, and C. Koh. 1972. Lithium and chlorpromazine: A controlled crossover study of hyperactive severely disturbed young children. *Journal of Autism and Childhood Schizophrenia* 2: 234-263.

Carr, E. G. 1979. Teaching autistic children to use sign language: Some research issues. *Journal of Autism and Developmental Disorders* 9: 345-359.

Cesaroni, L., and M. Garber. 1991. Exploring the experience of autism through firsthand accounts. *Journal of Autism and Developmental Disorders* 21: 303, 313.

Chess, S. 1972. Neurological dysfunction and childhood behavioral pathology. *Journal of Autism and Childhood Schizophrenia* 2: 299-311.

Churchill, D., and C. Q. Bryson. 1972. Looking and approach behavior of psychotic and normal children as a function of adult attention or preoccupation. *Comprehensive Psychiatry* 13: 171-177.

Ciesielski, K. T., E. Courchesne, and R. Elmasian. 1990. Effects of focused selective attention tasks on event-related potentials in autistic and normal individuals. *Electroencephalography and Clinical Neurophysiology* 75: 207-220.

Clark, P., and M. Rutter. 1977. Compliance and resistance in autistic children. *Journal of Autism and Childhood Schizophrenia* 7: 33-34.

Cohen, D. J., R. Paul, and F. R. Volkmar. 1987. Issues in the classification of pervasive developmental disorders and associated conditions. In *Handbook of Autism and Pervasive Developmental Disorders*, D. J. Cohen and A. M. Donnellan, eds., 20-40, New York: Wiley.

Comings, D. E., and B. G. Comings. 1991. Clinical and generic relationships between autism-pervasive developmental disorder and Tourette syndrome: A study of 19 cases. *American Journal of Medical Genetics* 39: 180-191.

Condon, W. S. 1975. Multiple response to sound in dysfunctional children. *Journal of Autism and Childhood Schizophrenia* 5: 37-56.

Courchesne, E., J. R. Hesselink, T. L. Jernigan, and R. Yeung-Courchesne. 1987. Abnormal neuroanatomy in a nonretarded person with autism: Unusual findings with magnetic resonance imaging. *Archives of Neurology* 44: 335-340.

Curcio, F. 1978. Sensorimotor functioning and communication in mute autistic children. *Journal of Autism and Childhood Schizophrenia* 8: 291-292.

Curcio, F., and E. A. Piserchia. 1978. Pantomimic representation in psychotic children. *Journal of Autism and Childhood Schizophrenia* 8: 181-189.

Damasio, A. 1994. *Descartes' Error: Emotion, reason, and the human brain*. New York: Putnam.

Damasio, A., and R. Maurer. 1978. A neurological model for childhood autism. *Archives of Neurology* 35: 777-786.

Darby, J. K., and L. Clark. 1992. Autism syndrome as a final common pathway of behavioral expression for many organic disorders [Letter to the editor]. *American Journal of Psychiatry* 149 (1): 146.

Dawson, G., and A. Adams. 1984. Imitation and social responsiveness in autistic children. *Journal of Abnormal Child Psychology* 12: 209-226.

Dawson, G., and A. Lewy. 1989. Arousal, attention, and the socioemotional impairments of individuals with autism. In *Autism: Nature, diagnosis, and treatment*, G. Dawson, ed., 49-74, New York: Guilford Press.

DeMyer, M. K. 1975. Research in infantile autism: A strategy and its results. *Biological Psychiatry* 10: 433-450.

DeMyer, M. K. 1976. Motor, perceptual-motor and intellectual disabilities of autistic children. In *Early Childhood Autism*, 2nd ed., L. Wing, ed., 169-196, Oxford: Pergamon.

DeMyer, M. K., G. D. Alpern, S. Barton, W. E. DeMyer, D. W. Churchill, J. N. Hingtgen, C. Q. Bryson, W. Pontius, and C. Kimberlin. 1972. Imitation in autistic, early schizophrenic, and non-psychotic subnormal children. *Journal of Autism and Childhood Schizophrenia* 2: 263-287.

DeMyer, M. K., J. N. Hingtgen, and R. K. Jackson. 1981. Infantile autism reviewed: A decade of research. *Schizophrenia Bulletin* 7: 388-451.

Duchan, J. F. 1986. Language intervention through sense-making and fine-tuning. In *Language Competence: Assessment and intervention*, R. Schiefelbush, ed., 187-212, San Diego: College-Hill.

Earl, C. J. C. 1934. The primitive catatonic psychosis of idiocy. *British Journal of Medical Psychology* 14: 230-253.

Edelman, G. M. 1992. *Bright Air, Brilliant Fire: On the matter of mind*. New York: Basic Books.

Favell, J. E., and J. W. Green. 1981. *How to Treat Self-Injurious Behavior*. Lawrence, KS: H & H Enterprises, Inc.

Favell, J. E., J. F. McGimsey, and M. L. Jones. 1978. The use of physical restraint in the treatment of self-injury and as a positive reinforcement. *Journal of Applied Behavior Analysis* 11: 225-241.

Fein, D., B. Skoff, and A. Mirsky. 1981. Clinical correlates of brainstem dysfunction in autistic children. *Journal of Autism and Developmental Disorders* 11: 303-315.

Foxx, R. M. 1982. *Decreasing Behaviors of Severely Retarded and Autistic Persons.* Champaign, IL: Research Press.

Frith, U. 1970. Studies in pattern detection in normal and autistic children. Journal of Abnormal Psychology 76: 413-420.

Frith, U. 1971. Spontaneous patterns produced by autistic, normal, and subnormal children. In *Infantile Autism: Concepts, characteristics, and treatment*, M. Rutter, ed., 113-131. London: Churchill-Livingstone.

Frith, U., and B. Hermelin. 1969. The role of visual and motor cues for normal, subnormal and autistic children. *Journal of Child Psychology and Psychiatry* 10: 153-163.

Gabony, P. 1991. Research supplement: Self-injurious behavior: A unitary phenomenon or a set of diverse behaviors? *British Journal of Special Education* 18 (Research Supplement): 59-63.

Garretson, H. B., D. Fein, and L. Waterhouse. 1990. Sustained attention in children with autism. *Journal of Autism and Developmental Disorders* 20: 101-114.

Gedye, A. 1989. Extreme self-injury attributed to frontal lobe seizures. *American Journal on Mental Retardation* 94: 20-26.

Gedye, A. 1991. Frontal lobe seizures in autism. *Medical Hypotheses* 34: 174-182.

Geller, B., L. B. Guttmacher, and M. Bleeg. 1981. Coexistence of childhood onset pervasive developmental disorder and attention deficit disorder with hyperactivity. *American Journal of Psychiatry* 138: 388-389.

Gillberg, C. 1991. Clinical and neurobiological aspects of Asperger syndrome in six family studies. In *Autism and Asperger Syndrome*, U. Frith, ed., 122-146, Cambridge, UK: Cambridge University Press.

Gillberg, C., U. Rosenhall, and E. Johansson. 1983. Auditory brainstem responses in childhood psychosis. *Journal of Autism and Developmental Disorders* 13: 181-195.

Gillberg, C., and P. Svendsen. 1983. Childhood psychosis and computed tomographic brain scan findings. *Journal of Autism and Developmental Disorders* 13: 19-32.

Gold, M. S., and J. R. Gold. 1975. Autism and attention. *Child Psychiatry and Human Development* 6: 68-80.

Golden, G. S. 1987. Neurological functioning. In *Handbook of Autism and Pervasive Developmental Disorders*, eds. D. J. Cohen, A. M. Donnellan, and R. Paul, 133-191, New York: Wiley.

Goldfarb, W. 1956. Receptor preferences in schizophrenic children. *Archives of Neurology and Psychiatry* 76: 643-653.

Grandin, T., and M. M. Scariano. 1986. *Emergence: Labeled autistic*. Novato, CA: Arena Press.

Grey-Walter, W., V. J. Aldridge, R. Cooper, G. O'Gorman, M. Cheyne, and A. L. Winter. 1971. Neurophysiological correlates of apparent defects of sensori-motor integration in autistic children. *Infantile Autism: Proceedings of the Indiana University Colloquium*, 265-276, Springfield, IL: Thomas.

Guess, D., and E. Carr. 1991. Emergence and maintenance of stereotypy and self-injury. *American Journal on Mental Retardation* 96: 299-319.

Hashimoto, T., M. Tayana, K. Mori, K. Fujino, M. Miyazaki, and Y. Kuroda. 1989. Magnetic resonance imaging in autism: Preliminary report. *Neuropediatrics* 20: 142-146.

Hauser, S. L., G. R. DeLong, and N. P. Rosman. 1975. Pneumographic findings in the infantile autism syndrome: A correlation with temporal lobe disease. *Brain* 98: 667-688.

Hermelin, B. 1972. Locating events in space and time: Experiments with autistic, blind, and deaf children. *Journal of Autism and Childhood Schizophrenia* 2: 288-298.

Hetzler, B. E., and J. L. Griffin. 1981. Infantile autism and the temporal lobe of the brain. *Journal of Autism and Developmental Disorders* 11: 317-330.

Hill, A. L. 1975. An investigation of calendar calculating by an idiot savant. *American Journal of Psychiatry* 132: 557-560.

Hoffman, W. L., and M. R. Prior. 1982. Neuropsychological dimensions of autism in children: A test of the hemispheric dysfunction hypothesis. *Journal of Clinical Neuropsychology* 4: 27-41.

Hutt, C., S. J. Hutt, D. Lee, and C. Ounsted. 1964. Arousal and childhood autism. *Nature* 204: 909-919.

Hutt, C., and C. Ounsted. 1966. The biological significance of gaze aversion with particular reference to the syndrome of infantile autism. *Behavioral Science* 11: 346-356.

Hutt, S. J., C. Hutt, D. Lee, and C. Ounsted. 1965. A behavioral and electroencephalographic study of autistic children. Journal of *Psychiatric Research* 3: 181-197.

Jolliffe, T., R. Lansdown, and C. Robinson. 1992. Autism: A personal account. *Communication* 26 (3): 12-19.

Jones, V., and M. Prior. 1985. Motor imitation abilities and neurological signs in autistic children. *Journal of Autism and Developmental Disorders* 15: 37-46.

Kahlbaum, K. [1874] 1973. *Catatonia*. Translated by Y. Levij and T. Pridan. Baltimore: Johns Hopkins University Press.

Kanner, L. 1943. Autistic disturbances of affective contact. *Nervous Child* 2: 217-250.

Kern, L., R. L. Koegel, and G. Dunlap. 1984. The influence of vigorous versus mild exercise on autistic stereotyped behaviors. *Journal of Autism and Developmental Disorders* 14: 57-67.

Konstantareas, M. M. 1985. Review of the evidence on the relevance of sign language in the early communication of autistic children. *Australian Journal of Human Communication Disorders* 13: 77-97.

LaVigna, G. 1977. Communication training in mute, autistic adolescents using the written word. *Journal of Autism and Childhood Schizophrenia* 7: 135-149.

Lohr, J. B., and A. A. Wisniewski. 1987. *Movement Disorders: A neuropsychiatric approach.* New York: Guilford Press.

Lovaas, O. I., L. Schreibman, R. Koegel, and R. Rehm. 1971. Selective responding by autistic children to multiple sensory input. *Journal of Abnormal Psychology* 77: 211-222.

Loveland, K. A., and S. H. Landry. 1986. Joint attention and language in autism and developmental language delay. *Journal of Autism and Developmental Disorders* 16: 335-349.

Lund, C. E., A. M. Mortimer, D. Rogers, and P. J. McKenna. 1991. Motor, volitional and behavioral disorders in schizophrenia 1: Assessment using the modified Rogers scale. *British Journal of Psychiatry* 158: 323-336.

Luria, A. R. [1932] 1976. *The Nature of Human Conflicts: Or emotion, conflict and will.* New York: Liveright.

Luria, A. R. 1979. *The Making of Mind: A personal account of Soviet psychology,* eds. M. Cole and S. Cole. Cambridge, MA: Harvard University.

Marsden, C. D. 1984a. Motor disorders in basal ganglia disease. *Human Neurobiology* 2: 245-250.

Marsden, C. D. 1984b. The pathophysiology of movement disorders. *Neurologic Clinics* 2: 435-459.

Masterton, B. A., and G. B. Biederman. 1983. Proprioceptive versus visual control in autistic children. *Journal of Autism and Developmental Disorders* 13: 141-152.

Maurer, R. G. 1992. *The neurology of facilitated communication* (Audiotape from proceedings, Autism Society of America). Albuquerque, NM: Audio Archives.

Maurer, R. G. 1993. *What autism and facilitated communication have to teach us about the neurology of relationship* (Audiotape from lecture). Toronto: MacKenzie Group International.

Maurer, R. G., and A. R. Damasio. 1982. Childhood autism from the point of view of behavioral neurology. *Journal of Autism and Developmental Disorders* 12: 195-205.

McKenna, P. J., C. E. Lund, A. M. Mortimer, and C. A. Biggins. 1991. Motor, volitional and behavioral disorders in schizophrenia 2: The "conflict of paradigms" hypothesis. *British Journal of Psychiatry* 158: 328-336.

McKinlay, I. 1989. Autism: The paediatric neurologist's tale. *British Journal of Disorders of Communication* 24: 201-207.

Meiselas, K., E. K. Spencer, R. Oberfield, E. D. Peselow, B. Angrist, and M. Campbell. 1989. Differentiation of stereotypies from neuroleptic-related dyskinesias in autistic children. *Journal of Clinical Psychopharmacology* 9: 207-209.

Mirenda, P. L., and A. M. Donnellan. 1986. The effects of adult interaction styles on conversation behavior in adolescents with handicaps. *Language, Speech and Hearing Services in Schools* 17: 126-141.

Mirenda, P. L., A. M. Donnellan, and D. E. Yoder. 1983. Gaze behavior: A new look at an old problem. *Journal of Autism and Developmental Disorders* 13: 397-409.

Morrison, D., D. Miller, and B. Meija. 1971. Effects of adult verbal requests on the behavior of autistic children. *American Journal of Mental Deficiency* 75: 510-518.

Mundy, P., M. Sigman, and C. Kasari. 1990. A longitudinal study of joint attention and language development in autistic children. *Journal of Autism and Developmental Disorders* 20: 115-128.

Nowell, M. A., D. B. Hackney, A. S. Muraki, and M. Coleman. 1990. Varied MR appearance of autism: Fifty-three pediatric patients having the full autistic syndrome. *Magnetic Resonance Imaging* 8: 811-816.

Olsson, I., S. Steffenburg, and C. Gillberg. 1988. Epilepsy in autism and autistic-like conditions: A population-based study. *Archives of Neurology* 45: 666-668.

Ornitz, E. M. 1974. The modulation of sensory input and motor output in autistic children. *Journal of Autism and Childhood Schizophrenia* 4: 197-215.

Ornitz, E. M., and E. R. Ritvo. 1968. Perceptual inconstancy in early infantile autism. *Archives of General Psychiatry* 18: 78-98.

Ornitz, E. M., and E. R. Ritvo. 1976. The syndrome of autism: A critical review. *American Journal of Psychiatry* 133: 609-621.

Paccia, J. M., and F. Curcio. 1982. Language processing and forms of immediate echolalia in autistic children. *Journal of Speech and Hearing Research* 25: 42-47.

Prior, M., and W. Hoffman. 1990. Brief report: Neuropsychological testing of autistic children through an exploration with frontal lobe tests. *Journal of Autism and Developmental Disorders* 20: 581-590.

Prior, M., and M. B. Macmillan. 1973. Maintenance of sameness in children with Kanner's syndrome. *Journal of Autism and Childhood Schizophrenia* 3: 154-167.

Prizant, B. M., and J. F. Duchan. 1981. The functions of immediate echolalia in autistic children. *Journal of Speech and Hearing Disorders* 46: 241-249.

Prizant, B. M., and P. Rydell. 1984. Analysis of functions of delayed echolalia in autistic children. *Journal of Speech and Hearing Research* 27: 183-192.

Prizant, B. M., and A. M. Wetherby. 1985. Intentional communicative behavior of children with autism: Theoretical and practical issues. *Australian Journal of Human Communication Disorders* 13: 21-59.

Rapin, I. 1987. Searching for the cause of autism: A neurologic perspective. In *Handbook of Autism and Pervasive Developmental Disorders*, eds. D. Cohen and Donnellan, 710-717. New York: Wiley.

Realmuto, G. M., and G. J. August. 1991. Catatonia in autistic disorder: A sign of comorbidity or variable expression? *Journal of Autism and Developmental Disorders* 21: 517-528.

Realmuto, G. M., and B. Main. 1982. Coincidence of Tourette's disorder and infantile autism. *Journal of Autism and Developmental Disorders* 12: 367-372.

Richer, J., and R. Coss. 1976. Gaze aversion in autistic and normal children. *Acta Psychiatrica Scandinavicas* 53: 193-210.

Rimland, B. 1978. Inside the mind of the autistic savant. *Psychology Today*, August: 71-76.

Ritvo, E. R., and B. J. Freeman. 1984. A medical model of autism: Etiology, pathology, and treatment. *Pediatric Annals* 13: 298-305.

Ritvo, E. R., and R. Ritvo. 1992. Dr. Ritvo and Ms. Ritvo reply [Letter to the editor]. *American Journal of Psychiatry* 149: 146-147.

Ritvo, E. R., A. Yuwiler, E. Geller, A. Kales, S. Rashkis, A. Schicor, S. Plotkin, R. Axelrod, and C. Howard. 1971. Effects of L-dopa in autism. *Journal of Autism and Childhood Schizophrenia* 1: 190-205.

Rogers, D. 1985. The motor disorders of severe psychiatric illness: A conflict of paradigms. *British Journal of Psychiatry* 147: 221-232.

Rogers, D. 1990. Psychiatric consequences of basal ganglia disease. *Seminars in Neurology* 10: 262-256.

Rogers, D. 1992. *Motor Disorder in Psychiatry: Towards a neurological psychiatry.* New York: Wiley.

Rogers, D., C. Karki, C. Bartlett, and P. Pocock. 1991. The motor disorders of mental handicap: An overlap with the motor disorders of severe psychiatric illness. *British Journal of Psychiatry* 158: 97-102.

Rolider, A., and R. Van Houten. 1985. Movement suppression time-out for undesirable behavior in psychotic and severely developmentally delayed children. *Journal of Applied Behavior Analysis* 18: 275-288.

Rosen, A. M. 1981. Adult calendar calculators in a psychiatric OPD: A report of two cases and comparative analysis of abilities. *Journal of Autism and Developmental Disorders* 11: 285-292.

Rutter, M. 1974. The development of infantile autism. *Psychological Medicine* 4: 147-163.

Sacks, O. 1987. *The Man Who Mistook His Wife for a Hat: And other clinical tales.* New York: Perennial Library.

Sacks, O. 1990. *Awakenings.* New York: Harper Perennial.

Schopler, E., R. J. Reichler, and B. R. Renner. 1986. *The Childhood Autism Rating Scale (CARS).* Los Angeles: Western Psychological Services.

Schreibman, L., and O. I. Lovaas. 1973. Overselective response to social stimuli by autistic children. *Journal of Abnormal Child Psychology* 1: 152-168.

Simon, N. 1975. Echolalic speech in childhood autism. *Archives of General Psychiatry* 32: 1439-1446.

Sorosky, A. D., E. M. Ornitz, M. B. Brown, and E. R. Ritvo. 1968. Systematic observations of autistic behavior. *Archives of General Psychiatry* 18: 439-449.

Steel, J. G., R. Gorman, and J. E. Flexman. 1984. Neuropsychiatric testing in an autistic mathematical idiot-savant: Evidence for non-verbal abstract capacity. *Journal of the American Academy of Child Psychiatry* 23: 704-707.

Sverd, J. 1991. Tourette syndrome and autistic disorder: A significant relationship. *American Journal of Medical Genetics* 39: 173-179.

Treffert, D. A. 1988. The idiot savant: A review of the syndrome. *American Journal of Psychiatry* 145: 563-572.

Treffert, D. A. 1989. *Extraordinary People*. New York: Harper and Row.

Vilensky, J. A., A. R. Damasio, and R. G. Maurer. 1981. Gait disturbances in patients with autistic behavior. *Archives of Neurology* 38: 646-649.

Volkmar, F. R. 1986. Compliance, noncompliance, and negativism. In *Social Behavior in Autism*, eds. E. Schopler and G. Mesibov, 171-188. New York: Plenum Press.

Volkmar, F. R., E. L. Hoder, and D. J. Cohen. 1985. Compliance, "negativism," and the effects of treatment structure in autism: A naturalistic, behavioral study. *Journal of Child Psychology and Psychiatry* 26: 865-877.

Walker, H. A., and M. Coleman. 1976. Characteristics of adventitious movements in autistic children. In *The Autistic Syndrome*, ed. M. Coleman, 135-144. Amsterdam: North Holland.

Wallace, B. R. 1975. Negativism in verbal and nonverbal responses of autistic children. *Journal of Abnormal Psychology* 84: 138-143.

Wetherby, A. M., R. L. Koegel, and M. Mendel. 1981. Central auditory nervous system dysfunction in echolalic autistic individuals. *Journal of Speech and Hearing Research* 24: 420-429.

Wilhelm, H., and I. O. Lovaas. 1976. Stimulus overselectivity: A common feature in autism and mental retardation. *American Journal of Mental Deficiency* 81: 26-31.

Winchel, R. M., and M. Stanley. 1991. Self-injurious behavior: A review of the behavior and biology of self-mutilation. *American Journal of Psychiatry* 148: 306-317.

Windsor, J., S. S. Doyle, and G. M. Siegel. 1994. Language acquisition after mutism: A longitudinal case study. *Journal of Speech and Hearing Research* 37: 96-105.

Wing, L., and A. Attwood. 1987. Syndromes of autism and atypical development. In *Handbook of Autism and Pervasive Developmental Disorders*, eds. D. Cohen and A. Donnellan, 3-19. New York: Wiley.

CHAPTER SEVEN

Invented Knowledge and Autism:
Highlighting Our Strengths and
Expanding the Conversation

Anne M. Donnellan

*Whenever the ratio of what is known to what needs to be
known approaches zero, we tend to invent knowledge and
assume that we understand more than we usually do. We
seem unable to acknowledge that we simply don't know.*
—Rosenhan 1984, 139

It is a pleasure to comment on this special *JASH* issue and to offer
thoughts about current and future directions. It is like revisiting my entire career. The approaches are familiar, often interesting and exciting,
yet perhaps more limited than this complex topic requires. As researchers and practitioners, we may have fallen into the conceptual trap that
Rosenhan (1984) called "invented knowledge." Invented knowledge is
not about deception but about self-delusion. It is about putting faith
and reliance on what we think we know in order to ease the burden of
working in complex human situations with less understanding than is
comfortable. The term comes from a landmark study in which mental
hospital personnel diagnosed researchers as mentally ill. Once they were
inpatients, the ordinary behavior of these researchers was recorded and
pathologized. Eventually, they were released with labels such as "schizophrenia in remission." Surrounded by a patina of confidence based on
professional objectivity, medical and scientific jargon and definitions,
these mental health professionals could not distinguish sanity from
insanity. I raise the question whether we in the field of autism may labor
under a similar burden of invented knowledge such that, confident in our

objectivity, we sometimes forget our limitations. I will suggest further that we would profit from an expansion of our conversation beyond the present data set and conceptual models of what we know and what we think we know.

I started out knowing everything. In the early 1970s, a naïve new college graduate with a psychology degree emphasizing operant conditioning, I developed one of the first preschool programs for children labeled autistic in the English speaking world (Donnellan-Walsh 1976). I received hands-on training in applied behavior analysis (ABA) and autism from one of the staff members of an early UCLA project (Lovaas 1967). I have maintained an interest in early childhood issues and teaching technology. I still question what we know about people with autism and how their disability should be accommodated (Cohen and Donnellan 1987; Donnellan and Leary 1995; Donnellan, Mirenda, Mesaros, and Fassbender 1984).

The lesson from my experience is great humility. Too many of the individuals I knew personally are now young adults who spent their entire lives getting over their autism (Lapin and Leigh 1998). They are still living what Thoreau might have called "lives of not so quiet desperation," surrounded by people paid to be with them. Their behavior was modified in their early years by some of us who are still arguing about the most effective treatment for young children with autism. Their parents are still desperate (Donnellan 1999). Desperate, too, are the hundreds of younger parents I meet, although they are more likely to believe that cure or recovery is at hand. I wonder what vision they have for their children's adulthood when/if the cure or recovery does not happen. After almost 60 years of studying individuals with autism, we have no cure, no clear definition of autism, we do not know what causes it, and we do not know which intervention is best for any given child (Bristol et al. 1996). I suggest that autism is not something that someone has, but a label for what we observe and experience. It is a partial and inadequate expression of the labeled individual's unique experience. What needs to be studied and known is the individual. I know far less today than I thought I knew when I began. Humility comes easy these days.

Throughout my career, behaviorism was considered by most the preferred scientific approach. Anderson and Romanczyk (1999) explicate that position very well. They present the model, clarify nuances that contribute to present controversies, highlight the considerable historical contribution of ABA, and note their own successful interventions. L. K. Koegel, Koegel, Harrower, and Carter (1999) and L. K. Koegel, Koegel, Shoshan, and McNerney (1999) offer their original approach to pivotal behaviors, focusing on self-initiation, self-management, motivation, and responses to multiple cues. Likewise, McGee, Morrier, and Daly (1999) describe a program that teaches children with and without autism in an inclusive preschool. Their attention to detail in supporting interactions with typically developing peers and focusing on child initiations and "careful planning of the interface between environment and procedures that the teacher will use to dispense preferred materials" is impressive.

These papers continue the dominant historical approach to autism. As Anderson and Romanczyk note, there are about 500 ABA/autism studies. This is an important part of our history, although it does not necessarily reflect the consistent march of scientific progress, hope, and understanding of this human condition that several of these papers suggests. The present collection reflects more recent and welcome changes as they emphasize ongoing review of child change in more natural social settings and interactions. Earlier, interventions were occasionally remarkable, at times reprehensible, but often geared to demonstrating a procedural nuance rather than clinical value for an individual (Evans and Meyer 1985; Guess 1990). When we reflect on what we think we know, it helps to acknowledge that we built a science in autism on research that, following Uri Bronfenbrenner (1979), too often looked like strangers doing strange things with strangely behaving children (and adults) in strange settings for the briefest possible period of time.

Greenspan and Wieder (1999) extend the autism issues beyond the traditional behavioral model. Their functional/developmental approach and case histories situate a child in a particular nervous system within a particular family and school/social situation. Within such contexts, they are willing to consider the child's "intention" which they, and I, see as essential when dealing with a child with severe sensory processing, motor, and other well documented problems (Donnellan and Leary 1995; Leary and Hill 1996).

The behavioral papers stop short of considering this intentionality, although several of the papers discuss "motivation." L. K. Koegel, Koegel, Harrower, et al. (1999) carefully limit their discussion of motivation to "observable characteristics of a child's responding, such that an improvement in motivation is broadly defined as an increase in responsiveness to social and environmental stimuli." Motivation is treated as a pivotal behavior and is targeted by varying child choice, tasks, and prompts. It is encouraging to see these useful strategies, although the limited definition does not address sufficiently one of the most complex topics in human learning (for a discussion of motivation and problems of will, see Damasio 1994, and Luria 1932, 1979). The careful way L. K. Koegel, Koegel, Harrower, et al. (1999) couch their brief discussion suggests that the authors know this.

Their caution may reflect an essential conundrum in the behavioral model when it addresses motivation, intention, or any private event. Anderson and Romanczyk (1999) present the topic in a way familiar to all of us who have been trained in the model: "The sine qua non of the applied behavior analytic approach is that objective measures are taken of the individual's behavior and that these measures must meet the boundary conditions of being operationally defined, reliable, and valid." They elaborate on their description of motivation and autism:

> It is also the case that some individuals, such as children with autism, have impairment in motivation. At times, motivation may be quite idiosyncratic and limited in its extensiveness. An example would be children who are not motivated by social attention and praise, physical contact, and the sense of accomplishment for completing a task or solving a problem. Rather these individuals might find their own repetitive and stereotyped behavior more interesting and enjoyable, and thus engage in it disproportionately compared to prosocial behaviors.

Descriptions such as this are common in autism. They are part of the invented knowledge, perhaps inevitable in an applied field where there is so much to be done compared to what is known. We make tentative proposals and use shorthand descriptions based on broad assumptions and abstract labels for real and complex phenomena that are barely understood. Inventions are necessary to move forward. The problem arises when these become conventional wisdom, no longer questioned or challenged. We begin to believe more than we actually know so that even strict behaviorists may assume that they can know whether a child has an "impairment in motivation" or a "sense of accomplishment," or finds stereotypical behavior "more enjoyable" by observing the child's external behavior.

There is a shared belief that we can define autism, and therefore the experience of autism, from an "etic" or outsider's perspective (Schwandt 1996a, 1996b). Certainly we have reliable information that individuals with autism prefer their own pursuits to social interactions (American Psychiatric Association 1994; Cohen and Volkmar 1997). Several of the authors acknowledge that our observational ability is based on our professional and social cultural bias, but assume that these can be overcome by our science (see Cole 1996 for an excellent review of social/cultural effects on knowing). Validating our assessment should be a constant challenge; so should validating our assumptions and perceived wisdom. We know what children with autism do but we do not know what they prefer to do unless we limit the definition of motivation to that which amounts to little more than an increase in responding in the presence of certain stimuli which we manipulate. Again, Koegel, Koegel, Harrower, et al. (1999) offer a potentially important contribution to our technology. However, if we were to use their work to assume that the motivation or preferences of typically developing people could be adequately assessed by the external interpretation of observers, we would be defying our own everyday experiences. Yet, our shared belief, our invented knowledge, permits us to move incautiously toward such an assumption in the case of children and adults whose differences and challenges ought, instead, call out for caution.

Greenspan and Wieder (1999) are more willing to take on private events such as intention during assessment. They are also willing to acknowledge that the observable behavior of these children can be affected by functional limitations in critical areas, including language, motor planning and sequencing, sensory process, and modulation. They present assessment as a complex nonlinear task that must include biological and social/historical variables. They stop short, however, of a clear acknowledgment of our limitations. They never say, for example, that what we are observing at any given moment might not be what a child is actually choosing to do. Each article in this special issue implies that a professional gaze can adequately assess what a child intends. In the article by Greenspan and Wieder, the invented knowledge about the emic (insider's) perspective (Schwandt 1996a, 1996b) is rooted less in behavioral precision than in a stance of advanced professional knowledge of child development and biology.

These articles reflect an ongoing and widespread belief in autism: that we can collect assessment data about children's deficits, pathologies, skill, and regulatory profiles relative to normal development or rating scales and, through this process, know them and their experience. Moreover, we believe that we can develop subtypes of such children based on this kind of information (Greenspan and Wieder 1999; L. K. Koegel, Koegel, Shoshan, et al. 1999), even though Anderson and Romanczyk caution that there are "as many differences between young children with autism as similarities among them." Although these approaches to assessment and grouping may be incrementally useful, they are risky if they contribute to our invented knowledge base, become part of our preconceptions of conventional wisdom, and, as such, are no longer challenged. We need to remind ourselves continually, clearly, and publicly that we cannot erase human variation by improving our reliability rates on diagnostic categories and subtypes nor wish away human complexity with reductionist observation models and behavioral definitions. I offer the following points to consider:

The possibility of complex and idiosyncratic movement differences that might confound our assessment and knowledge of an individual.

The need to include first-hand accounts in our story of autism.

Modern advances in biodynamic systems models of development and behavior, which can inform our knowledge base and practice.

Reports in the literature suggest that individuals with autism may be affected by movement differences and disturbances, which can render their performance, stereotypies, and behavior at any moment beyond their control or intent. Donnellan and Leary (1995), Leary and Hill (1996), and Rogers (1992) describe these differences in detail. Some well recognized movement disorders include Tourette's syndrome and Parkinson's disorder. Few today would assume that the motivation or intention of individuals so labeled could be validly discerned from their observable behavior alone, which often includes unusual and problematic speech, action, and emotional outbursts (Comings and Comings 1991; McGoon 1990; Sacks 1989, 1990). In *Awakenings,* Sacks (1990) describes postencephalitic Parkinson's patients and reminds us that although they all had the same kind of brain lesions, they each created their own unique form of the disorder.

Behavior, which in the typically developing population would be called a movement disorder or a neurologic symptom (defined here as not necessarily under the individual's volitional control), is likely to be called a behavior disturbance (i.e., purposeful or functional) or self-stimulating (i.e., preferred) behavior in people with developmental disabilities or who were mentally ill (Rogers 1992). In fact, the symptoms of autism fit remarkably well into the movement difference/disturbance category, which was first delineated and called catatonia more than a century ago (Kahlbaum 1874/1973).

Some argue that there are no movement (often called motor) problems in autism (Mulick, Jacobsen, and Kobe 1993; Rimland 1993). In the Leary and Hill (1996) review of the autism literature, 155 papers described the presence of such differences in sensory, motor, speech, and emotional processes. Maurer and Damasio (1982) specifically noted the similarity to Parkinson symptoms. They were ignored, perhaps because their findings did not fit into the conventional understanding of autism as a problem of the mind. Such differences have been given little focus. However, Greenspan and Wieder (1999) have covered this issue in their article. More typically, the symptoms have been used to both define and explain autism with very little attention to what these symptoms might indicate about the experience of the person with autism (Donnellan and Leary 1995). Consider the words of Temple Grandin, an adult with autism:

> As a child I wanted to feel the comfort of being held. I craved tender touching. At the same time I withdrew from touch. Being hugged was like being swallowed by a tidal wave ... I was intensely preoccupied with the movement of the spinning coin or lid and I saw nothing and heard nothing. I did it because it shut out sound that hurt my ears. No sound intruded on my fixation. It was like being deaf. Even a sudden noise didn't startle me out of my world. (British Film Institute 1992)

What would our etic view (Schwandt 1996a, 1996b) tell us of the preferences and accommodations of the young Temple? Would we say she had auditory or visual or tactile difficulties in her regulatory profile? Might we conclude she was not motivated to engage in social interaction?

Strandt-Conroy (1999) reviewed the literature on written reports by clinicians and parents and other adults with autism, and interviewed adults with autism who had verbal skills. Problems in starting, stopping, executing, combining, switching related to action, sensory-perception, motor, communication, thought, and memory were commonplace (Donnellan and Leary 1995), but were poorly accommodated by those who were meant to support these individuals. Researchers have been building an empirical base that suggests we have misunderstood, and misreported, the presence and implications of sensory and motor difficulties in the life experience of individuals with autism (Blakeslee 1999; Ghaziuddin and Butler 1998).

One possible area of misunderstanding concerns our unchallenged belief that most individuals with autism are also mentally retarded. Young (1998) reviewed the seminal research on the topic (e.g., Rutter, Greenfield, and Lockyer 1967) and found routine comments on the movement problems of the subjects, such as hypoactivity and hyperactivity and difficulty initiating movement. Yet, time-based criteria were used without reference to or accommodation of possible timing and performance difficulties. Today, the canon in autism, the invented knowledge, is that we can validly test people with standardized instruments since nothing significant interferes with their ability to respond except their retarded development (Jacobson, Mulick, and Schwartz 1995).

From the point of view of infant research, Zelazo (1997a, 1997b) is particularly instructive about this presumed relationship between production and ability. He used the standard-transformation-return (STR) paradigm (Zelazo, Kearslye, and Stack 1995), which measures clusters of visual fixation, cardiac changes, smiling, and vocalizing to test his hypothesis that performance difficulties might mask intact mental ability. He found that 75% of the two- and three-year-olds he studied, who had been diagnosed by other agencies as autistic and retarded, had typically developing processing. He then put these children into a developmentally based training program in which he taught parents to use shaping and other procedures. He found that 61% of these children misdiagnosed as retarded could "catch up" both in terms of school functioning and on standardized tests on 18-month follow-up. Moreover, Zelazo found that the optimal time for one-to-one sessions with the children was 12 minutes per day for at least 5 out of 7 days for 10 months. Today, there is a growing belief that "intensive" intervention by professionals of 30 to 40 hours a week is required for the reported positive results (McGee et al. 1999; Anderson and Romanczyk 1999). Zelazo's data highlight the intensity issues raised by Greene (1996) and Anderson and Romanczyk (1999) and perhaps should cause us to scrutinize our work for inadvertent selection bias. Zelazo's report also challenges us to broaden our database to include more biological and physiological measures in addition to other observable behavior.

We do not know if Zelazo's approach is more valid than others presented here. However, it is a cautionary tale to avoid claims that any research or any intervention approach is privileged over others, however large its database or long its history. We need more detailed data, including more case histories, to begin to account for what actually is making a difference for any given individual. Vygotskian research models could be useful as they assume that such data can be collected on the process of child change (Cole 1996). We need more first-person accounts.

Greenspan and Wieder (1999) acknowledge the value of sensory-movement differences, the value of speech and language, sensory integration, and other interventions. However, they do not explain clearly the cross modal and unpredictable nature of the regulatory process and other problems an individual might experience such as those described by Temple Grandin (1995) and by Strandt-Conroy's (1999) subjects. Donna Williams (1995b) refers to these as sudden "system shifts and shutdowns." Such shifts can cause a person to be unable to move or to speak or may contribute to behavior that is very confusing to the individual and the observer. Moreover, she stresses the inconsistent, idiosyncratic, and unpredictable nature of the daily experience:

... [S]ystem shifts and shutdowns which may be caused on one day by the excessive effect of shine, refracted light, fluorescent lighting, on another day by the allergic effect of perfume or the variation of a speaker's regular intonation ... lack of symmetry in the placement of things ... a sense of fullness in the bladder that hasn't been processed ...

She has written several books that are useful for teachers, parents, and researchers interested in autism (Williams 1992, 1994, 1995a, 1995b, 1995c). Her description of movement differences is entirely consistent with Strandt-Conroy's (1999) research into first-person accounts.

Whether or not the idea of movement disturbances ultimately is found to be generalizable to and useful for all people with autism, there is substantial data to make us cautious about our inferences about motivation or meaning of behavior based solely on the observable behavior of these individuals. As Leary and Hill (1996) explain:

Movement disturbance can clearly have a profound effect on a person's ability to regulate movement in order to effectively communicate, relate, and participate with others. Once this possibility is acknowledged, it becomes necessary to suspend absolute trust in one's intuitive interpretation of actions and intent. Behaviors may not be what they seem. (44)

There is much work to be done to understand these mind/body challenges (Sacks 1989). Individuals with the communication problems associated with autism present particularly great challenges. It is clear that the stated experience of individuals with autism must be taken into account. Perhaps this is even the larger point. Anderson and Romanczyk (1999) argue that case studies and anecdotal reports are not acceptable substitutes for the empirical research approach they espouse. It need not be a question of "either-or." It seems reasonable that those of us who claim an objective gaze be at least obligated to consider the widest possible database for defining the phenomenon under study. As Nobel laureate Gerald Edelman (1992) has suggested: "Objectivity is not absolute but depends on looking at a situation from as many viewpoints as possible" (250).

Anderson and Romanczyk note that autism is a "serious developmental disability that provides a complex challenge for parents, professionals, and all those who come in contact with the child." I would add that individuals labeled autistic face complex challenges and their perspective deserves mention when available. In particular, it would be instructive to hear from those individuals described as "recovered" or "indistinguishable" (Lovaas 1987; Maurice 1993; McEachin, Smith, and Lovaas 1993) who are old enough now to speak for themselves. Although the researchers must respect confidentiality, the individuals themselves are under no such constraints. Individuals with autism and their families have shown remarkable generosity in sharing their experiences in order to help others; see Strandt-Conroy (1999) for a review. Of course, we may not like all that we hear. Strandt-Conroy found that few of her informants, all of whom are successful enough to live independently, valued the behavior change interventions they experienced. Perhaps because we seldom publish negative findings (Davis 1998), we have developed invented knowledge around our interventions that assumes that if the target behavior improves for an individual, then all other aspects of functioning are either unchanged or improved. We ought not to presume that everything we do is helpful, neutral, or harmless even in our most successful programs. It is time to invite these successful graduates of our various intervention programs into the appropriate public forum to offer their perspective on our work.

The traditional autism database, while large, simply does not exhaust the universe of evidence and wealth of research on the human condition that can be applied to the challenges of autism. The child development literature is likewise limited and is also being challenged by newer approaches outside the traditional canon. The biodynamic systems models that attempt to explain child development through chaos theory (Gleick 1988; Guess and Sailor 1993; Thelen 1995; Thelen and Lockman 1993; Thelen and Smith 1996) argue that there is no "typical" developmental process. They provide compelling data on the truly unique nature of each individual's course of development. As Thelen and Smith explain, biodynamic systems are self-organizing, seeking preferred behavior modes as a function of the interactions of the components (e.g., thought, emotion, action, perception, memory, communication, posture) in a particular context. Through this interaction, behavior and development emerge: "Although behavior and development appear structured, there are no structures. Although behavior and development appear rule-driven, there are no rules. There is complexity" (xix).

Two critical aspects of the chaos model, "sensitive dependence on initial conditions" and the "butterfly effect" (which holds that small changes can have large effects), may be particularly useful for understanding the unusual development seen in people with autism and the idiosyncratic nature of their experience (Grandin 1995; Strandt-Conroy 1999; Williams 1992, 1994). At a minimum, the biodynamic systems research challenges our ideas of typical development and the notion of intensity in intervention. It also offers alternatives to the linear ways of thinking about research and intervention. With attention to the self-organizing and dynamic nature of human behavior and development, we may find that our invented knowledge base is larger than we imagined and that our interventions can be made more efficient and effective.

Summary

Each of the models discussed in this article has a good research and clinical base and contributes to our limited knowledge. I suggest that the study of context would pull together these approaches in a very useful fashion. As Bateson (1972) told us, context is not just what is left over when we take out the part we want to study. Context is every part of the experience of the individual as well as the cultural/social history in which learning is taking place (Cole 1996). Chaos and biodynamic systems models provide a greater understanding of the critical nature of context. Chaos theory makes clear that everything counts in context and biodynamic systems suggests that knowledge is fluid; knowledge only exists in context (Edelman 1992; Thelen and Smith 1994). Greenspan and Wieder (1999) suggest a wide range of variables that may contribute to context and ways to accommodate them. The self-reports make a similar contribution, especially those that include comments on movement differences and individuals' own accommodations, which may be difficult to observe from the "outside." The behavioral model provides a wealth of tools and experience for enhancing the environment (McGee et al. 1999) and clarifying and manipulating contextual contingencies (Anderson and Romanczyk 1999; L. K. Koegel, Koegel, Harrower et al. 1999; L. K. Koegel, Koegel, Shoshan et al. 1999). Each should be included in our conversation about the development of young children with autism. Through such an inclusive conversation, perhaps we will know more. At least we will be clearer about how little we presently know.

As I write these words, I am aware of the recent passing of Arthur Schawlow, Sr. (Browne 1999). Professor Schawlow won a Nobel Prize for his work on the laser and was one of the most honored scientists in the world. He was also a friend and advocate, and the parent of an adult son with autism, Arthur, Jr., who has lived through many behavior change programs that were considered state-of-the-art when he was a young child. These programs often exacerbated his problems (Schawlow and Schawlow 1985). One of the many gifts that friendship with Professor Schawlow brought to me was a story of his early work in applied physics. He and his mentors and colleagues would have three lists on the chalkboard: (1) What we know; (2) what we need to know; and (3) what we are learning. Each time they added something to list three, they found they had to take something away from the first list and add to the second because new information inevitably revealed how little was actually known and how little they would ever know for certain. Professor Schawlow kept that list going throughout an extraordinary career and, he said, it kept him humble. In autism, we are studying a complex human condition and the human brain is the most complex object in the known universe (Edelman 1992). Art Schawlow, Jr., others labeled autistic, and we as researchers, teachers, and advocates deserve no less than that to approach our task with hope, as these papers suggest, but also with a full measure of awe and humility.

Acknowledgments

The author thanks Martha Leary and Sally Young for their editorial comments.

Works Cited

American Psychiatric Association. 1994. *Diagnostic and Statistical Manual of Mental Disorders* (4h ed.). Washington, DC: Author.

Anderson, S. R., and R. G. Romanczyk. 1999. Early intervention for young children with autism: Continuum based on behavioral models. *The Journal of The Association for Persons with Severe Handicaps* 24: 162-173.

Bateson, G. 1972. *Steps to an Ecology of Mind.* New York: Ballantine.

Blakeslee, S. 1999, January 26. Movement may offer early clue to autism. *New York Times,* D3.

Bristol, M. M., D. J. Cohen, E. J. Costello, M. Denckla, T. J. Eckberg, R. Kallen, H. C. Kraemer, C. Lord, R. Maurer, W. J. McIlvane, N. Minshew, M. Sigman, and M. A. Spence. 1996. State of the science in autism: Report to the National Institutes of Health. *Journal of Autism and Developmental Disorders* 26 (2): 121-154.

British Film Institute. 1992. *A is for Autism.* Fine Take Production for Channel 4. Available through National Autism Society, London, UK.

Bronfenbrenner, U. 1979. *Ecology of Human Development: Experiments by nature and design.* Cambridge, MA: Harvard University Press.

Browne, M. W. 1999, April 30. Arthur Schawlow, 77, Novelist for Lasers, Dies. *New York Times,* C20.

Cohen, D. J., and A. M. Donnellan. 1987. *Handbook of Autism and Pervasive Developmental Disorders.* New York: Wiley.

Cohen, D. J., and F. Volkmar, eds. 1997. *Handbook of Autism and Pervasive Developmental Disorders* (2nd ed.). New York: Wiley.

Cole, M. 1996. *Cultural Psychology: A once and future discipline.* Cambridge, MA: Belknap Press.

Comings, D. E., and B. G. Comings. 1991. Clinical and genetic relationships between autistic-pervasive developmental disorder and Tourette syndrome: A study of 19 cases. *American Journal of Medical Genetics* 39: 180-191.

Damasio, A. R. 1994. *Descartes' Error: Emotion, reason, and the human brain*. New York: Putnam.

Danforth, S. 1997. On what basis hope? Modern progress and postmodern possibilities. *Mental Retardation* 35 (2): 93-106.

Davis, J. R. 1998. *Special education and behavioral literature reporting unsuccessful interventions: A review of published articles*. Unpublished manuscript, University of Wisconsin, Madison.

Donnellan, A., and G. LaVigna. 1990. Myths about punishment. In *Perspectives on the Use of Nonaversive and Aversive Interventions for Persons with Developmental Disabilities*, A. C. Repp and N. N. Singh, eds., 33-57. Sycamore, IL: Sycamore Publishing.

Donnellan, A. M. 1999, July. Issues, concerns and experiences of parents of a child with autism who is moving towards adulthood and independence. Paper presented at the annual meeting and conference of the Autism Society of America, Kansas City, MO.

Donnellan, A. M., and M. R. Leary. 1995. *Movement Differences and Diversity in Autism/Mental Retardation*. Madison, WI: DRI Press.

Donnellan, A. M., P. L. Mirenda, R. A. Mesaros, and L. L. Fassbender. 1984. Analyzing the communicative functions of aberrant behavior. *Journal of The Association for the Severely Handicapped* 9 (3): 201-212.

Edelman, G. M. 1992. *Bright Air, Brilliant Fire*. New York: Basic Books.

Evans, I., and L. Meyer. 1985. *An Educative Approach to Behavior Problems: A practical decision model for interventions with severely handicapped learners*. Baltimore: Paul H. Brookes.

Gelb, S. 1997. The problem of typological thinking in mental retardation. *Mental Retardation* 35 (6): 448-457.

Ghaziuddin, M., and E. Butler. 1998. Clumsiness in autism and Asperger syndrome: A further report. *Journal of Intellectual Disability Research* 42: 43-48.

Gleick, J. 1988. *Chaos: Making a new science*. New York: Penguin.

Grandin, T. 1995. *Thinking in Pictures: And other reports from my life with autism*. New York: Doubleday.

Greene, G. 1996. Early behavioral intervention for autism: What does research tell us? In *Behavioral Intervention for Young Children*, C. Maurice, G. Greene, and S. C. Luce, eds., 29-44. Austin: Pro-ed.

Greenspan, S. I., and S. Wieder. 1999. A functional developmental approach to autism spectrum disorders. *The Journal of The Association for Persons with Severe Handicaps* 24: 147-161.

Guess, D. 1990. Transmission of behavior management technologies from researchers to practitioners: A need for professional self-evaluation. In *Perspectives on the Use of Nonaversive and Aversive Interventions for Persons with Developmental Disabilities*, A. C. Repp and N. N. Singh, eds., 157-172. Sycamore, IL: Sycamore Publishing.

Guess, D., E. Helmstetter, H. R. Turnbull, and S. Knowlton. 1986. Use of aversive procedures with persons who are disabled: A historical review and critical analysis. Monograph. Seattle: The Association for Persons with Severe Handicaps.

Guess, D., and W. Sailor. 1993. Chaos theory and the study of human behavior: Implications for special education and developmental disabilities. *The Journal of Special Education* 27 (1): 16-34.

Jacobson, J. W., J. A. Mulick, and A. A. Schwartz. 1995. A history of facilitated communication: Science, pseudoscience, and antiscience. *American Psychologist* 50 (9): 750-765.

Kahlbaum, K. [1874] 1973. *Catatonia*. Translated by Y. Levij and T. Pridan. Baltimore: Johns Hopkins University Press.

Koegel, L. K., R. L. Koegel, J. K. Harrower, and C. M. Carter. 1999. Pivotal response intervention I: Overview of approach. *The Journal of The Association for Persons with Severe Handicaps* 24: 174-185.

Koegel, L. K., R. L. Koegel, Y. Shoshan, and E. McNerney. 1999. Pivotal response intervention II: Preliminary long-term outcome data. *The Journal of The Association for Persons with Severe Handicaps* 24: 186-198.

Lapin, S., and J. Leigh. 1998. Rocket man. In *Autism: The human touch*, A. M. Donnellan and M. R. Leary, eds. Manuscript in preparation.

Leary, M. R., and D. A. Hill. 1996. Moving on: Autism and movement disturbance. *Mental Retardation* 34 (1): 39-53.

Lovaas, O. I. 1987. Behavioral treatment and normal educational and intellectual functioning in young autistic children. *Journal of Consulting and Clinical Psychology* 55: 3-9.

Lovaas, O. I., L. Freitas, K. Nelson, and C. Whalen. 1967. The establishment of imitation and its use for the establishment of complex behavior in schizophrenic children. *Behavior Research and Therapy* 5: 171-181.

Luria, A. R. 1932. *The Nature of Human Conflicts.* New York: Liveright.

Luria, A. R. 1979. *The Making of Mind.* Cambridge, MA: Harvard University Press.

Maurer, R., and A. Damasio. 1982. Childhood autism from the point of view of behavioral neurology. *Journal of Autism and Developmental Disorders* 12: 195-205.

Maurice, C. 1993. *Let Me Hear Your Voice.* New York: Knopf.

McEachin, J. J., T. Smith, and O. I. Lovaas. 1993. Long-term outcome for children with autism who received early intensive behavioral treatment. *American Journal on Mental Retardation* 97 (4): 359-372.

McGee, G. G., M. J. Morrier, and T. Daly. 1999. An incidental teaching approach to early intervention for toddlers with autism. *The Journal of The Association for Persons with Severe Handicaps* 24: 133-146.

McGoon, D. C. 1990. *The Parkinson's Handbook.* New York: Norton.

Mulick, J. A., J. W. Jacobsen, and F. H. Kobe. 1993. Anguished silence and helping hands: Autism and facilitated communication. *Skeptical Inquirer* 17 (3): 270-280.

Rimland, B. 1993. Editor's notebook. *Autism Research Review International* 7 (3).

Rogers, D. 1992. *Motor Disorder in Psychiatry: Towards a neurological psychiatry.* Chichester, England: Wiley.

Rosenhan, D. L. 1984. On being sane in insane places. In *The Invented Reality: How do we know what we believe we know? Contributions to constructivism,* P. Watzlawick, ed., 117-144. New York: Norton.

Rutter, M., D. Greenfield, and L. Lockyer. 1967. A five to fifteen year follow-up study of infantile psychosis: II Social behavior and outcome. *British Journal of Psychiatry* 113: 1183-1199.

Sacks, O. 1989. Neuropsychiatry and Tourette's. In *Neurology and Psychiatry: A meeting of minds*, Mueller, ed., 156-174. Basel: Karger.

Sacks, O. 1990. *Awakenings* (6th ed.). New York: Harper Perennial.

Schawlow, A. T., and A. L. Schawlow. 1985. Our son: The endless search for help. In *Integrating Moderately and Severely Handicapped Learners: Strategies that work*, M. P. Brady and P. Gunter, eds., 5-15. Springfield, IL: Thomas.

Schwandt, T. A. 1996a. Notes on being an interpretivist. In *From Positivism to Interpretation and Beyond: Tales of transformation in educational and social research (The mind-body connection)*, L. Heshusuis and K. Ballard, eds., 77-84. New York: Teachers College Press.

Schwandt, T. A. 1996b. New songs of innocence and experiences (with apologies to William Blake). In *From Positivism to Interpretation and Beyond: Tales of transformation in educational and social research (The mind-body connection)*, L. Heshusuis and K. Ballard, eds., 155-160. New York: Teachers College Press.

Strandt-Conroy, K. 1999. *Exploring movement differences in autism through first-hand accounts*. Unpublished doctoral dissertation, University of Wisconsin, Madison.

Thelen, E. 1995. Motor development: A new synthesis. *American Psychologist* 50 (2): 79-95.

Thelen, E., and J. J. Lockman. 1993. Developmental biodynamics: Brain, body, behavior connections. *Child Development* 64 (4): 953-959.

Thelen, E., and L. B. Smith. 1996. *A Dynamic Systems Approach to the Development of Cognition and Action*. London: MIT Press.

Williams, D. 1992. *Nobody Nowhere*. London: Doubleday.

Williams, D. 1994. *Somebody Somewhere*. New York: Times Books.

Williams, D. 1995a. *Like Color to the Blind*. New York: Times Books.

Williams, D. 1995b, May. Self-other awareness. Lecture, Syracuse University.

Williams, D. 1995c. *Not Just Anything: A collection of thoughts on paper*. Arlington, TX: Future Education.

Young, S. R. 1998. *Autism and I.Q.* Unpublished manuscript, University of Wisconsin, Madison.

Zelazo, P. R. 1997a. Infant-toddler information processing assessments for children with pervasive developmental disorder and autism: I. *Infants and Young Children* 10 (1): 1-14.

Zelazo, P. R. 1997b. Infant-toddler information processing assessments for children with pervasive developmental disorder and autism: II. *Infants and Young Children* 10 (2): 1-13.

Zelazo, P. R., R. B. Kearslye, and D. M. Stack. 1995. Mental representations for visual sequences: Increased speed of central processing from 22 to 32 months. *Intelligence* 10: 41-63.

WONDER HOW THAT HAPPENS

SEE HIM?
YOU SEE THE NEED FOR MORE LOCKS
REALLY
I SEE SOMEONE ELSE
FUNNY

REALLY FUNNY
LIKE THE LOOK AROUND A CURVE IN SPACE
WONDER HOW THAT HAPPENS

SEE HIM?
THE ONE I SEE SITS LIKE A YOGI
REALLY
YOU SEE SOMEONE ELSE
FUNNY

REALLY FUNNY
LIKE THE SANDWICH THAT READS QUITE
WELL ON THE MENU
WONDER HOW THAT HAPPENS

—MRL